The classic science fiction ta⬚⬚⬚⬚⬚⬚⬚⬚⬚⬚⬚⬚⬚⬚⬚
space exploration than with ⬚⬚⬚⬚⬚⬚⬚⬚⬚⬚⬚⬚⬚⬚⬚
the more valued science fict⬚⬚⬚⬚⬚⬚⬚⬚⬚⬚⬚⬚⬚⬚
those in which scientific fa⬚⬚⬚⬚⬚⬚⬚⬚⬚⬚⬚⬚⬚
extrapolation is informed an⬚⬚⬚⬚⬚⬚⬚⬚⬚⬚⬚⬚

It seemed to us, then, tha⬚⬚⬚⬚⬚⬚⬚⬚⬚⬚⬚⬚⬚
gather together thirteen stories, at least one for each of the
nine planets, and for the Sun, the asteroids, and the comets in
addition, and to choose those that were reasonably accurate
for the time in which they were written.

How better and how more interestingly to indicate the speed
with which knowledge of our solar system has advanced in
this last generation of radio astronomy and space probes
than by seeing where these stories – all less than thirty years
old – are still accurate and where they have been outdated by
advancing knowledge.

From the Introduction
by Isaac Asimov

The Science Fictional Solar System

Edited by
Isaac Asimov,
Martin Harry Greenberg,
and
Charles G. Waugh

A PANTHER BOOK

GRANADA

London Toronto Sydney New York

Published by Granada Publishing Limited in 1982

ISBN 0 586 05228 3

First published in Great Britain by
Sidgwick and Jackson Limited 1980
Copyright © 1979 by Isaac Asimov,
Martin Harry Greenberg, and Charles G. Waugh

Granada Publishing Limited
Frogmore, St Albans, Herts AL2 2NF
and
36 Golden Square, London W1R 4AH
866 United Nations Plaza, New York, NY 10017, USA
117 York Street, Sydney, NSW 2000, Australia
100 Skyway Avenue, Rexdale, Ontario, M9W 3A6, Canada
61 Beach Road, Auckland, New Zealand

Printed and bound in Great Britain by
Cox & Wyman Ltd, Reading

Granada ®
Granada Publishing ®

CONTENTS

INTRODUCTION

BY ISAAC ASIMOV

The classic science fiction tale has more often dealt with space exploration than with any other theme. In addition, the more valued science fiction stories have always been those in which scientific fact is respected and scientific extrapolation is informed and rational.

It seemed to us, then, that it would be interesting to gather together thirteen stories, at least one for each of the nine planets, and for the Sun, the asteroids, and the comets in addition, and to choose those that were reasonably accurate for the time in which they were written.

How better and more interestingly to indicate the speed with which knowledge of our Solar system has advanced in this last generation of radio astronomy and space probes than by seeing where these stories—all less than thirty years old— are still accurate and where they have been outdated by advancing knowledge.

For that purpose I have added to each of the twelve sections a discussion of where we were and where we are. My own hope is that although the essays, like the stories, are interesting in themselves, the combination will prove more interesting than either separately.

THE SCIENCE FICTIONAL SOLAR SYSTEM

SUN

Any suggestion that the Sun might be changing is frightening. It is the constant on which all life depends. Make it slightly variable and life is destroyed. Extend the variation a little more and Earth is destroyed.

Yet it is only within the last half-century that human beings learned how the Sun worked and what kept it going. In 1938, Hans Albrecht Bethe and Carl Friedrich von Weizsäcker independently suggested the mechanism that might do the trick. They based their deduction on nuclear research in laboratories on Earth.

To begin with, the Sun is mostly hydrogen. That had been known for quite a while from spectroscopic studies. Therefore, any nuclear reaction designed to produce as much energy as the Sun has produced for billions of years must involve hydrogen. There wasn't enough of anything else for the job.

If hydrogen were to fuse to the slightly more complex atom of helium, enough energy would be produced. Given the nuclear reactions that were known to involve hydrogen; given the pressure and temperature of the Solar core; then the step-by-step succession of reacting nuclei could be worked out. With time the Bethe/von Weizsäcker mechanism was honed and made more precise, but the basic changes were not altered.

Eventually, the hydrogen-fuel of the Sun would run low and the helium-rich core would contract and heat up. New nuclear reactions would then begin to take place, and as a result of that the Sun would grow into a red giant. This, however, would not be for some billions of years yet, so there is no immediate need to worry.

The Sun, in other words, has been stable and will continue to be stable (so says the theory), and we are living in the healthy middle years of its lifetime. To be sure, there is a Sunspot cycle moving up and down in a slightly irregular period of about 21.4 years (counting alternations in the direction of the magnetic field), but that would seem a minor ripple on the vast sea of constant Solar energy we receive.

This was the view in 1970 when "The Weather on the Sun" was first published.

Scientists would naturally like to collect direct evidence concerning what is happening in the Sun's core, but how? Actually plunging into the Sun is not within the bounds of possibility right now—but perhaps something might come out of it. Neutrinos, for instance.

Neutrinos are subatomic particles that virtually do not interact with matter. They can go right through the Earth—or the Sun—or trillions of kilometers of solid lead and scarcely be affected. An occasional neutrino will be absorbed by an atomic nucleus en route, but countless trillions move on untouched and undisturbed.

The nuclear reactions at the Sun's core (if they are those predicted by theory) produce both photons and neutrinos. The photons, which make up light and lightlike radiations, are easy to detect, but they take a million years to get to the Sun's surface and have so complicated a history of absorption and re-emission that by the time we detect them, they tell us nothing about the core. The neutrinos, on the other hand, streak straight from core to us in eight minutes (like the photons, neutrinos move at the speed of light) and come to us fresh with news about the core.

The problem is to detect them. This task was undertaken by Raymond Davis, Jr., who took advantage of the fact that sometimes a neutrino will interact with a variety of chlorine atoms to produce a radioactive atom of the gas argon. The argon can be collected and detected even if only a few atoms are formed.

Davis used a huge tank containing 378,000 liters (100,000 gallons) of tetrachloroethylene, a common cleaning fluid that happens to be rich in chlorine atoms. He placed it deep in the Homestake gold mine in Lead, South Dakota, where there were 1.5 kilometers (almost one mile) of rock between itself and the surface. All that rock would absorb any particles coming from space except neutrinos.

It was then only a matter of waiting for argon atoms to form. If accepted theories of events in the Sun's core were correct, then a certain number of neutrinos should be formed each second; of these, a certain percentage should reach the Earth; of these, a certain percentage should pass through the tank of cleaning fluid; of these, a certain percentage should interact with chlorine atoms, and a certain number of argon atoms should be formed.

All these percentages were known and Davis was confident that he would be able to detect a certain number of neutrino absorptions per day. From fluctuations in the rate of absorption, he hoped that conclusions might be drawn concerning events at the Sun's core.

Almost at once, however, Davis had cause for astonishment. Very few neutrinos were detected, far fewer than had been expected. Only one-sixth as many neutrinos were detected as had been expected.

The Davis scheme of observation has been checked out and has been found to have no significant discoverable flaw. All the calculations that don't involve the Sun's core seem to be correct.

Conclusion: What is actually going on at the Sun's core doesn't seem to be what for forty years we have been thinking has been going on at the Sun's core.

It may be that there is some small point that scientists have overlooked—some side reaction they failed to take into account—some change of temperature and pressure that they haven't quite calculated correctly. A small correction might explain the missing neutrinos without raising any disturbing questions about the Sun's fate.

On the other hand, it is just possible that the reactions at the Sun's core have recently become slower. Can it be that the Sun may be dying?

If we don't find some explanation, it may be that we really don't understand how the Sun works or, by extension, any of the stars at all. If that is so, then we don't really know why the Sun is stable, or if it really is all that stable, and whether at some time in the future it might not suddenly begin to show unexpected changes.

Right now "The Weather on the Sun" seems just a tiny bit less fantastic than when it first appeared.

The Weather on the Sun

THEODORE L. THOMAS

> ... the name "Weather Bureau" continued to be used, although the organization itself was somewhat changed in form. Thus the Weather Congress consisted of three arms. First was the political arm, the Weather Council. Second was the scientific arm, the Weather Advisers. Third was the operating arm, the Weather Bureau.
>
> —The Columbia Encyclopedia, 32nd Edition, *Columbia University Press*

The mass of colors on the great globe shimmered and twisted in silence. The dials on the instruments along the curved walls dimmed and brightened each time the needles moved. The Weather Room presented an indecipherable complex of color to the untrained eye, but to the eyes of the Advisers who lounged there it presented an instantaneous picture of the world's weather, when they bothered to look at it. The day shift was near its end, and the mathemeteorologists were waiting to go home. Now and then one of them would look at some spot on the great globe to see how the weather pattern reacted—to check on a bit of his own work carried out earlier in the day. But he was not really interested; his mind was on the evening's date, or dinner, or a hockey game. Even Greenberg, head of the Weather Advisers, felt the general lassitude.

Anna Brackney was too bored to sit still. She got up and wandered into the computer room, plopped down again and punched a 2414 computer to check the day's match. It was 90.4 percent. She muttered, "Lousy," and then looked around guiltily. She punched the call-up to see what the match had been last week. Ninety point six. She started to say aloud, "Not bad," but stopped herself in time. James Eden would not approve of her talking to herself. Idly she punched call-up and looked at the results for last month and the month before that. Then she sat bolt upright and punched for data for the last six months. Very loudly she said, "Well, well, well, well, what do you know about that?" Ignoring the stares of two computer operators, she marched back into the Weather Room, right up to Greenberg.

"Do you realize," she said, "that our fit has been slipping a little each week? We are now operating on a fit' of a little better than ninety percent, when as recently as six months ago our fit was better than ninety-three percent? Did you realize that?"

Greenberg sat up and looked alert. "No. Are you sure?"

Anna did not bother to answer. Greenberg leaned aside and spoke into a communicator. "Charlie, get me a summary of the weekly fit for the last six months." He touched a button and said, "Upton, come on out to the Weather Room, will you? We may have a problem."

Greenberg touched several more buttons. In two minutes there was a circle of people around him, and he held a slip of paper in one hand. He said, "Somehow, in the last six months, we've slipped three percentage points in our match. How could that happen?"

The people looked at one another. Upton said, "Everybody thought somebody else was checking the long-term fit. I only compared it with the week before."

There was a chorus of "So did I," and Greenberg slapped his forehead. "How in hell could a thing like that happen?" He was a man who normally did not swear. "We've been drifting away from acceptable performance for six months and nobody even noticed it? What about the complaints?

What kind of complaints we been getting?"

The people shrugged, and Upton spoke for them again. "Nothing special. Just the usual gripes. Two weeks ago the Manitoba Council complained the breeze we made to blow away the mosquitoes was too strong, but—"

"Never you mind," said Anna Brackney. "That was my mathematical model on that problem, and the twenty-knot wind they got was just right to eliminate the mosquitoes because the foresters—"

"Knock it off," said Greenberg. "I take it there have been no serious complaints? I'd better check further." He talked into the phone with one of the secretaries, then said to the group, "Well, it seems we've been lucky. Anyhow, we've got to find out what's wrong. And we've got to find it before somebody else notices it, or we'll have the Weather Council on our necks. I wonder if I ought to call President Wilburn."

The people shook their heads, and Upton said, "I don't like to be sneaky or anything like that. But if we've somehow slipped in our procedures and got away with it, let's correct them without stirring up trouble. You know politicians."

Greenberg said, "We'll all have to stay on this until we find it. All of you willing?"

The people gave up their visions of dinner and dates and hockey games and nodded.

"Okay, then. Each of you set up a program designed to make independent repeat of your models for the last six months. Most of it was routine stuff, so it won't be bad. Call in the computer technicians and utilize all of the university's staff and equipment you need. If you need more, I'll set up a net and we can pull in everything we need from beyond Stockholm. Monitor your steps and when you find an error feed it into the 9680 as a collecting computer. Any other suggestions?"

The people shook their heads.

"All right. Let's get to work and solve this before anybody else even knows there's a problem. Good luck." A red light

flashed on the phone at Greenberg's elbow, and the operator's voice said, "Dr. Greenberg, President Wilburn is on the
phone. Some kind of emergency."

Greenberg looked startled. He picked up the phone and listened. In a moment he turned up the audio so that the people
could hear what Wilburn was saying.

The ox was almost done, and it smelled mighty good to Big
John Sommerville. He stood at the edge of the great patio
and looked across it through the morning groups of people to
where the ox slowly turned on the spit. A cloud of steam rose
above it and quickly disappeared in the still, dry air. Beyond
the barbecue pit with its automatic basters, auxiliary heaters,
powder sprinklers, temperature sensors and color detectors
stood one of the cattle barns, and beyond that the roll of the
prairie began. It was picture-pretty: a stand of oak and maple
on the forward slope, a road winding up, a stream meandering down the dip at the foot of the first hill fed from some
hidden subterranean channel that groped its way to the low
mountains. Big John Sommerville turned to look at the
house.

It rambled and twisted behind him, cloaked in brown-
stained shingles and roofed with cedar. It sprawled and
sprouted unexpected wings and went on for three hundred
feet. There was a story that two years ago there had been
eight guests in that house for a week before Big John found
out about it. It was a good house, built for comfort, and it
had a sense of belonging.

Big John Sommerville hooked his thumbs in his belt and
started to stroll over toward the roasting ox. His face was
craggy with little sags in the right places, and his body was
big with a thin layer of fat over hard muscles, a good Texas
face on a good Texas body.

"Hey, John, when do we eat?"

"Half an hour, I reckon." He walked on.

A hand slapped him on the shoulder, jolted him a little off

balance. As he turned he said, "You hungry, too, Brian?"

"Sure am." It was Brian Travers, mayor of Austin, the third most potent political figure in the area, and he held a large glass of straight bourbon. "I can wait through another pint or so of bourbon, but then I'm going to put me away a hindquarter of that ox. Hope it's as good as the last."

"Ought to be. Why, hello, Henry. Just get here?"

Henry Carpenter shook hands and looked around cautiously. "Everything under control? They all here?"

Travers said, "They're here. Quit worrying, Henry. We'll get it." The three of them had arranged the ox roast for a hundred of the major and minor citizens of the region to win over their support for a proposed monorail shipping line. It never hurt to line up the solid citizenry on your side before you tackled the local, state, and national officials. "We'll get them feeling comfortable on John's bourbon and ox, and then we'll tell them what we want to do. They'll go along, all right."

"Got a surprise," said Big John Sommerville. "I got to a few ears and I made out a case for a little water table replenishment around here. In exactly an hour and a half we will have a gentle rainfall on the mountains right behind the house, just over that near ridge. The time and position will be just right for the damnedest rainbow you ever saw in your life—the pot of gold will be right on top of that rise there. I'll announce the rainfall a half hour before it's due, and we'll let these fellows think I got extra-special connections at the Weather Council. When these fellows see what I can do with the Council, they'll split their britches to get behind us on the monoline. Right?"

Travers and Carpenter raised their glasses and took a long pull in honor of Big John Sommerville.

The bourbon was smooth, the ox was tender and tasty, and the announcement came at just the right time. The clouds formed on schedule. And then the rains came. The black heavens opened up and poured out their watery hell all over the spread of Big John Sommerville. Something like twelve inches of rain fell in the first twenty minutes, and the meandering stream turned into a devastating giant that swept away the barn and the stand of trees and the winding road. The water roared down the gentle slope behind the house and burst through the glass doors that opened out on the concealed porches and little hideaway nooks at the back of the house. The basement quickly filled with water, and the water lifted the floor joists from the plates. The little subterranean waterways built up pressure and quickly saturated the soil to a depth of fifteen feet. A mud slide started that transformed the entire house into a kind of roller coaster. Big John Sommerville felt it start and succeeded in getting everybody out of the house, so there were no casualties. In a final cloudburst, the rainstorm passed away.

One hundred and three men stood on a rocky ledge and looked in awe at all that was left of the house, garages, barns, corral, fences, and trees: a sea of soupy mud with occasional pieces of lumber protruding at crazy angles. The bare bones of the hill showed, and the barbecue pit lay somewhere downslope under fifty feet of mud.

"Big John," said Travers, "when you order yourself a rain, you really order yourself a rain."

It took Big John Sommerville three hours to reach a phone, and by that time his plans were made. First he called the Governor, explained what had happened and what he intended to do. It turned out that the Governor also had some information about a weather order or two that had gone wrong. So the Governor made a few calls himself, ending with a call to Wilburn's office to say that an important constituent named Big John Sommerville would soon be calling to talk to Wilburn about an important problem, and please arrange to have President Wilburn take the call. Big John Sommerville placed a few additional calls to other district councilmen, to three other governors, to several mayors and to half a dozen wealthy industrialists. As it happened, many of these people had some small pieces of information of their own about weather mishaps. When these folk called President Wilburn's office to suggest the President listen to what Big John Sommerville had to say, they also tossed into the conversation a few pointed remarks about weather control and sloppy management.

In two hours' time, the communications network surrounding President Wilburn's office in Sicily was in a snarled mess, out of which, nevertheless, two pertinent facts stood out: One, many good citizens were acutely unhappy about the weather control, and, two, Big John Sommerville was acoming.

When Big John Sommerville himself got on the line, President Wilburn was sitting there waiting. The five hours of pent-up anger burst into his office while he sat and marveled. The dirty red face that glared at him, the mud-caked hair, the ripped shirt, the glorious near-incoherence of the teeth-clenched stream of words were all fascinating. Never in his political life had President Wilburn received such a dressing down. Partway through it, Wilburn had to remind himself that the situation was not funny. He was, in fact, in the midst of a totally unexpected crisis.

The screen went blank. Big John Sommerville had had his say.

Wilburn sat quietly and reflected. The world government was not so mighty that one influential and irate citizen could not shake it a little. There should be no false moves now. First he had to find out what had gone wrong. He called Greenberg at the Advisers.

Greenberg had just turned up the audio.

"Let me make certain there is no misunderstanding," said Wilburn. "Every staff member of the Advisers and all associated personnel are hereby placed on an emergency basis, and you have authority to do whatever is necessary—I repeat, whatever is necessary—to get to the bottom of this and correct it. Money, time, people, equipment, anything you need you get. In twelve hours I want a preliminary report from you, and hopefully you will have the complete answers by that time. If not, your entire organization will stay on the problem until it is solved. Routine work will be suspended except for weather control requests you receive personally from me. Do you have any questions?"

"No, Mr. President," and they hung up.

Anna Brackney said, "Why didn't you tell him we had just discovered the problem ourselves?"

Greenberg gave her a look, then said to the group, "All right, let's go the way we planned. I guess we were dreaming a little to think we were going to solve this before anybody else caught on."

As they turned and walked away, Greenberg heard Anna Brackney say to Hiromaka, "But I don't understand why he didn't tell him we had already found out there was a problem."

Hiromaka said, "Aw, shut up."

At breakfast the next morning Harriet Wilburn said to Jonathan, "I guess this will be a bad one. We'd better make it a good breakfast; lunch may be a little tense." She poked the Diner for his coffee and then began making his onion-flavored eggs basted with pork sauce.

"Why is it," he said, "every time something pops I wind up having the breakfast I used to have when I was a boy? You suppose there's an element of regression there?"

"I certainly hope so. I'd hate to think it was some deep, undefined craving. Do you really think you ought to look at that now?" Wilburn had picked up a morning English-language newspaper.

"Oh, don't worry," he said. "I know I'm going to get the most severe castigation of my career. I'm sort of looking forward to how imaginative the press will be." He began to read.

When his eggs were ready he put down the paper and said, "Yes, they're in full cry. The editors, the seers, and columnists say they have been fully aware that things haven't been going right with the Weather Congress for several months, but they were just waiting to see if I would get going and do my job."

Harriet said, "Well, you know and I know and your friends know the truth. Eat your eggs, dear."

He ate his eggs. He sipped coffee when he was done, read through another paper, then went out into the soft Sicilian air, stepped on a walk, and rode a while. He got off and walked for a mile as was his custom, but a slight numbness crept into his legs, so he finished the trip on the slidewalk. He entered the Great Hall and went straight to his office through the private door.

Before he closed the door, Tongareva was there. Wilburn said, "Just the man I wanted to see. Come in, Gardner."

On his way to a seat, Tongareva started talking. "I have been reflecting on the events. I think we are caught up in some kind of world hysteria. I think the people have resented the Congress and the Council the way a small boy resents his authoritative father, and now they have found an excuse to let off steam. On top of that, elections are coming. I think we must be very careful."

Wilburn sank into his chair, ignoring the flashing lights on his phones and visuals. "Did you hear about that rained-out picnic in Texas?"

Tongareva nodded, a shade of a smile on his face. "That must have been the granddaddy of all rained-out picnics. The Texan knew just what to do to make an international issue out of it."

"The way he told it to me, it *was* an international issue. He led me to believe that everyone of any international importance was at that picnic, except you and me. Well, let me call Greenberg to see if he's found out what's gone haywire here. Please stay with me, Gardner."

Greenberg took the call in his office, with Upton and Hiromaka. "The information I have for you is incomplete, Mr. President. In fact, I hope it is so incomplete as to be incorrect. But you see, twelve hours is not really enough—"

"What are you trying to say, Dr. Greenberg?"

Greenberg glanced at Upton, took a deep breath and said, "A detailed check of all the procedures, all the mathematical models, all the parameters used here, shows that no error has been made and that our mathematical fit matches the prediction. This would indicate that the error was elsewhere. So we got in touch with Base Lieutenant Commander Markov; Hechmer and Eden are on vacation. We told Markov what we were doing and asked him to check out his results, too. We have his results now, and at least preliminarily, neither he nor we can find any fault with his operations. In short, the Weather Bureau on the Sun accomplished each of its missions within tolerance. There's no error there either." Greenberg stopped and rubbed his face.

Wilburn asked gently, "What is your conclusion?"

Greenberg said, "Well, since the data were used and applied as correctly as we know how, and since the theory checks out as well as ever—"

He fell silent. After a moment Wilburn said, "Well?"

Greenberg looked straight at him and said, "The trouble might be in the Sun itself. The Sun is changing, and our theories are no longer as valid as they used to be."

Wilburn's breath caught, and he felt his body grow cold. He understood what Greenberg had said, but he did not immediately allow the full thought to enter his mind. He held it in front of him where it could not really frighten him, where it hung like a rotted piece of meat that would have to be eaten eventually, but not now. No one spoke or moved in either office. Greenberg and Tongareva did not want to force the swallowing, and so they waited. Finally, Wilburn took it in.

He sat back and groaned, and then stood up and paced out of range of the viewer. Greenberg sat and waited. Then he heard Wilburn's voice asking, "If what you say is true, our whole system of weather control is faulty. Is that right?"

"Yes, if it proves out," said Greenberg.

"Our entire culture, our entire civilization, the world over, is built on weather control. It is the primary fact of life for every living being. If our ability to control weather is destroyed, our world will be destroyed. We go back to sectionalism, predatory individualism. The one factor that ties all men everywhere together would disappear. The only thing left—chaos."

No one answered him, and for another full minute they were all silent.

Wilburn came back and sat down at his desk. He said to Greenberg, "I have to think. How much time will you need to verify your findings so far?"

"Another twelve hours. The European computer net is on it now, and we are in the process of bringing in the United States net and the Asian net simultaneously. Both of them will be on line in an hour. I might say this is the most intensive effort the Advisers have ever made, and it is causing talk already. There will be no secrets about our findings when we finally get them."

"I understand. I have twelve hours to think of something, and I am going to assume you will confirm what you've already found; that's the worst result I can think of, so I'll get ready to face it." The snap was coming back to Wilburn's voice. "If anything comes up along the way that makes you change your mind, let me know immediately. And thanks for the effort, Dr. Greenberg."

Wilburn looked around his office. The men gathered there did not look happy, and several of them, his political enemies, were frowning. Yet Wilburn needed them all. This was the group that served as a kind of unofficial executive for the entire Council. But it was a difficult group to work with, primarily because they represented such diverse interests.

Councilman Maitland said, "I am afraid, President Wilburn, that you have brought the Council to its lowest point of public esteem that I can remember."

Barstow reared up. "Now just a minute here. How do you—"

Wilburn waved a hand. "It's all right, Arthur. We all agree we have an enormous problem. I called this meeting to ask this group to think about what we do now."

Barstow sat back and nodded. The others were quiet, and then Tongareva said, "You give the impression that you have a plan to solve our present crisis, Jonathan. Are you ready to discuss it?"

"Yes. Although it isn't much of a plan, really." He leaned forward. "We have been this route before. We are confronted with a scientific crisis. The Sun is changing. Our weather control is no longer as accurate, and we may have other dangers we don't even know about yet. The Advisers tell me that these unexpected changes in the Sun might be serious, far more so than our failure to control weather accurately. We don't know what's happening. So here we go again, but this time I'm afraid we will have to mount the largest and most expensive research program the world has ever seen. It is already possible to tell that the answers won't be easy to get. The Weather Bureau has not seen any changes at all, so the Advisers think things must be happening deep inside the Sun. We've never been able to go deep, so the first scientific order of business will be to solve that one."

"Costs, Jonathan?" It was Du Bois, always a worrier about other people's money.

"Enormous, Georges. This is why we will have to be so careful. The tax burden will be the largest we've ever asked our people to bear. But unless someone can think of another program, I think we'll have to sell it."

Barstow said, "Do you mind if I talk to Greenberg? I want to be able to assure my constituents that I've looked into this personally."

"I hope everyone here will do that, and more. Please talk to any person you want, scientific or not, on any possible solutions he may have. Let's adjourn now and meet here in twenty-four hours to thrash it out."

Tongareva stayed, as Wilburn knew he would. He said, "Who's going to head up the program?"

Wilburn looked at him and smiled. "Need you ask? Aren't Dr. Jefferson Potter and Senior Boatmaster James Eden the ones to do the job?"

Greenberg seemed upset. "Look, with all due respect to you two, I don't think you see the ramifications of the problem. First"—he counted on his fingers—"the trouble appears to lie deep within the Sun. Second, we don't have a vehicle that can penetrate deeper than about two miles; in fact, Jim"—he looked at Eden—"no one has ever equaled that depth you reached some years ago on that Anderson problem. Third, we can't even take measurements at those depths. Fourth, our theories of occurrences at those depths have never been proved out." He dropped his hands. "We are probably in a worse position than we were when we first approached the problem of Sun control as a means of weather control."

Potter and Eden stared reflectively at Greenberg. Then Potter said, "You know, he's just given us an overall breakdown." Greenberg wondered what he was talking about, then realized that Potter was talking to Eden.

Eden said, still looking at Greenberg, "Yes, and he's the man in the best position to make the judgment so far. Four main groups along those lines, with good cross liaison. He's come up with a great way to start out, at least."

Potter said, "Four scientific administrators, each with a cabinet of a dozen or so people with assigned responsibilities. Each of the four groups places its own R and D and hires its own people."

Eden said, "Each cabinet has a member responsible for

cross liaison with the other groups. In fact, each cabinet member has sole responsibility for an assigned area. He'll have his own staff to help administer his group."

It was Potter's turn again. "Any overlapping can be minimized by frequent meetings of the big four. Ought to work. Now let's see. All the problems come together on the Sun, so I guess that's where you ought to be. I'll stay here to keep things on the track. We can get together every month or so if necessary. How's that sound to you, Bob?"

Greenberg had caught the drift of the discussion and had been following it, fascinated. He nodded. "Sounds fine to me. Where do the Advisers come into this?"

"Seems to me you should be standing by for any extraordinary computing problems, of which there will be plenty. Don't forget you will also have the day-to-day work going on as usual. You had better increase your staff here, don't you think?"

Greenberg nodded. "Yes, but I can see some problems in getting enough scientific personnel to do all the work on the overall project. We'll wind up with one of our groups bidding against another."

"Bound to happen. We'll try to keep it to a minimum."

Potter said, "All right. I'll get on the horn and we'll start the ball rolling. Wilburn ought to be explaining things to everybody right about now."

Only two of the two hundred councilmen were absent, and Wilburn knew those two were in the hospital. Furthermore, the councilmen sat on the edge of their seats, listening intently to the voices booming over their desk speakers. Wilburn looked down impassively from his desk, but he was deeply shaken. The debate had gone on for three hours with no interruptions for any reason, and the opposition to the proposed research program was surprisingly strong. What was worse, the mood of the Council was emotional to a degree Wilburn had never seen before. Even Councilman Reardon of 35–50 E

30–45 N, normally a cool speaker, ended his five minutes with his voice broken and quavering. Wilburn frantically tried to think of a way to break the spell, to interject somehow a rational appeal. But he could not prevent the councilmen from obtaining their five minutes to speak. Many of them were so carried away with what they were saying that they did not see the thirty-second warning light on their desks, and they were cut off in mid-sentence by the sergeant at arms when their five minutes were up, left sobbing at a dead microphone.

Wilburn quietly turned to his desk, checked his directory, and dialed the desk of the next speaker, Francisco Espaiyat, 60–75 W 15–30 N. "Frank," he said, "you getting ready to speak?"

"I certainly am, Wilburn. I've come up with some reasons that haven't been mentioned yet, so I hope to do some good here. You got any particular suggestions?"

Wilburn hesitated. "Yes, I have, Frank, but I don't know whether to ask you to do it or not. See what you think. When you come on, simply state that you are in favor of the program, and then leave the rest of your time empty. Give us four minutes and fifty-five seconds of golden silence for a little somber reflection along with a quick trip to the bathroom. I don't like to ask you to give up your speaking time, but nobody yet has got through to these hotheads. What do you think?"

Espaiyat thought about it and then said slowly, "I don't know if it will work, Jonathan, but I'm willing to give it a try."

Three minutes later, when the sergeant at arms announced the speech of Councilman Espaiyat, the Council was startled to hear, "I speak in favor of the program, but I hereby devote the balance of my time to rest and relief from this interminable speechmaking." Espaiyat got up and started down the aisle. Immediately Wilburn got up and went out the door nearest him. After a moment's looking around the chamber in puzzlement, every other councilman suddenly got up and headed for a door, and as they pressed out to the corridors, some of them began to laugh. A low chant of "Yay, Espaiyat" started up from a few members and quickly spread over the entire chamber and up to the galleries, which were also emptying.

When they poured back to their desks a few minutes later, the spell was broken. Men and women chatted and called to one another. The next speaker, Madame Iwanowski, 45–60 E 45–60 N, spoke against the program, but she tried to marshal some facts. She yielded after two minutes twenty-eight seconds. The crisis had passed. Other speakers disgorged their thoughts, but the tenor of the speeches was only mildly argumentative, for the sake of the constituency back home. In half an hour the question was called and the vote taken. The tabulation flashed on the great board. A small cheer broke out from the floor and gallery. The vote was 133 for, 65 against. Wilburn sat impassively, staring out over the floor, ignoring the numbness that had come back in his legs. They had the required two-thirds vote, but it was much, much too close. On a project of this size he needed all the support in the Council he could get, but about one-third of the group was against him. He sighed. This would not do. There were hard times ahead. If this program didn't work out, he saw clearly who the scapegoat would be. For the first time a President of the Weather Congress would not so much step down as be thrown out. Well, that was politics. Harriet would be waiting for him when it was over, and they could always take up a pleasurable retirement. Key West, now, there was a place he had always loved, and perhaps the time had come to— He caught himself and straightened his shoulders. No time for retirement thoughts yet. There was work to be done. He headed for his office to call Greenberg.

"The trouble is," Senior Boatmaster James Eden said matter-of-factly, "the film of carbon vapor begins to collapse at these pressures. The rate of carbon consumption goes up, the sessile effect dissipates, and the boat itself is consumed."

"Very interesting," said Dr. John Plant. "Now don't you think we ought to get the hell out of here before you demonstrate the point?"

Eden nodded and said into the intercom, "Up. Forty degrees. Now." He fingered the keys and took the boat up to within five hundred yards of the surface before he leveled off. He said to Plant, "Don't wash it out, though. Those limitations I just mentioned will allow these boats to be consumed, but there may be a way around them."

"I don't know what they could be. Those limitations seem pretty fundamental to me. I think we need a whole new approach to get down to the center. We'll never do it with this kind of equipment."

Eden shook his head and said, "I never thought I'd be sitting in a sessile boat on the Sun and hear someone say it was obsolete. Look here. The carbon toruses that surround the boat act as a mirror. They absorb all the radiation from infrared down to the hard stuff to a depth of a fraction of a millimeter and then reflect it with an efficiency of ninety-nine point nine nine nine nine eight. That's the turnaround effect we've been telling you about. Carbon vaporization protects against the balance of the radiation, and the power difference is supplied by our internal reactors. So look. If we can increase the efficiency of the turnaround effect by a factor of a few thousand, we could cope with the increased temperatures and radiative effects at great depths. What's wrong with that?"

"Well, just how do you—"

"We can still balance out the gravitational force by channeling additional power to the bottom toruses, to take advantage of the radiative pressure on the bottom of the boat. Right?"

"Well, just how do you—?"

"That's your problem. I've told you how to do it. You're

the scientist. I'm just a boat captain. Now, stand by while we get this thing back to base. I'm going Earthside today."

Plant sighed and settled back in his harness while Eden picked up the beacon and followed it back to base, through the lock and into the bay. While they were stripping off their lead suits, Plant said, "Maybe a carbon alloy."

"What?" said Eden.

"Maybe a carbon alloy would improve the efficiency of the turnaround effect."

"Sounds promising to me. Give it a whirl. Nice going."

Plant looked at him wryly. "Thanks. Glad you like my ideas." Eden was too busy to pay any attention to the slight emphasis on the word "my," so Plant smiled at Eden's back, shrugged, and hung up his suit.

They found Base Commander Hechmer in the day room with some of the staff watching a teevee transmit Earthside. Wilburn was addressing the Weather Council, bringing the members up to date on the Sun program. He told them results were coming in. The Sun's core was behaving anomalously. Neutrino formation at the core had accelerated and apparently was going to accelerate even more. The Sun appeared to be moving out of the main sequence a billion years ahead of schedule. Hechmer said, to no one in particular, "Gives you a nice comfortable feeling, doesn't it?"

On the screen Wilburn said, "To finish my report to you, we should know in a few weeks exactly what is wrong with the Sun, and we should then be in a position to know what to do about it. In short, ladies and gentlemen of the Weather Council, this most massive of research efforts has borne fruit. It is isolating the problem, and it will arrive at a solution. Thank you." The applause was long and genuine, and Wilburn made a slight bow and quickly put his hand on the podium.

The Advisers had the jitters, so Greenberg called together his mathemeteorologists and said, "Now look. Just because we have the heavy artillery in the scientific world showing up here in a few minutes is no reason to get all upset. It's just a high-level meeting, and they're holding it here. After all, we've made an important contribution to the total research effort on this program."

"Yes, but why here? They going to change the Advisers?"

"I hear they're going to fire us."

"Yeah, clean shop and start again with a new group."

Greenberg said, "Oh, cut it out. They probably want our advice on the next steps in the program. You'll have to admit, we have a problem there. We may have accomplished everything we can in the program."

People began to drift in, and soon the room was full. Potter took over as chairman. "What we've got to do is see where we go from here. We've accomplished almost all the major objectives of the program. What's left?"

Kowalski said, "We've fallen down on boat design. We haven't been able to come up with a boat that will get us down to the center of the Sun and back up again. We don't know where to turn next. We've explored every alley we can think of, and we have some thirty thousand people working on the project, including some real bright ones, problem solvers. All we've done is improve the efficiency of the boats by a factor of a thousand. We don't know where to turn next."

Potter said, "You can get a boat down, but you can't get it back. That right?"

"Yes, and don't anybody here tell us about remote control or automation. Center-of-Sun conditions are such that we can't communicate twenty feet away. As to automation, we can't get into the boat a computer of the size we need to make a few critical decisions. The presence of the boat is going to change center-of-Sun conditions, so someone is going to have to make a quick evaluation. Well, let Frank Valko tell you what's there."

Dr. Frank Valko, senior scientist in charge of evaluation of the Sun's deep interior, smiled and rubbed his chin in embarrassment. "I wish I could tell you precisely what's there. Then perhaps we could automate. But here's what we have. Our Bomnak group came up with a neutrino detector of reasonable size, one we could get in a spaceship. This is a device we've been trying for a hundred years. If the program produced nothing else, the neutrino detector alone has been worth it. Well, we put it in a ship and orbited it around the Sun and did some scanning. This detector is adjustable— most remarkable. We ran the scale from the fastest neutrinos with the weakest interaction to the slowest with some slight interaction, and we were able to peel the core of the Sun like an onion. Each interior layer is a bit hotter than the one outside it. And when we got to the core—I mean the real core now—we found the trouble. We found the very center at a temperature of over half a billion degrees Kelvin. The neutrino energy was greater than the light energy. The electron-positron pairs do not annihilate back to high-energy photons completely. We get significant neutrino-antineutrino formation. There are also some neutrino-photon reactions. But the point is that with such neutrino formation, energy can escape from the core, right through the walls of the Sun. And there you are." He looked around at the others brightly.

The rest of them looked at him blankly, and Eden said it. "Where?"

"Why, the Sun is in the earliest stages of decay, unpredictably early. All we have to do is dampen the core, and we get our old Sun back."

Potter said sarcastically, "How do we do that? Throw some water on it?"

"Well, water might not be the best substance. We're working out the theory to improve on water. I think we'll come up with something."

Eden said, "From a practical point of view, wouldn't it take quite a bit of water?"

"Of course not. Oh, I forgot to tell you. The hot core—the

troublemaking part—is only about one hundred feet in diameter right now. But it's spreading. We ought to do something within the next six months."

Potter sat back and rubbed his face. "All right. We know what the trouble is. We know where the trouble is. And we will soon know what to do about it. Fair enough?" He looked around the room. Most of those present nodded. Anna Brackney and two other mathemeteorologists shrugged. Potter glared at them for a moment and continued. "We can even get down there to quench it. But we can't get back. Is that what's left of our problem?" No one said anything, and there were no shrugs this time. Potter waited a moment, then continued. "Well, if that's really all that's left, then we may be all done. I'm certain we can find a volunteer to take the sessile boat down to the core. The question is, should we allow the volunteer to do it? Do we continue to try to find a way to get him back up?"

Eden started to speak, but before he could form the words Anna Brackney cut in. "Now, just you don't say anything here at all. There's going to be a lot more thought put in on this problem before we go setting up a hero situation." She turned to Kowalski and said, "You have six months. Isn't there a chance you can come up with a suitable boat design in that time?"

Kowalski said, "A chance, yes. But it isn't very likely. We've reached the point where we know we need a major breakthrough. It could happen tomorrow—we're trying. Or it might not happen in the next ten years of intensive work. We've defined the problem sufficiently so that we know what's needed to solve it. I am not optimistic."

Potter said, "Any ideas from any others? McCormick, Metzger?"

Metzger said, "I think you've summarized it, Jeff. Let's try for another, say, four months to get a boat design and to check out what we think we know. If we finish up right where we are now, we won't have hurt anything. We can then find someone to take a boat down, and we'll give him a great big farewell party. Isn't that about it?"

More shrugs from the mathemeteorologists, and Anna Brackney glared at Eden. Potter said, "I think I'll go call President Wilburn and tell him our conclusion. Can I use your office, Bob?" Greenberg nodded, and Potter said, "Be back in a minute. Work out the details while I make the call."

He left, and a desultory conversation went on in his absence as the group set up priorities and discussed the beginnings of the phase-out of the giant program. Ten minutes passed. Potter reappeared and stood in the doorway. Eden looked up, leaped to his feet and ran around the table toward him. Potter was pale and his face was drawn. He leaned against the door jamb and said, "President Wilburn is dying."

"I'm going with you, Jonathan," said Harriet Wilburn. She sat across from Wilburn, dry-eyed, in their breakfast corner.

He smiled at her, and the cosmetics on his face wrinkled, giving his face an odd, ragged appearance. He reached across and patted her hand. "You have to stay behind to protect my good name. There's a bitterness in some people. As long as my wife is alive, they won't go too far."

"I don't care about them." The tears were in her eyes now, and she looked down at the table to hide them. She wiped her cheeks in annoyance and said in a steady voice, "When do you leave?"

"In three days. The doctors want to make one more attempt to find out what's causing the central myelitis; there's got to be *some* reason for spinal cord deterioration. They hope they can come up with a cure someday, but first they have to find out what causes it."

Harriet Wilburn burst out, "I don't care about all this

knowledge, all this good, all this benefit-of-man nonsense. I want you." She put her head down on the table and frankly sobbed. Wilburn reached over and patted the back of her head.

"I don't really believe all this, Boatmaster," said Technician O'Rourke. "When the first manlike creature put out the first fire something like a half million years ago, he almost certainly used water. Now here we are, quenching the core of a sun heading toward a nova, and what do we use? Water. I don't believe it."

Eden did not smile. His mind was on a sessile boat, now about thirty thousand miles deep within the Sun and heading deeper. He sat with Technician O'Rourke in front of the main viewer panel of the neutrino detector, monitoring the flux density at the various energy levels. Eden said, "The reaction we are trying to get back to is simply the high-energy reaction of two photons to produce an electron-positron pair. As it is now, in the core the temperature is so high that the electron-positron pair doesn't go back to two high-energy photons. Instead they are producing a neutrino-antineutrino pair, and these pour right out through the Sun and are lost to space. If we don't stop that energy loss, the core will collapse. Since all we have to do is reduce the temperature by absorbing photons, we have a choice of materials to use. Many substances will do it, but water is the safest to carry down there without decomposing or volatilizing and killing Wilburn. That's why the water."

"Well, thanks. I still say it's a mighty funny situation. Somebody's going to do a lot of philosophizing on it, I'll bet you. How deep is he now?"

"About forty thousand miles."

Wilburn thought, You never know. You never know until you're there. I thought I'd be reflecting on my life, the few things I did right, the many things I did wrong, wondering what it all meant. He glanced at a depth gauge that read 46,000, and he continued thinking: About ten percent of the way, ninety percent to go, many hours yet. He felt hungry, but his ability to swallow had deteriorated to the extent that it was no longer possible for him to eat normally. He sighed, and went about the business of hooking up a bottle of a solution of sugar and protein to the needle in his arm. There were other ingredients in the solution, too, so after the solution was all in, he took a long, painless nap. When he awoke, there were only forty thousand miles to go, and Wilburn realized with a shock that he had had his last meal.

He checked out the few gauges he was familiar with; his briefing period had been limited. He remembered once as a boy his father had taken him through a power plant, and the array of dials and gauges had been fantastic. There had been a large room, divided by a series of panels, and every square inch of the panels and walls of the room had been covered with dials and gauges. When the time came to kick in additional units, one of the operators had called him over and said, "Okay, son. Push that button." Wilburn did, and his father said to him, "Don't forget this. All the sensing instruments and dials in the world don't mean a thing without one human finger."

Wilburn looked at the one gauge he didn't like—the one that recorded outside temperature. It read 678,000°K, and Wilburn looked away quickly. He was not a scientific man, and he was incapable of really believing that any living creature could exist in an environment of six hundred and seventy-eight thousand degrees. He thought of Harriet.

He had found it necessary to take steps to prevent her from using her rather significant influence to stow away on this boat. He chuckled and felt the wave of warmth he always felt when he thought of her. For her sake it would have been better to allow her to come, but there were times when one could not take the easy and most desirable path. A soft chime sounded through the boat.

He was approaching the core. He focused his attention on the two instruments directly in front of him. He could feel the deceleration of the boat as the toruses, top and bottom, became more nearly balanced. The temperature inside the cabin was one hundred and forty-six degrees Fahrenheit, but Wilburn was not uncomfortable. He had the feeling that everything was going very well, and he wished he could tell Harriet. The deceleration continued; several of the gauges on the periphery of his vision went off scale. He was very close to the core. Conditions seemed to be as predicted.

He continued to watch, and a chime softly began a beat that slowly increased in tempo. He did not know it, because there was no instrument to record it, but the temperature outside approached the one billion mark. He watched the neutrino flux direction indicator, knowing that the great quantity of water aboard was no longer in the form of a liquid, vapor, or solid, and it crossed his mind to wonder how that could be. And when the neutrino flux direction indicator wavered, and changed direction to show he had just passed through the very center of the core, he placed his finger on the black button. The last thing he remembered were the words, still clear in his ears, "don't mean a thing without one human finger." Then the walls of the boat collapsed and released the water. And the electron-positron pairs appeared instead of the neutrino-antineutrino pairs. On the neutrino detector in the orbiting ship, Eden saw the tiny hot core fade and disappear. The technician made an adjustment to bring in the neutrinos with slightly greater interaction, and the normal core showed up again, with its normal neutrino flux. But Eden, though he stared at the screen with eyes wide open, could see nothing but a blur.

MERCURY

Mercury was known to the ancients, but it was only after the coming of the Copernican view of the Solar system in 1543 that it was clearly understood that Mercury was the planet nearest the Sun.

It was found to be a small planet only 4860 kilometers (3020 miles) in diameter—not quite two-fifths the diameter of Earth—and its orbit about the Sun was substantially elliptical.

Mercury's average distance from the Sun is 57,800,000 kilometers (35,900,000 miles), but when it is at its farthest point from the Sun it is 69,800,000 kilometers (43,400,000 miles) away from it. That is only 45 percent of Earth's distance from the Sun, but that is the farthest that Mercury can get. When it is closest to the Sun, at the opposite end of its orbit, Mercury is only 46,000,000 kilometers (28,600,000 miles) from the Sun, only 30 percent of Earth's distance.

It seemed clear under those circumstances that Mercury was bound to be the hottest of the planets, especially when closest to the Sun. When farthest from the Sun, Mercury sees it twice as wide as when seen from Earth, and the Sun then delivers 4.3 times as much heat to Mercury as it delivers to Earth. When the Sun is at its closest, it seems 3.3 times as wide to Mercury as when seen from Earth and delivers 10.6 times as much energy.

What effect this has on Mercury's surface temperature depends also on how fast Mercury rotates. How long does its swollen Sun shine down on a particular spot?

It's hard to tell. Mercury is so near the Sun in the sky and so small that it is very difficult to observe. Then, too, when it is farthest from the Sun and most easily seen, less than half the side we see is bathed in Sunlight. The rest is dark and invisible.

A logical guess, though, was that its rotational period was 88 days, equal to its time of revolution about the Sun. After all, when a small body is subjected to the gravitational pull of a nearby large body, tidal effects are produced which tend to slow the rotation of the small body till it matches the period of revolution. This has happened to the Moon, for instance, under the tidal effects of Earth's gravitation.

When the period of rotation equals the period of revolution, then the small body turns one side to the large body at all times. That is true of the Moon with respect to the Earth, and we see only one side of the Moon.

The Sun's tidal effects on Mercury are not quite as strong as Earth's on the Moon, but they might be strong enough. If so, Mercury would face only one side to the Sun as it turned. There would be a Brightside and a Darkside.

Since Mercury's orbit is quite lopsided, its speed of revolution would vary with position in orbit, being faster when closer to the Sun and slower when farther. Mercury's rotation, which would be constant, would alternately pull ahead of the revolution and fall behind. The Sun would therefore seem to oscillate in Mercury's sky, and there would be two broad sectors between the Brightside and the Darkside where the Sun would rise and set twice a revolution. These sectors would be relatively mild in temperature—for Mercury.

The Darkside, which never saw the Sun, would be at temperatures near absolute zero. The Brightside, especially when the Sun was at its closest, would blaze at temperatures hot enough to melt tin and lead. The fact that Mercury has no atmosphere would make the temperatures all the more extreme.

In the 1880s, Giovanni Virginio Schiaparelli set up the basis for the above analysis. He made out dim streaks on Mercury and decided that they always maintained the same position relative to the Sun. By 1890, he announced that Mercury definitely did keep one side to the Sun, and that was accepted for three-quarters of a century. It was still taken as truth in 1956, when "Brightside Crossing" appeared.

But then microwave astronomy developed in the decades after World War II. The Darkside of Mercury gave off no light, of course, but it could give off lightlike radiation of longer wave-length (such as microwaves) that was not visible to the eye but was detectable to other instruments. Such radiation is given off at any temperature, and the wavelength and intensity of such radiation is characteristic of the temperature. Study the radiation, in other words, and you know the temperature.

In the early 1960s, microwaves were detected to be radiated from the Darkside in surprising quantities. The Darkside had to be quite warm to produce that many microwaves, and it couldn't possibly be that warm if it never saw the Sun, especially as there was no atmosphere to circulate and bring warmth from the Brightside to the Darkside.

Microwaves can also be used to measure a planet's rate of rotation. If microwaves are sent out to a planet, and if they are reflected by the planetary surface, and if the reflected waves are detected, then that is all that is needed. The reflection is not quite the same from a moving surface as from a stationary one, and the changes increase with the speed of motion. By studying the reflected microwaves, in other words, Mercury's speed of rotation could be determined.

In 1965, it was discovered that Mercury rotated on its axis within a period of 58.7 days—just two-thirds its period of revolution. This could be brought about if the tidal effect were not quite strong enough to slow down the speed of rotation to an exact equality with the period of revolution.

It was something that might have been foreseen as a possibility, but hadn't been.

This means that every part of Mercury experiences both day and night. Each day is 88 Earth-days long and each night is 88 Earth-days long, but there is neither constant day nor constant night anywhere.

Still, one side of Mercury always experiences its Sunlight when the Sun is at or near its closest, and the other side when the Sun is at or near its farthest. This means that one hemisphere is hotter than the other, and so a "Brightside" crossing—that is, during daytime on the side of the planet that is then near the Sun—can still be spoken of.

It would not be quite as hot as had been thought, however, and if one traveled in the right direction, the night shadow would come to meet one and shave off some of the duration—but it would still be bad enough.

In 1974, by the way, the Mariner 10 probe passed close by Mercury and took photographs that finally revealed its surface in detail. It looks very much like a larger Moon, though it lacks "maria," the wide, relatively flat, and unscarred "seas" of the Moon.

Brightside Crossing

ALAN E. NOURSE

James Baron was not pleased to hear that he had had a visitor when he reached the Red Lion that evening. He had no stomach for mysteries, vast or trifling, and there were pressing things to think about at this time. Yet the doorman had flagged him as he came in from the street: "A thousand pardons, Mr. Baron. The gentleman—he would leave no name. He said you'd want to see him. He will be back by eight."

Now Baron drummed his fingers on the table top, staring about the quiet lounge. Street trade was discouraged at the Red Lion, gently but persuasively; the patrons were few in number. Across to the right was a group that Baron knew vaguely—Andean climbers, or at least two of them were. Over near the door he recognized old Balmer, who had mapped the first passage to the core of Vulcan Crater on Venus. Baron returned his smile with a nod. Then he settled back and waited impatiently for the intruder who demanded his time without justifying it.

Presently a small grizzled man crossed the room and sat down at Baron's table. He was short and wiry. His face held no key to his age—he might have been thirty or a thousand— but he looked weary and immensely ugly. His cheeks and forehead were twisted and brown, with scars that were still healing.

The stranger said, "I'm glad you waited. I've heard you're planning to attempt the Brightside."

Baron stared at the man for a moment. "I see you can read telecasts," he said coldly. "The news was correct. We are going to make a Brightside Crossing."

"At peribelion?"

"Of course. When else?"

The grizzled man searched Baron's face for a moment without expression. Then he said slowly, "No, I'm afraid you're not going to make the Crossing."

"Say, who are you, if you don't mind?" Baron demanded.

"The name is Claney," said the stranger.

There was a silence. Then: "Claney? *Peter* Claney?"

"That's right."

Baron's eyes were wide with excitement, all trace of anger gone. "Great balls of fire, man—*where have you been hiding?* We've been trying to contact you for months!"

"I know. I was hoping you'd quit looking and chuck the whole idea."

"Quit looking!" Baron bent forward over the table. "My friend, we'd given up hope, but we've never quit looking. Here, have a drink. There's so much you can tell us." His fingers were trembling.

Peter Claney shook his head. "I can't tell you anything you want to hear."

"But you've *got* to. You're the only man on Earth who's attempted a Brightside Crossing and lived through it! And the story you cleared for the news—it was nothing. We need *details*. Where did your equipment fall down? Where did you miscalculate? What were the trouble spots?" Baron jabbed a finger at Claney's face. "That, for instance—epithelioma? Why? What was wrong with your glass? Your filters? We've got to know those things. If you can tell us, we can make it across where your attempt failed—"

"You want to know. why we failed?" asked Claney.

"Of course we want to know. We *have* to know."

"It's simple. We failed because it can't be done. We couldn't do it and neither can you. No human beings will ever cross the Brightside alive, not if they try for centuries."

"Nonsense," Baron declared. "We will."

Claney shrugged. "I was there. I know what I'm saying. You can blame the equipment or the men—there were flaws in both quarters—but we just didn't know what we were fighting. It was the *planet* that whipped us, that and the *Sun.* They'll whip you, too, if you try it."

"Never," said Baron.

"Let me tell you," Peter Claney said.

I'd been interested in the Brightside for almost as long as I can remember (Claney said). I guess I was about ten when Wyatt and Carpenter made the last attempt—that was in 2082, I think. I followed the news stories like a tri-V serial and then I was heartbroken when they just disappeared.

I know now that they were a pair of idiots, starting off without proper equipment, with practically no knowledge of surface conditions, without any charts—they couldn't have made a hundred miles—but I didn't know that then, and it was a terrible tragedy. After that, I followed Sanderson's work in the twilight lab up there and began to get Brightside into my blood, sure as death.

But it was Mikuta's idea to attempt a Crossing. Did you ever know Tom Mikuta? I don't suppose you did. No, not Japanese—Polish-American. He was a major in the Interplanetary Service for some years and hung on to the title after he gave up his commission.

He was with Armstrong on Mars during his Service days, did a good deal of the original mapping and surveying for the Colony there. I first met him on Venus; we spent five years together up there doing some of the nastiest exploring since the Matto Grosso. Then he made the attempt on Vulcan Crater that paved the way for Balmer a few years later.

I'd always liked the Major—he was big and quiet and cool, the sort of guy who always had things figured a little further ahead than anyone else and always knew what to do in a tight place. Too many men in this game are all nerve and luck, with no judgment. The Major had both. He also had the kind of personality that could take a crew of wild men and make them work like a well-oiled machine across a thousand miles of Venus jungle. I liked him and I trusted him.

He contacted me in New York and he was very casual at first. We spent an evening here at the Red Lion, talking about old times; he told me about the Vulcan business, and how he'd been out to see Sanderson and the twilight lab on Mercury, and how he preferred a hot trek to a cold one any day of the year—and then he wanted to know what I'd been doing since Venus and what my plans were.

"No particular plans," I told him. "Why?"

He looked me over. "How much do you weigh, Peter?"

I told him one thirty-five.

"That much!" he said. "Well, there can't be much fat on you, at any rate. How do you take heat?"

"You should know," I said. "Venus was no icebox."

"No, I mean *real* heat."

Then I began to get it. "You're planning a trip."

"That's right. A hot trip." He grinned at me. "Might be dangerous, too."

"What trip?"

"Brightside of Mercury," the Major said.

I whistled cautiously. "At aphelion?"

He threw his head back. "Why try a Crossing at aphelion? What have you done then? Four thousand miles of butcherous heat, just to have some joker come along, use your data and drum you out of the glory by crossing at perihelion forty-four days later? No, thanks. I want the Brightside without any nonsense about it." He leaned across me eagerly. "I want to make a Crossing at perihelion and I want to cross on the surface. If a man can do that, he's got Mercury. Until then, *nobody's* got Mercury. I want Mercury—but I'll need help getting it."

I'd thought of it a thousand times and never dared consider

it. Nobody had, since Wyatt and Carpenter disappeared. Mercury turns on its axis in the same time that it wheels around the Sun, which means that the Brightside is always facing in. That makes the Brightside of Mercury at perihelion the hottest place in the Solar System, with one single exception: the surface of the Sun itself.

It would be a hellish trek. Only a few men had ever learned just *how* hellish, and they never came back to tell about it. It was a real hell's Crossing, but someday, I thought, somebody would cross it.

I wanted to be along.

The twilight lab, near the northern pole of Mercury, was the obvious jumping-off place. The setup there wasn't very extensive—a rocket landing, the labs and quarters for Sanderson's crew sunk deep into the crust, and the tower that housed the Solar 'scope that Sanderson had built up there ten years before.

Twilight lab wasn't particularly interested in the Brightside, of course—the Sun was Sanderson's baby and he'd picked Mercury as the closest chunk of rock to the Sun that could hold his observatory. He'd chosen a good location, too. On Mercury, the Brightside temperature hits 770° F. at perihelion and the Darkside runs pretty constant at −410° F. No permanent installation with a human crew could survive at either extreme. But with Mercury's wobble, the twilight zone between Brightside and Darkside offers something closer to survival temperatures.

Sanderson built the lab up near the pole, where the zone is about five miles wide, so the temperature only varies 50 to 60 degrees with the libration. The Solar 'scope could take that much change and they'd get good clear observation of the Sun for about seventy out of the eighty-eight days it takes the planet to wheel around.

The Major was counting on Sanderson knowing something

about Mercury as well as the Sun when we camped at the lab to make final preparations.

Sanderson did. He thought we'd lost our minds and he said so, but he gave us all the help he could. He spent a week briefing Jack Stone, the third member of our party, who had arrived with the supplies and equipment a few days earlier. Poor Jack met us at the rocket landing almost bawling, Sanderson had given him such a gloomy picture of what Brightside was like.

Stone was a youngster—hardly twenty-five, I'd say—but he'd been with the Major at Vulcan and had begged to join this trek. I had a funny feeling that Jack really didn't care for exploring too much, but he thought Mikuta was God, followed him around like a puppy.

It didn't matter to me as long as he knew what he was getting in for. You don't go asking people in this game why they do it—they're liable to get awfully uneasy and none of them can ever give you an answer that makes sense. Anyway, Stone had borrowed three men from the lab, and had the supplies and equipment all lined up when we got there, ready to check and test.

We dug right in. With plenty of funds—tri-V money and some government cash the Major had talked his way around—our equipment was new and good. Mikuta had done the designing and testing himself, with a big assist from Sanderson. We had four Bugs, three of them the light pillow-tire models, with special lead-cooled cut-in engines when the heat set in, and one heavy-duty tractor model for pulling the sledges.

The Major went over them like a kid at the circus. Then he said, "Have you heard anything from McIvers?"

"Who's he?" Stone wanted to know.

"He'll be joining us. He's a good man—got quite a name for climbing, back home." The Major turned to me. "You've probably heard of him."

I'd heard plenty of stories about Ted McIvers and I wasn't too happy to hear that he was joining us. "Kind of a daredevil, isn't he?"

"Maybe. He's lucky and skillful. Where do you draw the line? We'll need plenty of both."

"Have you ever worked with him?" I asked.

"No. Are you worried?"

"Not exactly. But Brightside is no place to count on luck."

The Major laughed. "I don't think we need to worry about McIvers. We understood each other when I talked up the trip to him and we're going to need each other too much to do any fooling around." He turned back to the supply list. "Meanwhile, let's get this stuff listed and packed. We'll need to cut weight sharply and our time is short. Sanderson says we should leave in three days."

Two days later, McIvers hadn't arrived. The Major didn't say much about it. Stone was getting edgy and so was I. We spent the second day studying charts of the Brightside, such as they were. The best available were pretty poor, taken from so far out that the detail dissolved into blurs on blow-up. They showed the biggest ranges of peaks and craters and faults, and that was all. Still, we could use them to plan a broad outline of our course.

"This range here," the Major said as we crowded around the board, "is largely inactive, according to Sanderson. But these to the south and west *could* be active. Seismograph tracings suggest a lot of activity in that region, getting worse down toward the equator—not only volcanic, but sub-surface shifting."

Stone nodded. "Sanderson told me there was probably constant surface activity."

The Major shrugged. "Well, it's treacherous, there's no doubt of it. But the only way to avoid it is to travel over the pole, which would lose us days and offer us no guarantee of less activity to the west. Now we might avoid some if we could find a pass through this range and cut sharp east—"

It seemed that the more we considered the problem, the further we got from a solution. We knew there were active volcanoes on the Brightside—even on the Darkside, though surface activity there was pretty much slowed down and localized.

But there were problems of atmosphere on Brightside, as well. There *was* an atmosphere and a constant atmospheric flow from Brightside to Darkside. Not much—the lighter gases had reached escape velocity and disappeared from Brightside millennia ago—but there was CO_2, and nitrogen, and traces of other heavier gases. There was also an abundance of sulfur vapor, as well as carbon disulfide and sulfur dioxide.

The atmospheric tide moved toward the Darkside, where it condensed, carrying enough volcanic ash with it for Sanderson to estimate the depth and nature of the surface upheavals on Brightside from his samplings. The trick was to find a passage that avoided those upheavals as far as possible. But in the final analysis, we were barely scraping the surface. The only way we would find out what was happening where was to be there.

Finally, on the third day, McIvers blew in on a freight rocket from Venus. He'd missed the ship that the Major and I had taken by a few hours, and had conned his way to Venus in hopes of getting a hop from there. He didn't seem too upset about it, as though this were his usual way of doing things and he couldn't see why everyone should get so excited.

He was a tall, rangy man with long, wavy hair prematurely gray, and the sort of eyes that looked like a climber's—half-closed, sleepy, almost indolent, but capable of abrupt alertness. And he never stood still; he was always moving, always doing something with his hands, or talking, or pacing about.

Evidently the Major decided not to press the issue of his arrival. There was still work to do, and an hour later we were running the final tests on the pressure suits. That evening, Stone and McIvers were thick as thieves, and everything was set for an early departure after we got some rest.

"And that," said Baron, finishing his drink and signaling the waiter for another pair, "was your first big mistake."

Peter Claney raised his eyebrows. "McIvers?"

"Of course."

Claney shrugged, glanced at the small quiet tables around them. "There are lots of bizarre personalities around a place like this, and some of the best wouldn't seem to be the most reliable at first glance. Anyway, personality problems weren't our big problem right then. *Equipment* worried us first and *route* next."

Baron nodded in agreement. "What kind of suits did you have?"

"The best insulating suits ever made," said Claney. "Each one had an inner lining of a fiberglass modification, to avoid the clumsiness of asbestos, and carried the refrigerating unit and oxygen storage which we recharged from the sledges every eight hours. Outer layer carried a monomolecular chrome reflecting surface that made us glitter like Christmas trees. And we had a half-inch dead-air space under positive pressure between the two layers. Warning thermocouples, of course—at 770 degrees, it wouldn't take much time to fry us to cinders if the suits failed somewhere."

"How about the Bugs?"

"They were insulated, too, but we weren't counting on them too much for protection."

"You weren't!" Baron exclaimed. "Why not?"

"We'd be in and out of them too much. They gave us mobility and storage, but we knew we'd have to do a lot of forward work on foot." Claney smiled bitterly. "Which meant that we had an inch of fiberglass and a half-inch of dead air between us and a surface temperature where lead flowed like water and zinc was almost at melting point and the pools of sulfur in the shadows were boiling like oatmeal over a camp-fire."

Baron licked his lips. His fingers stroked the cool wet glass as he set it down on the tablecloth.

"Go on," he said tautly. "You started on schedule?"

"Oh, yes," said Claney, "we started on schedule, all right. We just didn't quite end on schedule, that was all. But I'm getting to that."

He settled back in his chair and continued.

We jumped off from Twilight on a course due southeast with thirty days to make it to the Center of Brightside. If we could cross an average of seventy miles a day, we could hit Center exactly at perihelion, the point of Mercury's closest approach to the Sun—which made Center the hottest part of the planet at the hottest it ever gets.

The Sun was already huge and yellow over the horizon when we started, twice the size it appears on Earth. Every day that Sun would grow bigger and whiter, and every day the surface would get hotter. But once we reached Center, the job was only half done—we would still have to travel another two thousand miles to the opposite twilight zone. Sanderson was to meet us on the other side in the laboratory's scout ship, approximately sixty days from the time we jumped off.

That was the plan, in outline. It was up to us to cross those seventy miles a day, no matter how hot it became, no matter what terrain we had to cross. Detours would be dangerous and time-consuming. Delays could cost us our lives. We all knew that.

The Major briefed us on details an hour before we left. "Peter, you'll take the lead Bug, the small one we stripped down for you. Stone and I will flank you on either side, giving you a hundred-yard lead. McIvers, you'll have the job of dragging the sledges, so we'll have to direct your course pretty closely. Peter's job is to pick the passage at any given point. If there's any doubt of safe passage, we'll all explore ahead on foot before we risk the Bugs. Got that?"

McIvers and Stone exchanged glances. McIvers said, "Jack and I were planning to change around. We figured he could take the sledges. That would give me a little more mobility."

The Major looked up sharply at Stone. "Do you buy that, Jack?"

Stone shrugged. "I don't mind. Mac wanted—"

McIvers made an impatient gesture with his hands. "It doesn't matter. I just feel better when I'm on the move. Does it make any difference?"

"I guess it doesn't," said the Major. "Then you'll flank Peter along with me. Right?"

"Sure, sure." McIvers pulled at his lower lip. "Who's going to do the advance scouting?"

"It sounds like I am," I cut in. "We want to keep the lead Bug light as possible."

Mikuta nodded. "That's right. Peter's Bug is stripped down to the frame and wheels."

McIvers shook his head. "No, I mean the *advance* work. You need somebody out ahead—four or five miles, at least— to pick up the big flaws and active surface changes, don't you?" He stared at the Major. "I mean, how can we tell what sort of a hole we may be moving into, unless we have a scout up ahead?"

"That's what we have the charts for," the Major said sharply.

"Charts! I'm talking about *detail* work. We don't need to worry about the major topography. It's the little faults you can't see on the pictures that can kill us." He tossed the charts down excitedly. "Look, let me take a Bug out ahead and work reconnaissance, keep five, maybe ten miles ahead of the column. I can stay on good solid ground, of course, but scan the area closely and radio back to Peter where to avoid the flaws. Then—"

"No dice," the Major broke in.

"But why not? We could save ourselves days!"

"I don't care what we could save. We stay together. When we get to the Center, I want live men along with me. That means we stay within easy sight of each other at all times. Any climber knows that everybody is safer in a party than one man alone—any time, any place."

McIvers stared at him, his cheeks an angry red. Finally he gave a sullen nod. "Okay. If you say so."

"Well, I say so and I mean it. I don't want any fancy stuff. We're going to hit Center together, and finish the Crossing together. Got that?"

McIvers nodded. Mikuta then looked at Stone and me and we nodded, too.

"All right," he said slowly. "Now that we've got it straight, let's go."

It was hot. If I forget everything else about that trek, I'll never forget that huge yellow Sun glaring down, without a break, hotter and hotter with every mile. We knew that the first few days would be the easiest and we were rested and fresh when we started down the long ragged gorge southeast of the twilight lab.

I moved out first; back over my shoulder, I could see the Major and McIvers crawling out behind me, their pillow tires taking the rugged floor of the gorge smoothly. Behind them, Stone dragged the sledges.

Even at only 30 percent Earth gravity they were a strain on the big tractor, until the ski-blades bit into the fluffy volcanic ash blanketing the valley. We even had a path to follow for the first twenty miles.

I kept my eyes pasted to the big Polaroid binocs, picking out the track the early research teams had made out into the edge of Brightside. But in a couple of hours we rumbled past Sanderson's little outpost observatory and the tracks stopped. We were in virgin territory and already the Sun was beginning to bite.

We didn't *feel* the heat so much those first days out. We *saw* it. The refrig units kept our skins at a nice comfortable seventy-five degrees Fahrenheit inside our suits, but our eyes watched that glaring Sun and the baked yellow rocks going past, and some nerve pathways got twisted up, somehow. We poured sweat as if we were in a superheated furnace.

We drove eight hours and slept five. When a sleep period came due, we pulled the Bugs together into a square, threw up a light aluminum sun-shield and lay out in the dust and rocks. The sun-shield cut the temperature down sixty or seventy degrees, for whatever help that was. And then we ate from the forward sledge—sucking through tubes—protein, carbohydrates, bulk gelatin, vitamins.

The Major measured water out with an iron hand, because we'd have drunk ourselves into nephritis in a week otherwise. We were constantly, unceasingly thirsty. Ask the physiologists and psychiatrists why—they can give you half a dozen interesting reasons—but all we knew, or cared about, was that it happened to be so.

We didn't sleep the first few stops, as a consequence. Our eyes burned in spite of the filters and we had roaring headaches, but we couldn't sleep them off. We sat around looking at each other. Then McIvers would say how good a beer would taste, and off we'd go. We'd have murdered our grandmothers for one ice-cold bottle of beer.

After a few driving periods, I began to get my bearings at the wheel. We were moving down into desolation that made Earth's old Death Valley look like a Japanese rose garden. Huge sun-baked cracks opened up in the floor of the gorge, with black cliffs jutting up on either side; the air was filled with a barely visible yellowish mist of sulfur and sulfurous gases.

It was a hot, barren hole, no place for any man to go, but the challenge was so powerful you could almost feel it. No one had ever crossed this land before and escaped. Those who had tried it had been cruelly punished, but the land was still there, so it had to be crossed. Not the easy way. It had to be crossed the hardest way possible: overland, through anything the land could throw up to us, at the most difficult time possible.

Yet we knew that even the land might have been conquered before, except for that Sun. We'd fought absolute cold before and won. We'd never fought heat like this and won. The only worse heat in the Solar System was the surface of the Sun itself.

Brightside was worth trying for. We would get it or it would get us. That was the bargain.

I learned a lot about Mercury those first few driving periods. The gorge petered out after a hundred miles and we moved onto the slope of a range of ragged craters that ran south and east. This range had shown no activity since the first landing on Mercury forty years before, but beyond it there were active cones. Yellow fumes rose from the craters constantly; their sides were shrouded with heavy ash.

We couldn't detect a wind, but we knew there was a hot, sulfurous breeze sweeping in great continental tides across the face of the planet. Not enough for erosion, though. The craters rose up out of jagged gorges, huge towering spears of rock and rubble. Below were the vast yellow flatlands, smoking and hissing from the gases beneath the crust. Over everything was gray dust—silicates and salts, pumice and limestone and granite ash, filling crevices and declivities—offering a soft, treacherous surface for the Bug's pillow tires.

I learned to read the ground, to tell a covered fault by the sag of the dust; I learned to spot a passable crack, and tell it from an impassable cut. Time after time the Bugs ground to a halt while we explored a passage on foot, tied together with light copper cable, digging, advancing, digging some more until we were sure the surface would carry the machines. It was cruel work; we slept in exhaustion. But it went smoothly, at first.

Too smoothly, it seemed to me, and the others seemed to think so, too.

McIver's restlessness was beginning to grate on our nerves.

He talked too much, while we were resting or while we were driving—wisecracks, witticisms, unfunny jokes that wore thin with repetition. He took to making side trips from the route now and then, never far, but a little farther each time.

Jack Stone reacted quite the opposite; he grew quieter with each stop, more reserved and apprehensive. I didn't like it, but I figured that it would pass off after a while. I was apprehensive enough myself; I just managed to hide it better.

And every mile the Sun got bigger and whiter and higher in the sky and hotter. Without our ultraviolet screens and glare filters we would have been blinded; as it was our eyes ached constantly and the skin on our faces itched and tingled at the end of an eight-hour trek.

But it took one of those side trips of McIvers' to deliver the penultimate blow to our already fraying nerves. He had driven down a side branch of a long canyon running off west of our route and was almost out of sight in a cloud of ash when we heard a sharp cry through our earphones.

I wheeled my Bug around with my heart in my throat and spotted him through the binocs, waving frantically from the top of his machine. The Major and I took off, lumbering down the gulch after him as fast as the Bugs could go, with a thousand horrible pictures racing through our minds.

We found him standing stock-still, pointing down the gorge, and, for once, he didn't have anything to say. It was the wreck of a Bug; an old-fashioned half-track model of the sort that hadn't been in use for years. It was wedged tight in a cut in the rock, an axle broken, its casing split wide open up the middle, half buried in a rock slide. A dozen feet away were two insulated suits with white bones gleaming through the fiberglass helmets.

This was as far as Wyatt and Carpenter had gotten on *their* Brightside Crossing.

On the fifth driving period out, the terrain began to

change. It looked the same, but every now and then it *felt* different. On two occasions I felt my wheels spin, with a howl of protest from my engine. Then, quite suddenly, the Bug gave a lurch; I gunned my motor and nothing happened.

I could see the dull gray stuff seeping up around the hubs, thick and tenacious, splattering around in steaming gobs as the wheels spun. I knew what had happened the moment the wheels gave and, a few minutes later, they chained me to the tractor and dragged me back out of the mire. It looked for all the world like thick gray mud, but it was a pit of molten lead, steaming under a soft layer of concealing ash.

I picked my way more cautiously then. We were getting into an area of recent surface activity; the surface was really treacherous. I caught myself wishing that the Major had okayed McIvers' scheme for an advanced scout; more dangerous for the individual, maybe, but I was driving blind now and I didn't like it.

One error in judgment could sink us all, but I wasn't thinking much about the others. I was worried about *me,* plenty worried. I kept thinking, Better McIvers should go than me. It wasn't healthy thinking and I knew it, but I couldn't get the thought out of my mind.

It was a grueling eight hours and we slept poorly. Back in the Bug again, we moved still more slowly—edging out on a broad flat plateau, dodging a network of gaping surface cracks—winding back and forth in an effort to keep the machines on solid rock. I couldn't see far ahead, because of the yellow haze rising from the cracks, so I was almost on top of it when I saw a sharp cut ahead where the surface dropped six feet beyond a deep crack.

I let out a shout to halt the others; then I edged my Bug forward, peering at the cleft. It was deep and wide. I moved fifty yards to the left, then back to the right.

There was only one place that looked like a possible crossing—a long narrow ledge of gray stuff that lay down across a section of the fault like a ramp. Even as I watched it, I could feel the surface crust under the Bug trembling and saw the ledge shift over a few feet.

The Major's voice sounded in my ears. "How about it, Peter?"

"I don't know. This crust is on roller skates," I called back.

"How about that ledge?"

I hesitated. "I'm scared of it, Major. Let's backtrack and try to find a way around."

There was a roar of disgust in my earphones and McIvers' Bug suddenly lurched forward. It rolled down past me, picked up speed, with McIvers hunched behind the wheel like a race driver. He was heading past me straight for the gray ledge.

My shout caught in my throat; I heard the Major take a huge breath and roar, "Mac! *Stop that thing,* you fool!" and then McIvers' Bug was out on the ledge, lumbering across like a juggernaut.

The ledge jolted as the tires struck it; for a horrible moment it seemed to be sliding out from under the machine. And then the Bug was across in a cloud of dust, and I heard McIvers' voice in my ears, shouting in glee. "Come on, you slowpokes. It'll hold you!"

Something unprintable came through the earphones as the Major drew up alongside me and moved his Bug out on the ledge slowly and over to the other side. Then he said, "Take it slow, Peter. Then give Jack a hand with the sledges." His voice sounded tight as a wire.

Ten minutes later, we were on the other side of the cleft. The Major checked the whole column; then he turned on McIvers angrily. "One more trick like that," he said, "and I'll strap you to a rock and leave you. Do you understand me? *One more time—*"

McIvers' voice was heavy with protest. "Good Lord, if we leave it up to Claney, he'll have us out here forever! Any blind fool could see that that ledge would hold."

"*I* saw it moving," I shot back at him.

"All right, all right, so you've got good eyes. Why all the fuss? We got across, didn't we? But I say we've got to have a little nerve and use it once in a while if we're ever going to get across this lousy hotbox."

"We need to use a little judgment, too," the Major snapped. "All right, let's roll. But if you think I was joking, you just try me out once." He let it soak in for a minute. Then he geared his Bug on around to my flank again.

At the stopover, the incident wasn't mentioned again, but the Major drew me aside just as I was settling down for sleep. "Peter, I'm worried," he said slowly.

"McIvers? Don't worry. He's not as reckless as he seems—just impatient. We are over a hundred miles behind schedule and we're moving awfully slow. We only made forty miles this last drive."

The Major shook his head. "I don't mean McIvers. I mean the kid."

"Jack? What about him?"

"Take a look."

Stone was shaking. He was over near the tractor—away from the rest of us—and he was lying on his back, but he wasn't asleep. His whole body was shaking, convulsively. I saw him grip an outcropping of rock hard.

I walked over and sat down beside him. "Get your water all right?" I said.

He didn't answer. He just kept on shaking.

"Hey, boy," I said. "What's the trouble?"

"It's hot," he said, choking out the words.

"Sure it's hot, but don't let it throw you. We're in really good shape."

"*We're not,*" he snapped. "We're in rotten shape, if you ask me. *We're not going to make it,* do you know that? That crazy fool's going to kill us for sure—" All of a sudden, he was bawling like a baby. "I'm scared—I shouldn't be here—I'm *scared.* What am I trying to prove by coming out here, for God's sake? I'm some kind of hero or something? I tell you I'm scared—"

"Look," I said. "Mikuta's scared, *I'm* scared. So what? We'll make it, don't worry. And nobody's trying to be a hero."

"Nobody but Hero Stone," he said bitterly. He shook himself and gave a tight little laugh. "Some hero, eh?"

"We'll make it," I said.

"Sure," he said finally. "Sorry. I'll be okay."

I rolled over, but waited until he was good and quiet. Then I tried to sleep, but I didn't sleep too well. I kept thinking about that ledge. I'd known from the look of it what it was; a zinc slough of the sort Sanderson had warned us about, a wide sheet of almost pure zinc that had been thrown up white-hot from below, quite recently, just waiting for oxygen or sulfur to rot it through.

I knew enough about zinc to know that at these temperatures it gets brittle as glass. Take a chance like McIvers had taken and the whole sheet could snap like a dry pine board. And it wasn't McIvers' fault that it hadn't.

Five hours later, we were back at the wheel. We were hardly moving at all. The ragged surface was almost impass-able—great jutting rocks peppered the plateau; ledges crumbled the moment my tires touched them; long, open canyons turned into lead mires or sulfur pits.

A dozen times I climbed out of the Bug to prod out an uncertain area with my boots and pikestaff. Whenever I did, McIvers piled out behind me, running ahead like a schoolboy at the fair, then climbing back again red-faced and panting, while we moved the machines ahead another mile or two.

Time was pressing us now and McIvers wouldn't let me forget it. We had made only about three hundred twenty miles in six driving periods, so we were about a hundred miles or even more behind schedule.

"We're not going to make it," McIvers would complain angrily. "That Sun's going to be out to aphelion by the time we hit the Center—"

"Sorry, but I can't take it any faster," I told him. I was getting good and mad. I knew what he wanted, but didn't dare let him have it. I was scared enough pushing the Bug out on those ledges, even knowing that at least *I* was making the decisions. Put him in the lead and we wouldn't last for eight hours. Our nerves wouldn't take it, at any rate, even if the machines would.

Jack Stone looked up from the aluminum chart sheets. "Another hundred miles and we should hit a good stretch," he said. "Maybe we can make up distance there for a couple of days."

The Major agreed, but McIvers couldn't hold his impatience. He kept staring up at the Sun as if he had a personal grudge against it and stamped back and forth under the sunshield.

"That'll be just fine," he said. "*If* we ever get that far, that is."

We dropped it there, but the Major stopped me as we climbed aboard for the next run. "That guy's going to blow wide open if we don't move faster, Peter. I don't want him in the lead, no matter what happens. He's right though, about the need to make better time. Keep your head, but crowd your luck a little, okay?"

"I'll try," I said. It was asking the impossible and Mikuta knew it. We were on a long downward slope that shifted and buckled all around us, as though there were a molten underlay beneath the crust; the slope was broken by huge crevasses, partly covered with dust and zinc sheeting, like a vast glacier of stone and metal. The outside temperature registered 547° F. and getting hotter. It was no place to start rushing ahead.

I tried it anyway. I took half a dozen shaky passages, edging slowly out on flat zinc ledges, then toppling over and across. It seemed easy for a while and we made progress. We hit an even stretch and raced ahead. And then I quickly jumped on my brakes and jerked the Bug to a halt in a cloud of dust.

I'd gone too far. We were out on a wide flat sheet of gray stuff, apparently solid—until I'd suddenly caught sight of the crevasse beneath in the corner of my eye. It was an overhanging shell that trembled under me as I stopped.

McIvers' voice was in my ear. "What's the trouble now, Claney?"

"Move back!" I shouted. "It can't hold us!"

"Looks solid enough from here."

"You want to argue about it? It's too thin, it'll snap. Move back!"

I started edging back down the ledge. I heard McIvers swear; then I saw his Bug start to creep *outward* on the shelf. Not fast or reckless, this time, but slowly, churning up dust in a gentle cloud behind him.

I just stared and felt the blood rush to my head. It seemed so hot I could hardly breathe as he edged out beyond me, further and further—

I think I felt it snap before I saw it. My own machine gave a sickening lurch and a long black crack appeared across the shelf—and widened. Then the ledge began to upend. I heard a scream as McIvers' Bug rose up and up and then crashed down into the crevasse in a thundering slide of rock and shattered metal.

I just stared for a full minute, I think. I couldn't move until I heard Jack Stone groan and the Major shouting, "Claney! I couldn't see—what *happened?*"

"It snapped on him, that's what happened," I roared. I gunned my motor, edged forward toward the fresh broken edge of the shelf. The crevasse gaped; I couldn't see any sign of the machine. Dust was still billowing up blindingly from below.

We stood staring down, the three of us. I caught a glimpse of Jack Stone's face through his helmet. It wasn't pretty.

"Well," said the Major heavily, "that's that."

"I guess so." I felt the way Stone looked.

"Wait," said Stone. "I heard something."

He had. It was a cry in the earphones—faint, but unmistakable.

"Mac!" the Major called. "Mac, can you hear me?"

"Yeah, yeah. I can hear you." The voice was very weak.

"Are you all right?"

"I don't know. Broken leg, I think. It's—hot." There was a long pause. Then: "I think my cooler's gone out."

The Major shot me a glance, then turned to Stone. "Get a cable from the second sledge fast. He'll fry alive if we don't get him out of there. Peter, I need you to lower me. Use the tractor winch."

I lowered him; he stayed down only a few moments. When I hauled him up, his face was drawn. "Still alive," he panted. "He won't be very long, though." He hesitated for just an instant. "We've got to make a try."

"I don't like this ledge," I said. "It's moved twice since I got out. Why not back off and lower him a cable?"

"No good. The Bug is smashed and he's inside it. We'll need torches and I'll need one of you to help." He looked at me and then gave Stone a long look. "Peter, you'd better come."

"Wait," said Stone. His face was very white. "Let me go down with you."

"Peter is lighter."

"I'm not so heavy. Let me go down."

"Okay, if that's the way you want it." The Major tossed him a torch. "Peter, check these hitches and lower us slowly. If you see any kind of trouble, *anything*, cast yourself free and back off this thing, do you understand? This whole ledge may go."

I nodded. "Good luck."

They went over the ledge. I let the cable down bit by bit until it hit two hundred feet and slacked off.

"How does it look?" I shouted.

"Bad," said the Major. "We'll have to work fast. This whole side of the crevasse is ready to crumble. Down a little more."

Minutes passed without a sound. I tried to relax, but I couldn't. Then I felt the ground shift, and the tractor lurched to the side.

The Major shouted, *"It's going, Peter—pull back!"* and I threw the tractor into reverse, jerked the controls as the tractor rumbled off the shelf. The cable snapped, coiled up in front like a broken clockspring. The whole surface under me was shaking wildly now; ash rose in huge gray clouds. Then, with a roar, the whole shelf lurched and slid sideways. It teetered on the edge for seconds before it crashed into the crevasse, tearing the side wall down with it in a mammoth slide. I jerked the tractor to a halt as the dust and flame billowed up.

They were gone—all three of them, McIvers and the Major and Jack Stone—buried under a thousand tons of rock and zinc and molten lead. There wasn't any danger of anybody ever finding their bones.

Peter Claney leaned back, finishing his drink, rubbing his scarred face as he looked across at Baron.

Slowly, Baron's grip relaxed on the chair arm. *"You* got back," he said.

Claney nodded. "I got back, sure. I had the tractor and the sledges. I had seven days to drive back under that yellow Sun. I had plenty of time to think."

"You took the wrong man along," Baron said. "That was your mistake. Without him you would have made it."

"Never." Claney shook his head. "That's what I was thinking the first day or so—that it was *McIvers'* fault, that *he* was to blame. But that isn't true. He was wild, reckless, and had lots of nerve."

"But his judgment was bad!"

"It couldn't have been sounder. We had to keep to our schedule even if it killed us, because it would positively kill us if we didn't."

"But a man like that—"

"A man like McIvers was necessary. Can't you see that? It was the Sun that beat us, that surface. Perhaps we were licked the very day we started." Claney leaned across the table, his eyes pleading. "We didn't realize that, but it was *true*. There are places that men can't go, conditions men can't tolerate. The others had to die to learn that. I was lucky, I came back. But I'm trying to tell you what I found out—that *nobody* will ever make a Brightside Crossing."

"We will," said Baron. "It won't be a picnic, but we'll make it."

"But suppose you do," said Claney, suddenly. "Suppose I'm all wrong, suppose you *do* make it. Then what? *What comes next?*"

"The Sun," said Baron.

Claney nodded slowly. "Yes. That would be it, wouldn't it?" He laughed. "Good-by, Baron. Jolly talk and all that. Thanks for listening."

Baron caught his wrist as he started to rise. "Just one question more, Claney. Why did you come here?"

"To try to talk you out of killing yourself," said Claney.

"You're a liar," said Baron.

Claney stared down at him for a long moment. Then he crumpled in the chair. There was defeat in his pale blue eyes and something else.

"Well?"

Peter Claney spread his hands, a helpless gesture. "When do you leave, Baron? I want you to take me along."

VENUS

Venus is a frustrating planet, for it has long been a mystery even though it is the closest planet to ourselves. When it and the Earth are in appropriate positions in their orbits, they may be separated by only 38,900,000 kilometers (24,100,000 miles) or only 101 times the distance between the Earth and the Moon.

It is the brightest of the planets, far brighter than any star, brighter than any permanent object in our skies except the Sun and Moon, and with a larger apparent disc. You would suppose astronomers would have a field day studying it.

They don't. The closer it comes to us and the larger it gets, the more of the side that is facing us is dark. Venus is closer to the Sun than we are (its average distance from the Sun is only 0.72 that of Earth's distance) and it gets in between us and the Sun when it is close. We then see the wrong side.

Even if we could look at Venus completely Sun-lit, it would do us no good, for one of the earliest discoveries of the early telescopists was that Venus is covered with a solid layer of clouds that never breaks. Its visible "surface" is absolutely featureless.

Right down to the 1950s, we knew Venus's size and the nature of its orbit but nothing about its solid surface. We didn't even know what the planet's speed of rotation was.

One could guess, of course, and people did, fancying that they could measure the rotation from fugitive markings. Some reported that Venus rotated in 24 hours as Earth did; some reported that it faced one side to the Sun at all times (as Mercury was thought to do), so that it rotated once in 224.7 days, which is the planet's period of revolution.

Most people suspected a relatively fast rotation. Between that and the cloudy layer (which reflected three-fourths of the incoming Solar radiation) it was felt that Venus's surface, while warm, would not be too warm for life. The planet, it was felt, would be a tropical one everywhere, dark by night, rather gray by day.

Clouds are naturally associated with rain, so it seemed natural to suppose that Venus was a rainy planet. Some even felt that Venus might have a planetary ocean, with little or no land surface.

By the mid-1950s, however, astronomers began to come up with some puzzling news. Microwaves from Venus seemed to be coming in unexpectedly large quantities. To give off so much in the way of microwaves, Venus would have to be very hot— hotter than the boiling point of water. If that were so, Venus would have to be a hot desert, a super-Sahara.

It didn't seem likely and, for a while, many astronomers felt that there might be some mistake, that the data were being misinterpreted. Still, science fiction writers seized on the reports to write stories based on new versions of the Venus environment, such as "Prospector's Special," which was published in 1959.

If anything, though, the initial suggestions of Venerian heat were conservative. On December 14, 1962, a probe, Mariner 2, flew by Venus at a nearest approach of 35,000 kilometers (22,000 miles) and was able to measure the microwave emission with great precision. It seemed clear that Venus's surface temperature approached an unbelievable 500°C. on both the sunny side and the dark side.

There couldn't be a drop of liquid water anywhere on the surface of Venus, and even the world of "Prospector's Special" is now out of date.

Why should Venus be so hot? The answer probably lies in the

atmosphere. It was expected to be thicker than Earth's and to be rich in carbon dioxide, but the full extent of the thickness and richness wasn't known until 1967, when a Soviet probe, Venera IV, finally actually entered the atmosphere and passed through it to the solid surface of the planet.

It was supposed that the atmosphere might be 20 times as dense as Earth's; it was actually over 90 times as dense. And 95 percent of that souplike atmosphere was carbon dioxide.

Carbon dioxide is transparent to visible light and quite opaque to infrared. Sunlight passes through to hit the surface, be absorbed, and converted to heat. The hot surface reradiates energy as infrared, which cannot get through the atmosphere. The heat is trapped and Venus's temperature goes up till the infrared is forced through. The result is called a "runaway greenhouse effect" (so called because the glass in a greenhouse performs a similar function).

According to the data we are now receiving from Venus by way of our probes, not only is there not a drop of liquid water on the planet, but even the clouds are not simply water droplets. There is very likely sulfuric acid present; and if it could ever rain on Venus, which it can't, it would rain a wildly corrosive liquid.

And what about Venus's period of rotation? Scientists have sent microwave beams to Venus and these can pierce the clouds and bounce off the solid surface. Using microwave reflection, they can even make crude maps of that surface and have located what seem to be mountain ranges and volcanoes.

What's more, the microwave reflections measure the period of rotation, which turns out to be slow—even slower than its period of revolution. Venus turns on its axis only once in 243.1 Earth-days, and does so in a retrograde fashion—east to west, rather than west to east.

This means that the length of time between sunrise and sunset on Venus is 117 Earth-days.

Venus may be farther from the Sun than Mercury is, but Venus is the more hostile world of the two. It is hotter all over its surface than Mercury is even under the blaze of its Sun at its largest.

On Mercury, the temperature drops when the Sun is not at zenith, and during the night its surface gets cold, even very cold. Venus's thick atmosphere, whipping about in gales, equalizes the temperature everywhere and makes it hell everywhere.

Considering the surface temperature, the atmospheric pressure, and the sulfuric acid clouds, it doesn't seem as though manned exploration of Venus is going to take place in a hurry.

Prospector's Special

ROBERT SHECKLEY

The sandcar moved smoothly over the rolling dunes, its six fat wheels rising and falling like the ponderous rumps of tandem elephants. The hidden sun beat down from a dead-white sky, pouring heat into the canvas top, reflecting heat back from the parched sand.

"Stay awake," Morrison told himself, pulling the sandcar back to its compass course.

It was his twenty-first day on Venus's Scorpion Desert, his twenty-first day of fighting sleep while the sandcar rocked across the dunes, forging over humpbacked little waves. Night travel would have been easier, but there were too many steep ravines to avoid, too many house-sized boulders to dodge. Now he knew why men went into the desert in teams; one man drove while the other kept shaking him awake.

"But it's better alone," Morrison reminded himself. "Half the supplies and no accidental murders."

His head was beginning to droop; he snapped himself erect. In front of him, the landscape shimmered and danced through the Polaroid windshield. The sandcar lurched and rocked with treacherous gentleness. Morrison rubbed his eyes and turned on the radio.

He was a big sunburned, rangy young man with close-cropped black hair and gray eyes. He had come to Venus with a grubstake of twenty thousand dollars, to find his fortune in the Scorpion Desert as others had done before him.

He had outfitted in Presto, the last town on the edge of the wilderness, and spent all but ten dollars on the sandcar and equipment.

In Presto, ten dollars just covered the cost of a drink in the town's only saloon. So Morrison ordered rye and water, drank with the miners and prospectors, and laughed at the oldtimers' yarns about the sandwolf packs and the squadrons of voracious birds that inhabited the interior desert. He knew all about sunblindness, heatstroke, and telephone breakdown. He was sure none of it would happen to him.

But now, after twenty-one days and eighteen hundred miles, he had learned respect for this waterless waste of sand and stone three times the area of the Sahara. You really *could* die here!

But you could also get rich, and that was what Morrison planned to do.

His radio hummed. At full volume, he could hear the faintest murmur of dance music from Venusborg. Then it faded and only the hum was left.

He turned off the radio and gripped the steering wheel tightly in both hands. He unclenched one hand and looked at his watch. Nine-fifteen in the morning. At ten-thirty he would stop and take a nap. A man had to have rest in this heat. But only a half-hour nap. Treasure lay somewhere ahead of him, and he wanted to find it before his supplies got much lower.

The precious outcroppings of goldenstone *had* to be up ahead! He'd been following traces for two days now. Maybe he would hit a real bonanza, as Kirk did in '89, or Edmonson and Arsler in '93. If so, he would do just what they did. He'd order up a Prospector's Special, and to hell with the cost.

The sandcar rolled along at an even thirty miles an hour, and Morrison tried to concentrate on the heat-blasted yellow-brown landscape. That sandstone patch over there was just the tawny color of Janie's hair.

After he struck it rich, he and Janie would get married,

and he'd go back to Earth and buy an ocean farm. No more prospecting. Just one rich strike so he could buy his spread on the deep blue Atlantic. Maybe some people thought fish-herding was tame; it was good enough for him.

He could see it now, the mackerel herds drifting along and browsing at the plankton pens, himself and his trusty dolphin keeping an eye out for the silvery flash of a predatory barra-cuda or a steel-gray shark coming along behind the branch-ing coral. . . .

Morrison felt the sandcar lurch. He woke up, grabbed the steering wheel and turned it hard. During his moments of sleep, the vehicle had crept over the dune's crumbling edge. Sand and pebbles spun under the fat tires as the sandcar fought for traction. The car tilted perilously. The tires shrieked against the sand, gripped, and started to pull the ve-hicle back up the slope.

Then the whole face of the dune collapsed.

Morrison held on to the steering wheel as the sandcar flipped over on its side and rolled down the slope. Sand filled his mouth and eyes. He spat and held on while the car rolled over again and dropped into emptiness.

For seconds, he was in the air. The sandcar hit bottom squarely on its wheels. Morrison heard a double boom as the two rear tires blew out. Then his head hit the windshield.

When he recovered consciousness, the first thing he did was look at his watch. It read 10:35.

"Time for that nap," Morrison said to himself. "But I guess I'll survey the situation first."

He found that he was at the bottom of a shallow fault strewn with knife-edged pebbles. Two tires had blown on im-pact, his windshield was gone, and one of the doors was sprung. His equipment was strewn around, but appeared to be intact.

"Could have been worse," Morrison said.

He bent down to examine the tires more carefully.

"It *is* worse," he said.

The two blown tires were shredded beyond repair. There wasn't enough rubber left in them to make a child's balloon. He had used up his spares ten days back crossing Devil's Grill. Used them and discarded them. He couldn't go on without tires.

Morrison unpacked his telephone. He wiped dust from its black plastic face, then dialed Al's Garage in Presto. After a moment, the small video screen lighted up. He could see a man's long, mournful grease-stained face.

"Al's Garage. Eddie speaking."

"Hi, Eddie. This is Tom Morrison. I bought that GM sandcar from you about a month ago. Remember?"

"Sure I remember you," Eddie said. "You're the guy doing a single into the Southwest Track. How's the bus holding out?"

"Fine. Great little car. Reason I called—"

"Hey," Eddie said, "what happened to your face?"

Morrison put his hand to his forehead and felt blood. "Nothing much," he said. "I went over a dune and blew out two tires."

He turned the telephone so that Eddie could see the tires.

"Unrepairable," said Eddie.

"I thought so. And I used up all my spares crossing Devil's Grill. Look, Eddie, I'd like you to 'port me a couple of tires. Retreads are fine. I can't move the sandcar without them."

"Sure," Eddie said, "except I haven't any retreads. I'll have to 'port you new ones at five hundred apiece. Plus four hundred dollars 'porting charges. Fourteen hundred dollars, Mr. Morrison."

"All right."

"Yes, sir. Now if you'll show me the cash, or a money order which you can send back with the receipt, I'll get moving on it."

"At the moment," Morrison said, "I haven't got a cent on me."

"Bank account?"

"Stripped clean."

"Bonds? Property? Anything you can convert into cash?"

"Nothing except this sandcar, which you sold me for eight thousand dollars. When I come back, I'll settle my bill with the sandcar."

"*If* you get back. Sorry, Mr. Morrison. No can do."

"What do you mean?" Morrison asked. "You know I'll pay for the tires."

"And you know the rules on Venus," Eddie said, his mournful face set in obstinate lines. "No credit! Cash and carry!"

"I can't run the sandcar without tires," Morrison said. "Are you going to strand me out here?"

"Who in hell is stranding you?" Eddie asked. "This sort of thing happens to prospectors every day. You know what you have to do now, Mr. Morrison. Call Public Utility and declare yourself a bankrupt. Sign over what's left of the sandcar, equipment, and anything you've found on the way. They'll get you out."

"I'm not turning back," Morrison said. "Look!" He held the telephone close to the ground. "You see the traces, Eddie? See those red and purple flecks? There's precious stuff near here!"

"Every prospector sees traces," Eddie said. "Damned desert if full of traces."

"These are rich," Morrison said. "These are leading straight to big stuff, a bonanza lode. Eddie, I know it's a lot to ask, but if you could stake me to a couple of tires—"

"I can't do it," Eddie said. "I just work here. I can't 'port you any tires, not unless you show me money first. Otherwise I get fired and probably jailed. You know the law."

"Cash and carry," Morrison said bleakly.

"Right. Be smart and turn back now. Maybe you can try again some other time."

"I spent twelve years getting this stake together," Morrison said. "I'm not going back."

He turned off the telephone and tried to think. Was there

anyone else on Venus he could call? Only Max Krandall, his jewel broker. But Max couldn't raise fourteen hundred dollars in that crummy two-by-four office near Venusborg's jewel market. Max could barely scrape up his own rent, much less take care of stranded prospectors.

"I can't ask Max for help," Morrison decided. "Not until I've found goldenstone. The real stuff, not just traces. So that leaves it up to me."

He opened the back of the sandcar and began to unload, piling his equipment on the sand. He would have to choose carefully; anything he took would have to be carried on his back.

The telephone had to go with him, and his lightweight testing kit. Food concentrates, revolver, compass. And nothing else but water, all the water he could carry. The rest of the stuff would have to stay behind.

By nightfall, Morrison was ready. He looked regretfully at the twenty cans of water he was leaving. In the desert, water was a man's most precious possession, second only to his telephone. But it couldn't be helped. After drinking his fill, he hoisted his pack and set a southwest course into the desert.

For three days he trekked to the southwest; then on the fourth day he veered to due south, following an increasingly rich trace. The sun, eternally hidden, beat down on him, and the dead-white sky was like a roof of heated iron over his head. Morrison followed the traces, and something followed him.

On the sixth day, he sensed movement just out of the range of his vision. On the seventh day, he saw what was trailing him.

Venus's own brand of wolf, small, lean, with a yellow coat and long, grinning jaws, it was one of the few mammals that made its home in the Scorpion Desert. As Morrison watched, two more sandwolves appeared beside it.

He loosened the revolver in its holster. The wolves made no attempt to come closer. They had plenty of time.

Morrison kept on going, wishing he had brought a rifle

with him. But that would have meant eight pounds more, which meant eight pounds less water.

As he was pitching camp at dusk the eighth day, he heard a crackling sound. He whirled around and located its source, about ten feet to his left and above his head. A little vortex had appeared, a tiny mouth in the air like a whirlpool in the sea. It spun, making the characteristic crackling sounds of 'porting.

"Now who could be 'porting anything to me?" Morrison asked, waiting while the whirlpool slowly widened.

Solidoporting from a base projector to a field target was a standard means of moving goods across the vast distances of Venus. Any inanimate object could be 'ported; animate beings couldn't because the process involved certain minor but distressing molecular changes in protoplasm. A few people had found this out the hard way when 'porting was first introduced.

Morrison waited. The aerial whirlpool became a mouth three feet in diameter. From the mouth stepped a chrome-plated robot carrying a large sack.

"Oh, it's you," Morrison said.

"Yes, sir," the robot said, now completely clear of the field. "Williams Four at your service with the Venus Mail."

It was a robot of medium height, thin-shanked and flat-footed, humanoid in appearance, amiable in disposition. For twenty-three years it had been Venus's entire postal service—sorter, deliverer, and dead storage. It had been built to last, and for twenty-three years the mails had always come through.

"Here we are, Mr. Morrison," Williams 4 said. "Only twice-a-month mail call in the desert, I'm sorry to say, but it comes promptly and that's a blessing. This is for you. And this. I think there's one more. Sandcar broke down, eh?"

"It sure did," Morrison said, taking his letters.

Williams 4 went on rummaging through its bag. Although it was a superbly efficient postman, the old robot was known as the worst gossip on three planets.

"There's one more in here somewhere," Williams 4 said. "Too bad about the sandcar. They just don't build 'em like they did in my youth. Take my advice, young man. Turn back if you still have the chance."

Morrison shook his head.

"Foolish, downright foolish," the old robot said. "Pity you don't have my perspective. Too many's the time I've come across you boys lying in the sand in the dried-out sack of your skin, or with your bones gnawed to splinters by the sandwolves and the filthy black kites. Twenty-three years I've been delivering mail to fine-looking young men like you, and each one thinking he's unique and different."

The robot's eyecells became distant with memory. "But they *aren't* different," Williams 4 said. "They're as alike as robots off the assembly line—especially after the wolves get through with them. And then I have to send their letters and personal effects back to their loved ones on Earth."

"I know," Morrison said. "But some get through, don't they?"

"Sure they do," the robot said. "I've seen men make one, two, three fortunes. And then die on the sands trying to make a fourth."

"Not me," Morrison said. "I just want one. Then I'm going to buy me an undersea farm on Earth."

The robot shuddered. "I have a dread of salt water. But to each his own. Good luck, young man."

The robot looked Morrison over carefully—probably to see what he had in the way of personal effects—then climbed back into the aerial whirlpool. In a moment, it was gone. In another moment, the whirlpool had vanished.

Morrison sat down to read his mail. The first letter was from his jewel broker, Max Krandall. It told about the depression that had hit Venusborg, and hinted that Krandall might have to go into bankruptcy if some of his prospectors didn't strike something good.

The second letter was a statement from the Venus Telephone Company. Morrison owed two hundred and ten dollars and eight cents for two months' telephone service. Unless he remitted this sum at once, his telephone was liable to be turned off.

The last letter, all the way from Earth, was from Janie. It was filled with news about his cousins, aunts and uncles. She told him about the Atlantic farm sites she had looked over, and the wonderful little place she had found near Martinique in the Caribbean. She begged him to give up prospecting if it looked dangerous; they could find another way of financing the farm. She sent all her love and wished him a happy birthday in advance.

"Birthday?" Morrison asked himself. "Let's see, today is July twenty-third. No, it's the twenty-fourth, and my birthday's August first. Thanks for remembering Janie."

That night he dreamed of Earth and the blue expanse of the Atlantic Ocean. But toward dawn, when the heat of Venus became insistent, he found he was dreaming of mile upon mile of goldenstone, of grinning sandwolves, and of the Prospector's Special.

Rock gave way to sand as Morrison plowed his way across the bottom of a long-vanished lake. Then it was rock again, twisted and tortured into a thousand gaunt shapes. Reds, yellows, and browns swam in front of his eyes. In all that desert, there wasn't one patch of green.

He continued his trek into the tumbled stone mazes of the interior desert, and the wolves trekked with him, keeping pace far out on either flank.

Morrison ignored them. He had enough on his mind just to negotiate the sheer cliffs and the fields of broken stone that blocked his way to the south.

By the eleventh day after leaving the sandcar, the traces were almost rich enough for panning. The sandwolves were tracking him still, and his water was almost gone. Another day's march would finish him.

Morrison thought for a moment, then unstrapped his telephone and dialed Public Utility in Venusborg.

The video screen showed a stern, severely dressed woman

with iron-gray hair. "Public Utility," she said. "May we be of service?"

"Hi," Morrison said cheerfully. "How's the weather in Venusborg?"

"Hot," the woman said. "How's it out there?"

"I hadn't even noticed," Morrison said, grinning. "Too busy counting my fortune."

"You've found goldenstone?" the woman asked, her expression becoming less severe.

"Sure have," Morrison said. "But don't pass ·the word around yet. I'm still staking my claim. I think I can use a refill on these."

Smiling easily, he held up his canteens. Sometimes it worked. Sometimes, if you showed enough confidence, Public Utility would fill you up without checking your account. True, it was embezzling, but this was no time for niceties.

"I suppose your account is in order?" asked the woman.

"Of course," Morrison said, feeling his smile grow stiff. "The name's Tom Morrison. You can just check—"

"Oh, I don't do that personally," the woman said. "Hold that canteen steady. Here we go."

Gripping the canteen in both hands, Morrison watched as the water, 'ported four thousand miles from Venusborg, appeared as a slender crystal stream above the mouth of his canteen. The stream entered the canteen, making a wonderful gurgling sound. Watching it, Morrison found his dry mouth actually was beginning to salivate.

Then the water stopped.

"What's the matter?" Morrison asked.

His video screen went blank. Then it cleared, and Morrison found himself staring into a man's narrow face. The man was seated in front of a large desk. The sign in front of him read *Milton P. Reade, Vice President, Accounts.*

"Mr. Morrison," Reade said, "your account is overdrawn. You have been obtaining water under false pretenses. That is a criminal offense."

"I'm going to pay for the water," Morrison said.

"When?"

"As soon as I get back to Venusborg."

"With what," asked Mr. Reade, "do you propose to pay?"

"With goldenstone," Morrison said. "Look around here, Mr. Reade. The traces are rich! Richer than they were for the Kirk claim! I'll be hitting the outcroppings in another day—"

"That's what every prospector thinks," Mr. Reade said. "Every prospector on Venus is only a day from goldenstone. And they all expect credit from Public Utility."

"But in this case—"

"Public Utility," Mr. Reade continued inexorably, "is not a philanthropic organization. Its charter specifically forbids the extension of credit. Venus is a frontier, Mr. Morrison, a *farflung* frontier. Every manufactured article on Venus must be imported from Earth at outrageous cost. We do have our own water, but locating it, purifying it, then 'porting it is an expensive process. This company, like every other company on Venus, necessarily operates on a very narrow margin of profit, which is invariably plowed back into further expansion. That is why there can be no credit on Venus."

"I know all that," Morrison said. "But I'm telling you, I only need a day or two more—"

"Absolutely impossible. By the rules, we shouldn't even help you out now. The time to report bankruptcy was a week ago, when your sandcar broke down. Your garage man reported, as required by law. But you didn't. We would be within our rights to leave you stranded. Do you understand that?"

"Yes, of course," Morrison said wearily.

"However, the company has decided to stretch a point in your favor. If you turn back immediately, we will keep you supplied with water for the return trip."

"I'm not turning back yet. I'm almost on the real stuff."

"You must turn back! Be reasonable, Morrison! Where would we be if we let every prospector wander over the desert while we supplied his water? There'd be ten thousand men out there, and we'd be out of business inside of a year. I'm stretching the rules now. Turn back."

"No," said Morrison.

"You'd better think about it. If you don't turn back now, Public Utility takes no further responsibility for your water supply."

Morrison nodded. If he went on, he would stand a good chance of dying in the desert. But if he turned back, what then? He would be in Venusborg, penniless and in debt, looking for work in an overcrowded city. He'd sleep in a community shed and eat at a soup kitchen with the other prospectors who had turned back. And how would he be able to raise the fare back to Earth? When would he ever see Janie again?

"I guess I'll keep on going," Morrison said.

"Then Public Utility takes no further responsibility for you," Reade repeated, and hung up.

Morrison packed up his telephone, took a sip from his meager water supply, and went on.

The sandwolves loped along at each side, moving in closer. Overhead, a delta-winged kite found him. It balanced on the updrafts for a day and a night, waiting for the wolves to finish him. Then a flock of small flying scorpions sighted the waiting kite. They drove the big creature upstairs into the cloud bank. For a day the flying reptiles waited. Then they in turn were driven off by a squadron of black kites.

The traces were very rich now, on the fifteenth day since he had left the sandcar. By rights, he should be walking over goldenstone. He should be surrounded by goldenstone. But still he hadn't found any.

Morrison sat down and shook his last canteen. It gave off no wet sound. He uncapped it and turned it up over his mouth. Two drops trickled down his parched throat.

It was about four days since he had talked to Public Utility. He must have used up the last of his water yesterday. Or had it been the day before?

He recapped the empty canteen and looked around at the heat-blasted landscape. Abruptly he pulled the telephone out of his pack and dialed Max Krandall in Venusborg.

Krandall's round worried face swam into focus on the screen. "Tommy," he said, "you look like hell."

"I'm all right," Morrison said. "A little dried out, that's all. Max, I'm near goldenstone."

"Are you sure?" Krandall asked.

"See for yourself," Morrison said, swinging the telephone around. "Look at the stone formations! Do you see the red and purple markings over there?"

"Traces, all right," Krandall admitted dubiously.

"There's rich stuff just beyond it," Morrison said. "There has to be! Look, Max, I know you're short on money, but I'm going to ask you a favor. Send me a pint of water. Just a pint, so I can go on for another day or two. We can both get rich for the price of a pint of water."

"I can't do it," Krandall said sadly.

"You can't?"

"That's right. Tommy, I'd send you water even if there wasn't anything around you but sandstone and granite. Do you think I'd let you die of thirst if I could help it? But I can't do a thing. Take a look."

Krandall rotated his telephone. Morrison saw that the chairs, table, desk, filing cabinet and safe were gone from the office. All that was left in the room was the telephone.

"I don't know why they haven't taken out the phone," Krandall said. "I owe two months on my bill."

"I do too," said Morrison.

"I'm stripped," Krandall said. "I haven't got a dime. Don't get me wrong, I'm not worried about myself. I can always eat at a soup kitchen. But I can't 'port you any water. Not you or Remstaater."

"Jim Remstaater?"

"Yeah. He was following a trace up north past Forgotten River. His sandcar broke an axle last week and he wouldn't turn back. His water ran out yesterday."

"I'd bail him out if I could," said Morrison.

"And he'd bail you out if he could," Krandall said. "But he can't and you can't and I can't. Tommy, you have only one hope."

"What's that?"

"Find goldenstone. Not just traces, find the real thing worth real money. Then phone me. If you really have goldenstone, I'll bring in Wilkes from Tri-Planet Mining and get him to advance us some money. He'll probably want fifty per cent of the claim."

"That's plain robbery!"

"No, it's just the high cost of credit on Venus," Krandall answered. "Don't worry, there'll still be plenty left over. But you have to find goldenstone first."

"OK," Morrison said. "It should be around here somewhere. Max, what's today's date?"

"July thirty-first. Why?"

"Just wondering. I'll call you when I've found something."

After hanging up, Morrison sat on a little boulder and stared dully at the sand. July thirty-first. Tomorrow was his birthday. His family would be thinking about him. Aunt Bess in Pasadena, the twins in Laos, Uncle Ted in Durango. And Janie, of course, waiting for him in Tampa.

Morrison realized that tommorow might be his last birthday unless he found goldenstone.

He got to his feet, strapped the telephone back in his pack beside the empty canteens, and set a course to the south.

He wasn't alone. The birds and beasts of the desert marched with him. Overhead, the silent black kites circled endlessly. The sandwolves crept closer on his flanks, their red tongues lolling out, waiting for the carcass to fall.

"I'm not dead yet!" Morrison shouted at them.

He drew his revolver and fired at the nearest wolf. At twenty feet, he missed. He went down on one knee, held the revolver tightly in both hands and fired again. The wolf yelped in pain. The pack immediately went for the wounded animal, and the kites swooped down for their share.

Morrison put the revolver back in its holster and went on. He could tell he was in a badly dehydrated state. The landscape jumped and danced in front of him, and his footing was unsure. He discarded the empty canteens, threw away everything but the testing kit, telephone, and revolver. Either he was coming out of the desert in style or he wasn't coming out at all.

The traces continued to run rich. But still he came upon no sign of tangible wealth.

That evening he found a shallow cave set into the base of a cliff. He crawled inside and built a barricade of rocks across the entrance. Then he drew his revolver and leaned back against the far wall.

The sandwolves were outside, sniffing and snapping their jaws. Morrison propped himself up and got ready for an all-night vigil.

He didn't sleep, but he couldn't stay awake, either. Dreams and visions tormented him. He was back on Earth and Janie was saying to him, "It's the tuna. Something must be wrong with their diet. Every last one of them is sick."

"It's the darnedest thing," Morrison told her. "Just as soon as you domesticate a fish, it turns into a prima donna."

"Are you going to stand there philosophizing," Jane asked, "while your fish are sick?"

"Call the vet."

"I did. He's off at the Blakes' place, taking care of their dairy whale."

"All right, I'll go out and take a look." He slipped on his face mask. Grinning, he said, "I don't even have time to dry off before I have to go out again."

His face and chest were wet.

Morrison opened his eyes. His face and chest *were* wet— from perspiration. Staring at the partially blocked mouth of the cave, he could see green eyes, two, four, six, eight.

He fired at them, but they didn't retreat. He fired again, and his bullet ricocheted off the cave wall, stinging him with stone splinters. With his next shots, he succeeded in winging one of the wolves. The pack withdrew.

That emptied the revolver. Morrison searched through his pockets and found five more cartridges. He carefully loaded the gun. Dawn couldn't be far away now.

And then he was dreaming again, this time of the Prospector's Special. He had heard about it in every little saloon that bordered the Scorpion. Bristly-bearded old prospectors told a hundred different stories about it, and the cynical bartenders chimed in with their versions. Kirk had it in '89, ordered up big and special just for him. Edmonson and Arsler received it in '93. That was certain. And other men had had it too, as they sat on their precious goldenstone claims. Or so people said.

But was it real? Was there such a thing as the Prospector's Special? Would he live to see that rainbow-hued wonder, tall as a church steeple, wide as a house, more precious than goldenstone itself?

Sure he would! Why, he could almost see it now . . .

Morrison shook himself awake. It was morning. Painfully, he crawled out of the cave to face the day.

He stumbled and crawled to the south, escorted closely by wolves, shaded by predatory flying things. His fingers scrabbled along rock and sand. The traces were rich, rich!

But where in all this desolation was the goldenstone?

Where? He was almost past caring. He drove his sunburned, dried-out body, stopping only to fire a single shot when the wolves came too close.

Four bullets left.

He had to fire again when the kites, growing impatient, started diving at his head. A lucky shot tore into the flock, downing two. It gave the wolves something to fight over. Morrison crawled on blindly.

And fell over the edge of a little cliff.

It wasn't a serious fall, but the revolver was knocked from his hand. Before he could find it, the wolves were on him.

Only their greed saved Morrison. While they fought over him, he rolled away and retrieved his revolver. Two shots scattered the pack. That left one bullet.

He'd have to save that one for himself, because he was too tired to go on. He sank to his knees. The traces were rich here. Fantastically rich. Somewhere nearby . . .

"Well, I'll be damned," Morrison said.

The little ravine into which he had fallen was solid goldenstone.

He picked up a pebble. Even in its rough state he could see the deep luminous golden glow, the fiery red and purple flecks deep in the shining stone.

"Make sure," Morrison told himself. "No false alarms, no visions, no wild hopes. Make sure."

He broke off a chunk of rock with the butt of his revolver. It still looked like goldenstone. He took out his testing kit and spilled a few drops of white solution on the rock. The solution foamed green.

"Goldenstone, sure as sure," Morrison said, looking around at the glowing cliff walls. "Hey, I'm rich!"

He took out his telephone. With trembling fingers he dialed Krandall's number.

"Max!" Morrison shouted. "I've hit it! I've hit the real stuff!"

"My name is not Max," a voice over the telephone said.

"Huh?"

"My name is Boyard," the man said.

The video screen cleared, and Morrison saw a thin sallow-faced man with a hairline mustache.

"I'm sorry, Mr. Boyard," Morrison said. "I must have gotten the wrong number. I was calling—"

"It doesn't matter who you were calling," Mr. Boyard said. "I am District Supervisor of the Venus Telephone Company. Your bill is two months overdue."

"I can pay it now," Morrison said, grinning.

"Excellent," said Mr. Boyard. "As soon as you do, your service will be resumed."

The screen began to fade.

"Wait!" Morrison cried. "I can pay as soon as I reach your office. But I must make one telephone call. Just one call, so that I—"

"Not a chance," Mr. Boyard said decisively. "*After* you have paid your bill, your service will be turned on immediately."

"I've got the money right here!" Morrison said. "Right here in my hand!"

Mr. Boyard paused. "Well, it's unusual, but I suppose we could arrange for a special robot messenger if you are willing to pay the expenses."

"I am!"

"Hm. It's irregular, but I daresay we . . . Where is the money?"

"Right here," Morrison said. "You recognize it, don't you? It's goldenstone!"

"I am sick and tired of the tricks you prospectors think you can put over on us. Holding up a handful of pebbles—"

"But this is really goldenstone! Can't you see it?"

"I am a businessman," Mr. Boyard said, "not a jeweler. I wouldn't know goldenstone from goldenrod."

The video screen went blank.

Frantically, Morrison tried to reach the operator. There was nothing, not even a dial tone. His telephone was disconnected.

He put the instrument down and surveyed his situation. The narrow crevice into which he had fallen ran straight for about twenty yards, then curved to the left. No cave was visible in the steep walls, no place where he could build a barricade.

He heard a movement behind him. Whirling around, he saw a huge old wolf in full charge. Without a moment's hesitation, Morrison drew and fired, blasting off the top of the beast's head.

"Damn it," Morrison said. "I was going to save that bullet for myself."

It gave him a moment's grace. He ran down the ravine, looking for an opening in its sides. Goldenstone glowed at him and sparkled red and purple. And the sandwolves loped along behind him.

Then Morrison stopped. In front of him, the curving ravine ended in a sheer wall.

He put his back against it, holding the revolver by its butt. The wolves stopped five feet from him, gathering themselves for a rush. There were ten or twelve of them, and they were packed three deep in the narrow pass. Overhead, the kites circled, waiting for their turn.

At that moment, Morrison heard the crackling sound of 'porting equipment. A whirlpool appeared above the wolves' heads and they backed hastily away.

"Just in time!" Morrison said.

"In time for what?" asked Williams 4, the postman.

The robot climbed out of the vortex and looked around.

"Well, young man," Williams 4 said, "this is a fine fix you've gotten yourself into. Didn't I warn you? Didn't I advise you to turn back? And now look!"

"You were perfectly right," Morrison said. "What did Max Krandall send me?"

"Max Krandall did not, and could not, send a thing."

"Then why are you here?"

"Because it's your birthday," Williams 4 said. "We of the Postal Department always give special service for birthdays. Here you are."

Williams 4 gave him a handful of mail, birthday greetings from Janie, and from his aunts, uncles, and cousins on Earth.

"Something else here," Williams 4 said, rummaging in his bag. "I *think* there was something else here. Let me see . . . Yes, here it is."

He handed Morrison a small package.

Hastily, Morrison tore off the wrappings. It was a birthday present from his Aunt Mina in New Jersey. He opened it. It was a large box of salt-water taffy, direct from Atlantic City.

"Quite a delicacy, I'm told," said Williams 4, who had

been peering over his shoulder. "But not very satisfactory under the circumstances. Well, young man, I hate to see anyone die on his birthday. The best I can wish you is a speedy and painless departure."

The robot began walking toward the vortex.

"Wait!" Morrison cried. "You can't just leave me like this! I haven't had any water in days! And those wolves—"

"I know," Williams 4 said. "Do you think I feel *happy* about it? Even a robot has some feelings!"

"Then help me."

"I can't. The rules of the Postal Department expressly and categorically forbid it. I remember Abner Lathe making much the same request of me in '97. It took three years for a burial party to reach him."

"You have an emergency telephone, haven't you?" Morrison asked.

"Yes. But I can use it only for personal emergencies."

"Can you at least carry a letter for me? A special delivery letter?"

"Of course I can," the robot postman said. "That's what I'm here for. I can even lend you pencil and paper."

Morrison accepted the pencil and paper and tried to think. If he wrote to Max now, special delivery, Max would have the letter in a matter of hours. But how long would Max need to raise some money and send him water and ammunition? A day, two days? Morrison would have to figure out some way of holding out.

"I assume you have a stamp," the robot said.

"I don't," Morrison replied. "But I'll buy one from you. Solidoport special."

"Excellent," said the robot. "We have just put out a new series of Venusborg triangulars. I consider them quite an esthetic accomplishment. They cost three dollars apiece."

"That's fine. Very reasonable. Let me have one."

"There is the question of payment."

"Here," Morrison said, handing the robot a piece of gold-enstone worth about five thousand dollars in the rough.

The postman examined the stone, then handed it back. "I'm sorry, I can accept only cash."

"But this is worth more than a thousand postage stamps!" Morrison said. "This is goldenstone!"

"It may well be," Williams 4 said. "But I have never had any assaying knowledge taped into me. Nor is the Venus Postal Service run on a barter system. I'll have to ask for three dollars in bills or coins."

"I don't have it."

"I am very sorry." Williams 4 turned to go.

"You can't just go and let me die!"

"I can and must," Williams 4 said sadly. "I am only a robot, Mr. Morrison. I was made by men, and naturally I partake of some of their sensibilities. That's as it should be. But I also have my limits, which, in their nature, are similar to the limits most humans have on this harsh planet. And, unlike humans, I cannot transcend my limits."

The robot started to climb into the whirlpool. Morrison stared at him blankly, and saw beyond him the waiting wolf pack. He saw the soft glow of several million dollars' worth of goldenstone shining from the ravine's walls.

Something snapped inside him.

With an inarticulate yell, Morrison dived, tackling the robot around the ankles. Williams 4, half in and half out of the 'porting vortex, struggled and kicked, and almost succeeded in shaking Morrison loose. But with a maniac's strength Morrison held on. Inch by inch he dragged the robot out of the vortex, threw him on the ground and pinned him.

"You are disrupting the mail service," said Williams 4.

"That's not all I'm going to disrupt," Morrison growled. "I'm not afraid of dying. That was part of the gamble. But I'm damned if I'm going to die fifteen minutes after I've struck it rich!"

"You have no choice."

"I do. I'm going to use that emergency telephone of yours."

"You can't," Williams 4 said. "I refuse to extrude it. And

you could never reach it without the resources of a machine shop."

"Could be," said Morrison. "I plan to find out." He pulled out his empty revolver.

"What are you going to do?" Williams 4 asked.

"I'm going to see if I can smash you into scrap metal *without* the resources of a machine shop. I think your eyecells would be a logical place to begin."

"They would indeed," said the robot. "I have no personal sense of survival, of course. But let me point out that you would be leaving all Venus without a postman. Many would suffer because of your antisocial action."

"I hope so," Morrison said, raising the revolver above his head.

"Also," the robot said hastily, "you would be destroying government property. That is a serious offense."

Morrison laughed and swung the pistol. The robot moved its head quickly, dodging the blow. It tried to wriggle free, but Morrison's two hundred pounds was seated firmly on its thorax.

"I won't miss this time," Morrison promised, hefting the revolver.

"Stop!" Williams 4 said. "It is my duty to protect government property, even if that property happens to be myself. You may use my telephone, Mr. Morrison. Bear in mind that this offense is punishable by a sentence of not more than ten and not less than five years in the Solar Swamp Penitentiary."

"Let's have that telephone," Morrison said.

The robot's chest opened and a small telephone extruded. Morrison dialed Max Krandall and explained the situation.

"I see, I see," Krandall said. "All right, I'll try to find Wilkes. But, Tom, I don't know how much I can do. It's after business hours. Most places are closed—"

"Get them open again," said Morrison. "I can pay for it. And get Jim Remstaater out of trouble, too."

"It can't be done just like that. You haven't established

any rights to your claim. You haven't even proved that your claim is valuable."

"Look at it." Morrison turned the telephone so that Krandall could see the glowing walls of the ravine.

"Looks real," Krandall said. "But unfortunately, all that glitters is not goldenstone."

"What can we do?" Morrison asked.

"We'll have to take it step by step. I'll 'port you the Public Surveyor. He'll check your claim, establish its limits, and make sure no one else has filed on it. You give him a chunk of goldenstone to take back. A big chunk."

"How can I cut goldenstone? I don't have any tools."

"You'll have to figure out a way. He'll take the chunk back for assaying. If it's rich enough, you're all set."

"And if it isn't?"

"Perhaps we better not talk about that," Krandall said. "I'll get right to work on this, Tommy. Good luck!"

Morrison signed off. He stood up and helped the robot to its feet.

"In twenty-three years of service," Williams 4 said, "this is the first time anybody has threatened the life of a government postal employee. I must report this to the police authorities at Venusborg, Mr. Morrison. I have no choice."

"I know," Morrison said. "But I guess five or ten years in the penitentiary is better than dying."

"I doubt it. I carry mail there, you know. You will have the opportunity of seeing for yourself in about six months."

"What?" said Morrison, stunned.

"In about six months, after I have completed my mail calls around the planet and returned to Venusborg. A matter like this must be reported in person. But first and foremost, the mails must go through."

"Thanks, Williams. I don't know how——"

"I am simply performing my duty," the robot said as it climbed into the vortex. "If you are still on Venus in six months, I will be delivering your mail to the penitentiary."

"I won't be here," Morrison said. "So long, Williams!"

The robot disappeared into the 'porting vortex. Then the vortex disappeared. Morrison was alone in the Venusian twilight.

He found an outcropping of goldenstone larger than a man's head. He chipped at it with his pistol butt, and tiny particles danced and shimmered in the air. After an hour, he had put four dents in his revolver, but he had barely scratched the highly refractory surface of the goldenstone.

The sandwolves began to edge forward. Morrison threw stones at them and shouted in his dry, cracked voice. The wolves retreated.

He examined the outcropping again and found a hairline fault running along one edge. He concentrated his blows along the fault.

The goldenstone refused to crack.

Morrison wiped sweat from his eyes and tried to think. A chisel, he needed a chisel . . .

He pulled off his belt. Putting the edge of the steel buckle against the crack, he managed to hammer it in a fraction of an inch. Three more blows drove the buckle firmly into the fault. With another blow, the outcropping sheared off cleanly. He had separated a twenty-pound piece from the cliff. At fifty dollars a troy ounce, this lump should be worth about twelve thousand dollars—if it assayed out as pure as it looked.

The twilight had turned a deep gray when the Public Surveyor 'ported in. It was a short, squat robot with a conservative crackle-black finish.

"Good day, sir," the surveyor said. "You wish to file a claim? A standard unrestricted mining claim?"

"That's right," Morrison said.

"And where is the center of the aforesaid claim?"

"Huh? The center? I guess I'm standing on it."

"Very well," the robot said.

Extruding a steel tape, it walked rapidly away from Morrison. At a distance of two hundred yards, it stopped. More steel tape fluttered as it walked, flew, and climbed a square with Morrison at the center. When it had finished, the surveyor stood for a long time without moving.

"What are you doing?" Morrison asked.

"I'm making depth-photographs of the terrain," the robot said. "It's rather difficult in this light. Couldn't you wait till morning?'

"No!"

"Well, I'll just have to cope," the robot said.

It moved and stood, moved and stood, each subterranean exposure taking longer than the last as the twilight deepened. If it had had pores, it would have sweated.

"There," said the robot at last, "that takes care of it. Do you have a sample for me to take back?"

"Here it is," Morrison said, hefting the slab of goldenstone and handing it to the surveyor. "Is that all?"

"Absolutely all," the robot said. "Except, of course, that you haven't given me the Deed of Search."

Morrison blinked. "I haven't given you the what?"

"The Deed of Search. That is a government document showing that the claim you are filing on is free, as per government order, of fissionable material in excess of fifty per cent of the total mass to a depth of sixty feet. It's a mere formality, but a necessary one."

"I never heard of it," Morrison said.

"It became a requirement last week," explained the surveyor. "You don't have the Deed? Then I'm afraid your standard unrestricted claim is invalid."

"Isn't there anything I can do?"

"Well," the robot said, "you *could* change your standard unrestricted claim to a special restricted claim. That requires no Deed of Search."

"What does the special restricted part mean?"

"It means that in five hundred years all rights revert to the Government of Venus."

"All right!" Morrison shouted. "Fine! Good! Is that all?"

"Absolutely all," the surveyor said. "I shall bring this sample back and have it assayed and evaluated immediately. From it and the depth-photographs we can extrapolate the value and extent of your claim."

"Send me back something to take care of the wolves," Morrison said. "And food. And listen—I want a Prospector's Special."

"Yes, sir. It will all be 'ported to you—if your claim is of sufficient value to warrant the outlay."

The robot climbed into the vortex and vanished.

Time passed, and the wolves edged forward again. They snarled at the rocks Morrison threw, but they didn't retreat. Jaws open and tongues lolling, they crept up the remaining yards between them and the prospector.

Then the leading wolf leaped back and howled. A gleaming vortex had appeared over his head and a rifle had fallen from the vortex, striking him on a forepaw.

The wolves scrambled away. Another rifle fell from the vortex. Then a large box marked *Grenades, Handle With Care*. Then another box marked *Desert Ration K*.

Morrison waited, staring at the gleaming mouth of the vortex. It crossed the sky to a spot a quarter of a mile away and paused there, and then a great round brass base emerged from the vortex, and the mouth widened to allow an even greater bulge of brass to which the base was attached. The bulge grew higher as the base was lowered to the sand. When the last of it appeared, it stood alone in the horizon-to-horizon expanse, a gigantic ornate brass punchbowl in the desert. The vortex rose and paused again over the bowl.

Morrison waited, his throat raw and aching. Now a small trickle came out of the vortex and splashed down into the bowl. Still Morrison didn't move.

And then it came. The trickle became a roar that sent the wolves and kites fleeing in terror, and a cataract poured from the vortex to the huge punchbowl.

Morrison began staggering toward it. He should have ordered a canteen, he told himself thirstily, stumbling across the quarter of a mile of sand. But at last he stood beneath the Prospector's Special, higher than a church steeple, wider than a house, filled with water more precious than goldenstone itself. He turned the spigot at the bottom. Water soaked the yellow sands and ran in rivulets down the dune.

He should have ordered a cup or glass, Morrison thought, lying on his back with open mouth.

EARTH

Since we live on Earth, you might very well suppose we know a great deal about it—and we do. You might even suppose we know all about it—but we don't. Some very basic discoveries have been made only in the last couple of decades.

For instance if you look at the map of the world, you will see that the eastern coast of South America and the western coast of Africa are amazingly similar. In fact Francis Bacon pointed this out as long ago as 1620, when the coasts were first being outlined accurately.

Could it be that Africa and South America were once joined? That they split apart along the line of the present coasts and then drifted apart?

The first person to deal thoroughly with this notion of "continental drift" was Alfred Lothar Wegener, who published a book on the subject in 1912. He suggested that the continents, which are essentially large blocks of granite, floated on the denser basalt that made up the sea bottom and very slowly drifted this way and that. Originally, he felt, the world contained a single supercontinent ("Pan-Gaea" or "All-Earth") which split up and drifted apart into pieces.

If this were so, it would account for a variety of puzzles. There are similar species of plants and animals in widely different parts of the world. Perhaps they had evolved when those parts of the world were close together. There are signs of glaciation in the far past in regions which are now tropical—perhaps they were once polar. Whereas fossils from some rocks on the continents are up to 600 million years old, fossils from the Atlantic sea bottom are much younger, as though the Atlantic Ocean had been only recently formed.

Geologists were quite certain, however, that the continental granite could not drift through basalt, and Wegener's notions were dismissed.

The dismissal was only possible, however, because we knew so little about 70 percent of the Earth's solid surface, that portion which was hidden by the ocean. All we knew about the sea bottom was an occasional depth, obtained by dropping a plumb line overboard here and there.

Even so, as long ago as 1853, when soundings were made in connection with laying a transatlantic cable, it seemed that the Atlantic was shallower in its middle than at either side. The central shallow was named "Telegraph Plateau" in honor of the cable.

During World War I, Paul Langevin developed a method of judging distance by the time it takes shortwave sound ("ultrasonic waves") to reach an object and be reflected back to its starting point. This is now called "sonar."

Sonar was enormously more efficient than plumb lines, and by 1925 sonar soundings showed that a vast undersea mountain range wound down the center of the Atlantic Ocean through all its length. Eventually, this was shown to curve into the other oceans as well and, indeed, to encircle the globe in a long, winding "Mid-Oceanic Ridge."

By 1953, William Maurice Ewing and Bruce Charles Heezen showed that running down the length of the ridge was a deep canyon. This was eventually found to exist in all portions of the Mid-Oceanic Ridge, so it is sometimes called the "Great Global Rift."

Such findings increased world consciousness of the exciting nature of the ocean floor, and the number of science fiction stories dealing with it—like "Waterclap," published in 1970—increased.

The Great Global Rift seems to divide the Earth's crust into large plates, which are in some cases thousands of kilometers across and some 70 to 150 kilometers (40 to 90 miles) deep. These are called "tectonic plates," from the Greek word for "carpenter," since they seem so tightly joined. The study of the Earth's crust in terms of these plates is called "plate tectonics"—a science which is only a quarter of a century old, and yet without which almost nothing in geology can be understood properly.

The discovery of the tectonic plates established continental drift, but not in the Wegener fashion. The continents were not floating and adrift; they were integral parts of the plate they rested upon. The plates, however, moved. They did not float; they were actively pushed apart.

In 1960, Harry Hammond Hess presented evidence in favor of "sea-floor spreading." Hot molten rock slowly welled up from great depths into the Great Global Rift in the mid-Atlantic, for instance, and solidified at or near the surface. This upwelling of solidifying rock forced the two plates on either side apart, in places at the rate of from 2 to 18 centimeters (1 to 7 inches) a year. As the plates moved apart, South America and Africa were separated and the Atlantic Ocean formed.

The whole history of the Earth can be worked out in terms of plate tectonics. With tectonic plates moving apart here and crushing together there, mountains rise, deeps depress, oceans widen, and continents separate and rejoin.

Every once in a while the continents join into one huge land mass and then split up again, over and over. The last occasion on which Pan Gaea seems to have formed was 225 million years ago, when the dinosaurs were just beginning to evolve; and it began to break up about 180 million years ago.

As the sea bottom came to be better known through sonar sounding, human beings began to invade it.

As recently as 1934, Charles William Beebe could only get down to a point 0.9 kilometers (0.57 miles) below the ocean surface, and that made headlines. He used a bathysphere, an inert thick-walled object, just large enough to hold a man, and suspended from a surface vessel by a cable.

A maneuverable ship of the abyss, a "bathyscaphe," was invented by Auguste Piccard in 1947. It used a heavy ballast of iron pellets which could be automatically jettisoned in case of emergency. This took it down while a gasoline-filled balloon provided buoyancy and stability. In its first test in 1948, an unmanned bathyscaphe descended 1.4 kilometers (0.85 miles) below the ocean surface.

On January 14, 1960, Jacques Piccard (son of Auguste) and Don Walsh took a bathyscaphe to the bottom of the Marianas Trench, plumbing 11 kilometers (7 miles) below the ocean surface to the deepest part of the abyss. The world of "Waterclap" seems possible.

Waterclap

ISAAC ASIMOV

Stephen Demerest looked at the textured sky. He kept looking at it and found the blue opaque and revolting.

Unwarily, he had looked at the Sun, for there was nothing to blank it out automatically, and then he had snatched his eyes away in panic. He wasn't blinded; just a few after-images. Even the Sun was washed out.

Involuntarily, he thought of Ajax's prayer in Homer's *Iliad*. They were fighting over the body of Patroclus in the mist and Ajax said, "O Father Zeus, save the Achaeans out of this mist! Make the sky clean, grant us to see with our eyes! Kill us in the light, since it is thy pleasure to kill us!"

Demerest thought: Kill us in the light—

Kill us in the clear light on the Moon, where the sky is black and soft, where the stars shine brightly, where the cleanliness and purity of vacuum make all things sharp.

—Not in this low-clinging, fuzzy blue.

He shuddered. It was an actual physical shudder that shook his lanky body, and he was annoyed. He was going to die. He was sure of it. And it wouldn't be under the blue, either, come to think of it, but under the black—but a different black.

It was as though in answer to that thought that the ferry pilot, short, swarthy, crisp-haired, came up to him and said, "Ready for the black, Mr. Demerest?"

Demerest nodded. He towered over the other as he did over

93

most of the men of Earth. They were thick, all of them, and took their short, low steps with ease. He himself had to feel his footsteps, guide them through the air; even the impalpable bond that held him to the ground was textured.

"I'm ready," he said. He took a deep breath and deliberately repeated his earlier glance at the Sun. It was low in the morning sky, washed out by dusty air, and he knew it wouldn't blind him. He didn't think he would ever see it again.

He had never seen a bathyscaphe before. Despite everything, he tended to think of it in terms of prototypes, an oblong balloon with a spherical gondola beneath. It was as though he persisted in thinking of space flight in terms of tons of fuel spewed backward in fire, and an irregular module feeling its way, spiderlike, toward the Lunar surface.

The bathyscaphe was not like the image in his thoughts at all. Under its skin, it might still be buoyant bag and gondola, but it was all engineered sleekness now.

"My name is Javan," said the ferry pilot. "Omar Javan."

"Javan?"

"Queer name to you? I'm Iranian by descent; Earthman by persuasion. Once you get down there, there are no nationalities." He grinned and his complexion grew darker against the even whiteness of his teeth. "If you don't mind, we'll be starting in a minute. You'll be my only passenger, so I guess you carry weight."

"Yes," said Demerest dryly. "At least a hundred pounds more than I'm used to."

"You're from the Moon? I thought you had a queer walk on you. I hope it's not uncomfortable."

"It's not exactly comfortable, but I manage. We exercise for this."

"Well, come on board." He stood aside and let Demerest walk down the gangplank. "I wouldn't go to the Moon myself."

"You go to Ocean-Deep."

"About fifty times so far. That's different."

Demerest got on board. It was cramped, but he didn't mind that. It might be a space module except that it was more——well, textured. There was that word again. There was the clear feeling everywhere that mass didn't matter. Mass was held up; it didn't have to be hurled up.

They were still on the surface. The blue sky could be seen greenishly through the clear thick glass. Javan said, "You don't have to be strapped in. There's no acceleration. Smooth as oil, the whole thing. It won't take long; just about an hour. You can't smoke."

"I don't smoke," said Demerest.

"I hope you don't have claustrophobia."

"Moon-men don't have claustrophobia."

"All that open—"

"Not in our cavern. We live in a"—he groped for the phrase—"a Lunar-Deep, a hundred feet deep."

"A hundred feet!" The pilot seemed amused, but he didn't smile. "We're slipping down now."

The interior of the gondola was fitted into angles but here and there a section of wall beyond the instruments showed its basic sphericity. To Javan, the instruments seemed to be an extension of his arms; his eyes and hands moved over them lightly, almost lovingly.

"We're all checked out," he said, "but I like a last-minute look-over; we'll be facing a thousand atmospheres down there." His finger touched a contact, and the round door closed massively inward and pressed against the beveled rim it met.

"The higher the pressure, the tighter that will hold," said Javan. "Take your last look at sunlight, Mr. Demerest."

The light still shone through the thick glass of the window. It was wavering now; there was water between the Sun and them now.

"The last look?" said Demerest.

Javan snickered. "Not the *last* look. I mean for the trip.

. . . I suppose you've never been on a bathyscaphe before."

"No, I haven't. Have many?"

"Very few," admitted Javan. "But don't worry. It's just an underwater balloon. We've introduced a million improvements since the first bathyscaphe. It's nuclear-powered now and we can move freely by water jet up to certain limits, but cut it down to basics and it's still a spherical gondola under buoyancy tanks. And it's still towed out to sea by a mother ship because it needs what power it carries too badly to waste it on surface travel. Ready?"

"Ready."

The supporting cable of the mother ship flicked away and the bathyscaphe settled lower; then lower still, as sea water fed into the buoyancy tanks. For a few moments, caught in surface currents, it swayed, and then there was nothing. The bathyscaphe sank slowly through a deepening green.

Javan relaxed. He said, "John Bergen is head of Ocean-Deep. You're going to see him?"

"That's right."

"He's a nice guy. His wife's with him."

"She is?"

"Oh, sure. They have women down there. There's a bunch down there, fifty people. Some stay for months."

Demerest put his finger on the narrow, nearly invisible seam where door met wall. He took it away and looked at it. He said, "It's oily."

"Silicone, really. The pressure squeezes some out. It's suppose to. . . . Don't worry. Everything's automatic. Everything's fail-safe. The first sign of malfunction, any malfunction at all, our ballast is released and up we go."

"You mean nothing's ever happened to these bathyscaphes?"

"What can happen?" The pilot looked sideways at his passenger. "Once you get too deep for sperm whales, nothing can go wrong."

"Sperm whales?" Demerest's thin face creased in a frown.

"Sure, they dive as deep as half a mile. If they hit a bathyscaphe—well, the walls of the buoyancy chambers aren't particularly strong. They don't have to be, you know. They're open to the sea and when the gasoline, which supplies the buoyancy, compresses, sea water enters."

It was dark now. Demerest found his gaze fastened to the viewport. It was light inside the gondola, but it was dark in that window. And it was not the darkness of space; it was a thick darkness.

Demerest said sharply. "Let's get this straight, Mr. Javan. You are not equipped to withstand the attack of a sperm whale. Presumably you are not equipped to withstand the attack of a giant squid. Have there been any actual incidents of that sort?"

"Well, it's like this—"

"No games, please, and don't try ragging the greenhorn. I am asking out of professional curiosity. I am head safety engineer at Luna City and I am asking what precautions this bathyscaphe can take against possible collision with large creatures."

Javan looked embarrassed. He muttered, "Actually, there have been no incidents."

"Are any expected? Even as a remote possibility?"

"Anything is remotely possible. But actually sperm whales are too intelligent to monkey with us and giant squid are too shy."

"Can they see us?"

"Yes, of course. We're lit up."

"Do you have floodlights?"

"We're already past the large-animal range, but we have them, and I'll turn them on for you."

Through the black of the window there suddenly appeared a snowstorm, an inverted upward-falling snowstorm. The blackness had come alive with stars in three-dimensional array, and all moving upward.

Demerest said, "What's that?"

"Just crud. Organic matter. Small creatures. They float, don't move much, and they catch the light. We're going down past them. They seem to be going up in consequence."

Demerest's sense of perspective adjusted itself and he said, "Aren't we dropping too quickly?"

"No, we're not. If we were, I could use the nuclear engines, if I wanted to waste power; or I could drop some ballast. I'll be doing that later, but for now everything is fine. Relax, Mr. Demerest. The snow thins as we dive and we're not likely to see much in the way of spectacular life forms. There are small angler fish and such but they avoid us."

Demerest said, "How many do you take down at a time?"

"I've had as many as four passengers in this gondola, but that's crowded. We can put two bathyscaphes in tandem and carry ten, but that's clumsy. What we really need are trains of gondolas, heavier on the nukes—the nuclear engines—and lighter on the buoyancy. Stuff like that is on the drawing board, they tell me. Of course, they've been telling me that for years."

"There are plans for large-scale expansion of Ocean-Deep, then?"

"Sure, why not? We've got cities on the continental shelves, why not on the deep-sea bottom? The way I look at it, Mr. Demerest, where man can go, he will go and he should go. The Earth is ours to populate and we will populate it. All we need to make the deep sea habitable are completely maneuverable 'scaphes. The buoyancy chambers slow us, weaken us, and complicate the engineering."

"But they also save you, don't they? If everything goes wrong at once, the gasoline you carry will still float you to the surface. What would do that for you if your nuclear engines go wrong and you had no buoyancy?"

"If it comes to that, you can't expect to eliminate the chances of accident altogether, not even fatal ones."

"I know that very well," said Demerest feelingly.

Javan stiffened. The tone of his voice changed. "Sorry. Didn't mean anything by that. Tough about that accident."

"Yes," said Demerest. Fifteen men and five women had died. One of the individuals listed among the "men" had been fourteen years old. It had been pinned down to human failure. What could a head safety engineer say after that?

"Yes," he said.

A pall dropped between the two men, a pall as thick and as turgid as the pressurized sea water outside. How could one allow for panic and for distraction and for depression all at once? There were the Moon-Blues—stupid name—but they struck men at inconvenient times. It wasn't always noticeable when the Moon-Blues came but it made men torpid and slow to react.

How many times had a meteorite come along and been averted or smothered or successfully absorbed? How many times had a Moonquake done damage and been held in check? How many times had human failure been backed up and compensated for? How many times had accidents *not* happened?

But you don't pay off on accidents not happening. There were twenty dead—

Javan said (how many long minutes later?), "There are the lights of Ocean-Deep!"

Demerest could not make them out at first. He didn't know where to look. Twice before, luminescent creatures had flicked past the windows at a distance and with the floodlights off again, Demerest had thought them the first sign of Ocean-Deep. Now he saw nothing.

"Down there," said Javan, without pointing. He was busy now, slowing the drop and edging the 'scaphe sideways.

Demerest could hear the distant sighing of the water jets, steam-driven, with the steam formed by the heat of momentary bursts of fusion power.

Demerest thought dimly: Deuterium is their fuel and it's all around them. Water is their exhaust and it's all around them.

Javan was dropping some of his ballast, too, and began a

kind of distant chatter. "The ballast used to be steel pellets and they were dropped by electromagnetic controls. Anywhere up to fifty tons of them were used in each trip. Conservationists worried about spreading rusting steel over the ocean floor, so we switched to metal nodules that are dredged up from the continental shelf. We put a thin layer of iron over them so they can still be electromagnetically handled and the ocean bottom gets nothing that wasn't sub-ocean to begin with. Cheaper, too. . . . But when we get out real nuclear 'scaphes, we won't need ballast at all."

Demerest scarcely heard him. Ocean-Deep could be seen now. Javan had turned on the floodlights and far below was the muddy floor of the Puerto Rican Trench. Resting on that floor like a cluster of equally muddy pearls was the spherical conglomerate of Ocean-Deep.

Each unit was a sphere such as the one in which Demerest was now sinking toward contact, but much larger, and as Ocean-Deep expanded—expanded—expanded, new spheres were added.

Demerest thought: They're only five and a half miles from home, not a quarter of a million.

"How are we going to get through?" asked Demerest.

The 'scaphe had made contact. Demerest heard the dull sound of metal against metal but then for minutes there had been nothing more than a kind of occasional scrape as Javan bent over his instruments in rapt concentration.

"Don't worry about that," Javan said at last, in belated answer. "There's no problem. The delay now is only because I have to make sure we fit tightly. There's an electromagnetic joint that holds at every point of a perfect circle. When the instruments read correctly, that means we fit over the entrance door."

"Which then opens?"

'It would if there were air on the other side, but there isn't. There's sea water, and that has to be driven out. *Then* we enter."

Demerest did not miss this point. He had come here on this, the last day of his life, to give that same life meaning and he intended to miss nothing.

He said, "Why the added step? Why not keep the air lock, if that's what it is, a real air lock, and have air in it at all times?"

"They tell me it's a matter of safety," said Javan. *"Your* specialty. The interface has equal pressure on both sides at all times, *except* when men are moving across. This door is the weakest point of the whole system, because it opens and closes; it has joints; it has seams. You know what I mean?"

"I do," murmured Demerest. There was a logical flaw here and that meant there was a possible chink through which— but later.

He said, "Why are we waiting now?"

"The lock is being emptied. The water is being forced out."

"By air."

"Hell, no. They can't afford to waste air like that. It would take a thousand atmospheres to empty the chamber of its water, and filling the chamber with air at that density, even temporarily, is more air than they can afford to expend. Steam is what does it."

"Of course. Yes."

Javan said cheerfully, "You heat the water. No pressure in the world can stop water from turning to steam at a temperature of more than 374° C. And the steam forces the sea water out through a one-way valve."

"Another weak point," said Demerest.

"I suppose so. It's never failed yet. The water in the lock is being pushed out now. When hot steam starts bubbling out the valve, the process automatically stops and the lock is full of overheated steam."

"And then?"

"And then we have a whole ocean to cool it with. The temperature drops and the steam condenses. Once that happens, ordinary air can be let in at a pressure of one atmosphere and *then* the door opens."

"How long must we wait?"

"Not long. If there were anything wrong, there'd be sirens sounding. At least, so they say. I never heard one in action."

There was silence for a few minutes, and then there was a sudden sharp clap and a simultaneous jerk.

Javan said, "Sorry, I should have warned you. I'm so used to it I forgot. When the door opens, a thousand atmospheres of pressure on the other side forces us hard against the metal of Ocean-Deep. No electromagnetic force can hold us hard enough to prevent that last hundredth-of-an-inch slam."

Demerest unclenched his fist and released his breath. He said, "Is everything all right?"

"The walls didn't crack, if that's what you mean. It sounds like doom, though, doesn't it? It sounds even worse when I've got to leave and the air lock fills up again. Be prepared for that."

But Demerest was suddenly weary. Let's get on with it, he thought. I don't want to drag it out. He said, "Do we go through now?"

"We go through."

The opening in the 'scaphe wall was round and small; even smaller than the one through which they had originally entered. Javan went through it sinuously, muttering that it always made him feel like a cork in a bottle.

Demerest had not smiled since he entered the 'scaphe. Nor did he really smile now, but a corner of his mouth quirked as he thought that a skinny Moon-man would have no trouble.

He went through also, feeling Javan's hands firmly at his waist, helping him through.

Javan said, "It's dark in here. No point in introducing an additional weakness by wiring for lighting. But that's why flashlights were invented."

Demerest found himself on a perforated walk, its stainless metallic surface gleaming dully. And through the perforations he could make out the wavering surface of water.

He said, "The chamber hasn't been emptied."

"You can't do any better, Mr. Demerest. If you're going to

use steam to empty it, you're left with that steam, and to get the pressures necessary to do the emptying, that steam must be compressed to about one-third the density of liquid water. When it condenses, the chamber remains one-third full of water—but it's water at just one-atmosphere pressure.... Come on, Mr. Demerest."

John Bergen's face wasn't entirely unknown to Demerest. Recognition was immediate. Bergen, as head of Ocean-Deep for nearly a decade now, was a familiar face on the TV screens of Earth—just as the leaders of Luna City had become familiar.

Demerest had seen the head of Ocean-Deep both flat and in three dimensions, in black-and-white and in color. Seeing him in life added little.

Like Javan, Bergen was short and thickset; opposite in structure to the traditional (already traditional?) Lunar pattern of physiology. He was fairer than Javan by a good deal and his face was noticeably asymmetrical, with his somewhat thick nose leaning just a little to the right.

He was not handsome. No Moon-man would think he was, but then Bergen smiled and there was a sunniness about it as he held out his large hand.

Demerest placed his own thin one within, steeling himself for a hard grip, but it did not come. Bergen took the hand and let it go, then said, "I'm glad you're here. We don't have much in the way of luxury, nothing that will make our hospitality stand out, we can't even declare a holiday in your honor—but the spirit is there. Welcome!"

"Thank you," said Demerest softly. He remained unsmiling now, too. He was facing the enemy and he knew it. Surely Bergen must know it also and, since he did, that smile of his was hypocrisy.

And at that moment a clang like metal against metal sounded deafeningly and the chamber shuddered. Demerest leaped back and staggered against the wall.

Bergen did not budge. He said quietly, "That was the

bathyscaphe unhitching and the waterclap of the air lock filling. Javan ought to have warned you."

Demerest panted and tried to make his racing heart slow. He said, "Javan did warn me. I was caught by surprise anyway."

Bergen said, "Well, it won't happen again for a while. We don't often have visitors, you know. We're not equipped for it and so we fight off all kinds of big wheels who think a trip down here would be good for their careers. Politicians of all kinds, chiefly. Your own case is different of course."

Is it? thought Demerest. It had been hard enough to get permission to make the trip down. His superiors back at Luna City had not approved in the first place and had scouted the idea that a diplomatic interchange would be of any use. ("Diplomatic interchange" was what they had called it.) And when he had overborne them, there had been Ocean-Deep's own reluctance to receive him.

It had been sheer persistence alone that had made his present visit possible. In what way then was Demerest's case different?

Bergen said, "I suppose you have your junketing problems on Luna City, too?"

"Very little" said Demerest. "Your average politican isn't as anxious to travel a half-million-mile round trip as he is to travel a ten-mile one."

"I can see that," agreed Bergen, "and it's more expensive out to the Moon, of course.... In a way, this is the first meeting of inner and outer space. No Ocean-man has ever gone to the Moon as far as I know, and you're the first Moon-man to visit a sub-sea station of any kind. No Moonman has ever been to one of the settlements on the continental shelf."

"It's a historic meeting, then," said Demerest, and tried to keep the sarcasm out of his voice.

If any leaked through, Bergen showed no sign. He rolled up his sleeves as though to emphasize his attitude of informality (or the fact that they were very busy, so that there would be little time for visitors?) and said, "Do you want coffee? I assume you've eaten. Would you like to rest before I show you around? Do you want to wash up, for that matter, as they say euphemistically?"

For a moment, curiosity stirred in Demerest; yet not entirely aimless curiosity. Everything involving the interface of Ocean-Deep with the outside world could be of importance. He said, "How are sanitary facilities handled here?"

"It's cycled mostly; as it is on the Moon, I imagine. We can eject if we want to or have to. Man has a bad record of fouling the environment, but as the only deep-sea station, what we eject does no perceptible damage. Adds organic matter." He laughed.

Demerest filed that away, too. Matter was ejected; there were therefore ejection tubes. Their workings might be of interest and he, as a safety engineer, had a right to be interested.

"No," he said, "I don't need anything at the moment. If you're busy—"

"That's all right. We're always busy, but I'm the least busy, if you see what I mean. Suppose I show you around. We've got over fifty units here, each as big as this one, some bigger—"

Demerest looked about. Again, as in the 'scaphe, there were angles everywhere, but beyond the furnishings and equipment there were signs of the inevitable spherical outer wall. Fifty of them!

"Built up," went on Bergen, "over a generation of effort. The unit we're standing in is actually the oldest and there's been some talk of demolishing and replacing it. Some of the men say we're ready for second-generation units, but I'm not sure. It would be expensive—everything's expensive down here—and getting money out of the Planetary Project Council is always a depressing experience."

Demerest felt his nostrils flare involuntarily and a spasm of anger shot through him. It was a thrust, surely. Luna City's miserable record with the PPC must be well known to Bergen.

But Bergen went on, unnoticing. "I'm a traditionalist, too—just a little bit. This is the first deep-sea unit ever constructed. The first two people to remain overnight on the floor of an ocean trench slept here with nothing else beyond this bare sphere except for a miserable portable fusion unit to work the escape hatch. I mean the air lock, but we called it the escape hatch to begin with—and just enough controls for the purpose. Reguera and Tremont, those were the men. They never made a second trip to the bottom, either; stayed Topside forever after. Well, well, they served their purpose and both are dead now. And here we are with fifty people and with six months as the usual tour of duty. I've spent only two weeks Topside in the last year and a half."

He motioned vigorously to Demerest to follow him, slid open a door which moved evenly into a recess, and took him into the next unit. Demerest paused to examine the opening. There were no seams that he could notice between the adjacent units.

Bergen noted the other's pause and said, "When we add on our units, they're welded under pressure into the equivalent of a single piece of metal and then reinforced. We can't take chances, as I'm sure you understand, since I have been given to understand that you're the head safe—"

Demerest cut him off. "Yes," he said. "We on the Moon admire your safety record."

Bergen shrugged. "We've been lucky. Our sympathy, by the way, on the rotten break you fellows had. I mean that fatal—"

Demerest cut him off again. "Yes."

Bergen, the Moon-man decided, was either a naturally voluble man or else was eager to drown him in words and get rid of him.

"The units," said Bergen, "are arranged in a highly

branched chain—three-dimensional actually. We have a map we can show you, if you're interested. Most of the end units represent living-sleeping quarters. For privacy, you know. The working units tend to be corridors as well, which is one of the embarrassments of having to live down here.

"This is our library; part of it, anyway. Not big, but it's got our records, too, on carefully indexed and computed microfilm, so that for its kind it's not only the biggest in the world, but the best and the only. And we have a special computer to handle the references to meet our needs exactly. It collects, selects, coordinates, weighs, then gives us the gist.

"We have another library, too, book films and even some printed volumes. But that's for amusement."

A voice broke in on Bergen's cheerful flow. "John? May I interrupt?"

Demerest started; the voice had come from behind him. Bergen said, "Annette! I was going to get you. This is Stephen Demerest of Luna City. Mr. Demerest, may I introduce my wife, Annette?"

Demerest had turned. He said stiffly, a little mechanically, "I'm pleased to meet you, Mrs. Bergen." But he was staring at her waistline.

Annette Bergen seemed in her early thirties. Her brown hair was combed simply and she wore no makeup. Attractive, not beautiful, Demerest noted vaguely. But his eyes kept returning to that waistline.

She shrugged a little. "Yes, I'm pregnant, Mr. Demerest. I'm due in about two months."

"Pardon me," Demerest muttered. "So rude of me. . . . I didn't—" He faded off and felt as though the blow had been a physical one. He hadn't expected women, though he didn't know why. He *knew* there would have to be women in Ocean-Deep. And the ferry pilot had said Bergen's wife was with him.

He stammered as he spoke. "How many women are there in Ocean-Deep, Mr. Bergen?"

"Nine at the moment," said Bergen. "All wives. We look forward to a time when we can have the normal ratio of one to one, but we still need workers and researchers primarily, and unless women have important qualifications of *some* sort—"

"They all have important qualifications of *some* sort, dear," said Mrs. Bergen. "You could keep the men for longer duty if—"

"My wife," said Bergen, laughing, "is a convinced feminist but is not above using sex as an excuse to enforce equality. I keep telling her that that is the feminine way of doing it and not the feminist way, and she keeps saying— Well, that's why she's pregnant. You think it's love, sex mania, yearning for motherhood? Nothing of the sort. She's going to have a baby down here to make a philosophical point."

Annette said coolly, "Why not? Either this is going to be home for humanity or it isn't going to be. If it *is,* then we're going to have babies here, that's all. I want a baby born in Ocean-Deep. There are babies born in Luna City, aren't there, Mr. Demerest?"

Demerest took a deep breath. "*I* was born in Luna City, Mrs. Bergen."

"And well she knew it," muttered Bergen.

"And you are in your late twenties, I think?" she said.

"I am twenty-nine," said Demerest.

"And well she knew that, too," said Bergen with a short laugh. "You can bet she looked up all possible data on you when she heard you were coming."

"That is quite beside the point," said Annette. "The point is that for twenty-nine years at least children have been born in Luna City and no children have been born in Ocean-Deep."

"Luna City, my dear," said Bergen, "is longer-established. It is over half a century old; we are not yet twenty."

"Twenty years is quite enough. It takes a baby nine months." .

Demerest interposed, "Are there any children in Ocean-Deep?"

"No," said Bergen. "No. Someday, though."

"In two months, anyway," said Annette Bergen positively.

The tension grew inside Demerest and when they returned to the unit in which he had first met Bergen, he was glad to sit down and accept a cup of coffee.

"We'll eat soon," said Bergen matter-of-factly. "I hope you don't mind sitting here meanwhile. As the prime unit, it isn't used for much except, of course, for the reception of vessels, an item I don't expect will interrupt us for a while. We can talk, if you wish."

"I *do* wish," said Demerest.

"I hope I'm welcome to join in," said Annette.

Demerest looked at her doubtfully, but Bergen said to him, "You'll have to agree. She's fascinated by you and by Moon-men generally. She thinks they're—uh—*you're* a new breed, and I think that when she's quite through being a Deep-woman she wants to be a Moon-woman."

"I just want to get a word in edgewise, John, and when I get that in, I'd like to hear what Mr. Demerest has to say. What do you think of us, Mr. Demerest?"

Demerest said cautiously, "I've asked to come here, Mrs. Bergen, because I'm a safety engineer. Ocean-Deep has an enviable safety record—"

"Not one fatality in almost twenty years," said Bergen cheerfully. "Only one death by accident in the C-shelf settlements and none in transit by either sub or 'scaphe. I wish I could say, though, that this was the result of wisdom and care on our part. We do our best, of course, but the breaks have been with us—"

"John," said Annette, "I really wish you'd let Mr. Demerest speak."

"As a safety engineer," said Demerest, "I can't afford to believe in luck and breaks. We cannot stop Moonquakes or large meteorites out at Luna City, but we are designed to minimize the effects even of those. There are no excuses or there should be none for human failure. We have not avoided that on Luna City; our record recently has been"—his voice dropped—"bad. While humans are imperfect, as we all know, machinery should be designed to take that imperfection into account. We lost twenty men and women—"

"I know. Still, Luna City has a population of nearly one thousand, doesn't it? Your survival isn't in danger."

"The people on Luna City number nine hundred and seventy-two, including myself, but our survival *is* in danger. We depend on Earth for essentials. That need not always be so; it wouldn't be so right now if the Planetary Project Council could resist the temptation toward pygmy economics—"

"There, at least, Mr. Demerest," said Bergen, "we see eye to eye. We are not self-supporting either, and we could be. What's more, we can't grow much beyond our present level unless nuclear 'scaphes are built. As long as we keep that buoyancy principle, we are limited. Transportation between Deep and Top is slow; slow for men; slower still for matériel and supplies. I've been pushing, Mr. Demerest, for—"

"Yes, and you'll be getting it now, Mr. Bergen, won't you?"

"I hope so, but what makes you so sure?"

"Mr. Bergen, let's not play around. You know very well that Earth is committed to spending a fixed amount of money on expansion projects—on programs designed to expand the human habitat—and that it is not a terribly large amount. Earth's population is not going to lavish resources in an effort to expand either outer space or inner space if it thinks this will cut into the comfort and convenience of Earth's prime habitat, the land surface of the planet."

Annette broke in. "You make it sound callous of Earthmen, Mr. Demerest, and that's unfair. It's only human, isn't it, to want to be secure? Earth is overpopulated and it is only slowly reversing the havoc inflicted on the planet by the Mad Twentieth. Surely man's original home must come first, ahead of either Luna City or Ocean-Deep. Heavens, Ocean-Deep is almost *home* to me, but I can't want to see it flourish at the expense of Earth's land."

"It's not an either-or, Mrs. Bergen," said Demerest earnestly. "If the ocean and outer space are firmly, honestly, and intelligently exploited, it can only redound to Earth's benefit. A small investment will be lost but a large one will redeem itself with profit."

Bergen held up his hand. "Yes, I know. You don't have to argue with me on that point. You'd be trying to convert the converted. Come, let's eat. I tell you what. We'll eat here. If you'll stay with us overnight, or several days for that matter—you're quite welcome—there will be ample time to meet everybody. Perhaps you'd rather take it easy for a while, though."

"Much rather," said Demerest. "Actually, I want to stay here. . . . I would like to ask, by the way, why I met so few people when we went through the units."

"No mystery," said Bergen genially. "At any given time, some fifteen of our men are asleep and perhaps fifteen more are watching films or playing chess or, if their wives are with them—"

"Yes, John," said Annette.

"—And it's customary not to disturb them. The quarters are constricted and what privacy a man can have is cherished. A few are out at sea; three right now, I think. That leaves a dozen or so at work in here and you met them."

"I'll get lunch," said Annette, rising.

She smiled and stepped through the door, which closed automatically behind her.

Bergen looked after her. "That's a concession. She's playing woman for your sake. Ordinarily, it would be just as likely for me to get the lunch. The choice is not defined by sex but by the striking of random lightning."

Demerest said, "The doors between units, it seems to me, are of dangerously limited strength."

"Are they?"

"If an accident happened, and one unit was punctured—"

"No meteorites down here," said Bergen, smiling.

"Oh yes, wrong word. If there were a leak of any sort, for any reason, then could a unit or a group of units be sealed off against the full pressure of the ocean?"

"You mean, in the way that Luna City can have its component units automatically sealed off in case of meteorite puncture in order to limit damage to a single unit."

"Yes," said Demerest with a faint bitterness. "As did *not* happen recently."

"In theory, we could do that, but the chances of accident are much less down here. As I said, there are no meteorites and, what's more, there are no currents to speak of. Even an earthquake centered immediately below us would not be damaging, since we make no fixed or solid contact with the ground beneath and are cushioned by the ocean itself against the shocks. So we can afford to gamble on no massive influx."

"Yet if one happened?"

"Then we could be helpless. You see, it is not so easy to seal off component units here. On the Moon, there is a pressure differential of just one atmosphere; one atmosphere inside and the zero atmosphere of vacuum outside. A thin seal is enough. Here at Ocean-Deep the pressure differential is roughly a thousand atmospheres. To secure absolute safety against that differential would take a great deal of money, and you know what you said about getting money out of PPC. So we gamble and so far we've been lucky."

"And we haven't," said Demerest.

Bergen looked uncomfortable, but Annette distracted both by coming in with lunch at this moment.

She said, "I hope, Mr. Demerest, that you're prepared for Spartan fare. All our food in Ocean-Deep is prepackaged and requires only heating. We specialize in blandness and non-surprise here, and the non-surprise of the day is a bland chicken à la king, with carrots, boiled potatoes, a piece of something that looks like a brownie for dessert, and, of course, all the coffee you can drink."

Demerest rose to take his tray and tried to smile. "It sounds very like Moon fare, Mrs. Bergen, and I was brought up on that. We grow our own micro-organismic food. It is patriotic to eat that but not particularly enjoyable. We hope to keep improving it, though."

"I'm sure you *will* improve it."

Demerest said, as he ate with a slow and methodical chewing, "I hate to ride my specialty, but how secure are you against mishaps in your air-lock entry?"

"It *is* the weakest point of Ocean-Deep," said Bergen. He had finished eating, well ahead of the other two, and was half through with his first cup of coffee. "But there's got to be an interface, right? The entry is as automatic as we can make it and as fail-safe. Number one: there has to be contact at every point about the outer lock before the fusion generator begins to heat the water within the lock. What's more, the contact has to be metallic and of a metal with just the magnetic permeability we use on our 'scaphes. Presumably a rock or some mythical deep-sea monster might drop down and make contact at just the right places; but if so, nothing happens.

"Then, too, the outer door doesn't open until the steam has pushed the water out and then condensed; in other words, not till both pressure and temperature have dropped below a certain point. At the moment the outer door begins to open, a relatively slight increase in internal pressure, as by water entry, will close it again."

Demerest said, "But then, once men have passed through the lock, the inner door closes behind them and sea water must be allowed into the lock again. Can you do that gradually against the full pressure of the ocean outside?"

"Not very." Bergen smiled. "It doesn't pay to fight the ocean too hard. You have to roll with the punch. We slow it down to about one-tenth free entry, but even so it comes in like a rifle shot—louder, a thunderclap, or waterclap, if you prefer. The inner door can hold it, though, and it is not subjected to the strain very often. Well, wait, you heard the waterclap when we first met, when Javan's 'scaphe took off again. Remember?"

"I remember," said Demerest. "But here is something I don't understand. You keep the lock filled with ocean at high pressure at all times to keep the outer door without strain. But that keeps the inner door at full strain. Somewhere there has to be strain."

"Yes, indeed. But if the outer door, with a thousand-atmosphere differential on its two sides, breaks down, the full ocean in all its millions of cubic miles tries to enter and that would be the end of all. If the inner door is the one under strain and it gives, then it will be messy indeed, but the only water that enters Ocean-Deep will be the very limited quantity in the lock, and its pressure will drop at once. We will have plenty of time for repair, for the outer door will certainly hold a long time."

"But if both go simultaneously—"

"Then we are through." Bergen shrugged. "I need not tell you that neither absolute certainty nor absolute safety exists. You have to live with some risk, and the chance of double and simultaneous failure is so microscopically small that it can be lived with easily."

"If all your mechanical contrivances fail—"

"They fail safe," said Bergen stubbornly.

Demerest nodded. He finished the last of his chicken. Mrs. Bergen was already beginning to clean up. "You'll pardon my questions, Mr. Bergen, I hope."

"You're welcome to ask. I wasn't informed, actually, as to the precise nature of your mission here. 'Fact finding' is a weasel phrase. However, I assume there is keen distress on the Moon over the recent disaster and as safety engineer you rightly feel the responsibility of correcting whatever shortcomings exist and would be interested in learning, if possible, from the system used in Ocean-Deep."

"Exactly. But, see here, if all your automatic contrivances fail safe for some reason, for any reason, you would be alive, but all your escape-hatch mechanisms would be sealed permanently shut. You would be trapped inside Ocean-Deep and would exchange a slow death for a fast one."

"It's not likely to happen but we'd *hope* we could make repairs before our air supply gave out. Besides we *do* have a manual backup system."

"Oh?"

"Certainly. When Ocean-Deep was first established and this was the only unit—the one we're sitting in now—manual controls were all we had. *That* was unsafe, if you like. There they are, right behind you—covered with friable plastic."

"In emergency, break glass," muttered Demerest, inspecting the covered setup.

"Pardon me?"

"Just a phrase commonly used in ancient fire-fighting systems ... Well, do the manuals still work, or has the system been covered with your friable plastic for twenty years to the point where it has all decayed into uselessness with no one noticing?"

"Not at all. It's periodically checked, as all our equipment is. That's not my job personally, but I know it is done. If any electrical or electronic circuit is out of its normal working condition, lights flash, signals sound, everything happens but a nuclear blast. ... You know, Mr. Demerest, we are as curious about Luna City as you are about Ocean-Deep. I presume you would be willing to invite one of our young men—"

"How about a young woman?" interposed Annette at once.

"I am sure you mean yourself, dear," said Bergen, "to which I can only answer that you are determined to have a baby here and to keep it here for a period of time after birth, and that effectively eliminates you from consideration."

Demerest said stiffly, "We hope you will send men to Luna City. We are anxious to have you understand our problems."

"Yes, a mutual exchange of problems and of weeping on

each other's shoulders might be of great comfort to all. For instance, you have one advantage on Luna City that I wish we could have. With low gravity and a low pressure differential, you can make your caverns take on any irregular and angular fashion that appeals to your aesthetic sense or is required for convenience. Down here we're restricted to the sphere, at least for the foreseeable future, and our designers develop a hatred for the spherical that surpasses belief. Actually it isn't funny. It breaks them down. They eventually resign rather than continue to work spherically."

Bergen shook his head and leaned his chair back against a microfilm cabinet. "You know," he continued, "when William Beebe built the first deep-sea chamber in history in the 1930s—it was just a gondola suspended from a mother ship by a half-mile cable, with no buoyancy chambers and no engines, and if the cable broke, good night, only it never did. . . . Anyway, what was I saying? Oh, when Beebe built his first deep-sea chamber, he was going to make it cylindrical; you know, so a man would fit in it comfortably. After all, a man is essentially a tall, skinny cylinder. However, a friend of his argued him out of that and into a sphere on the very sensible grounds that a sphere would resist pressure more efficiently than any other possible shape. You know who that friend was?"

"No, I'm afraid I don't."

"The man who was President of the United States at the time of Beebe's descents—Franklin D. Roosevelt. All these spheres you see down here are the great-grandchildren of Roosevelt's suggestion."

Demerest considered that briefly but made no comment. He returned to the earlier topic. "We would particularly like someone from Ocean-Deep," he said, "to visit Luna City because it might lead to a great enough understanding of the need, on Ocean-Deep's part, for a course of action that might involve considerable self-sacrifice."

"Oh?" Bergen's chair came down flat-leggedly on all fours. "How's that?"

"Ocean-Deep is a marvelous achievement; I wish to detract nothing from that. I can see where it will become greater still, a wonder of the world. *Still—*"

"Still?"

"Still, the oceans are only a part of the Earth; a major part, but only a part. The deep sea is only part of the ocean. It is inner space indeed; it works inward, narrowing constantly to a point."

"I think," broke in Annette, looking rather grim, "that you're about to make a comparison with Luna City."

"Indeed I am," said Demerest. "Luna City represents outer space, widening to infinity. There is nowhere to go down here in the long run; everywhere to go out there."

"We don't judge by size and volume alone, Mr. Demerest," said Bergen. "The ocean is only a small part of Earth, true, but for that very reason it is intimately connected with over five billion human beings. Ocean-Deep is experimental, but the settlements on the continental shelf already deserve the name of cities. Ocean-Deep offers mankind the chance of exploiting the whole planet—"

"Of polluting the whole planet," broke in Demerest excitedly. "Of raping it, of ending it. The concentration of human effort to Earth itself is unhealthy and even fatal if it isn't balanced by a turning outward to the frontier."

"There is nothing at the frontier," said Annette, snapping out the words. "The Moon is dead, all the other worlds out there are dead. If there are live worlds among the stars, light-years away, they can't be reached. This ocean is *living.*"

"The Moon is living, too, Mrs. Bergen, and if Ocean-Deep allows it, the Moon will become an independent world. We Moon-men will then see to it that other worlds are reached and made alive and, if mankind but has patience, we will reach the stars. We! We! It is only we Moon-men, used to space, used to a world in a cavern, used to an engineered environment, who could endure life in a spaceship that may have to travel centuries to reach the stars."

"Wait, wait, Demerest," said Bergen, holding up his hand.

"Back up! What do you mean, if Ocean-Deep allows it? What have we to do with it?"

"You're competing with us, Mr. Bergen. The Planetary Project Commission will swing your way, give you more, give us less, because in the short term, as your wife says, the ocean is alive and the Moon, except for a thousand men, is not; because you are a half-dozen miles away and we a quarter of a million; because you can be reached in an hour and we only in three days. And because you have an ideal safety record and we have had—misfortunes."

"The last, surely, is trivial. Accidents can happen any time, anywhere."

"But the trivial can be used," said Demerest angrily. "It can be made to manipulate emotions. To people who don't see the purpose and the importance of space exploration, the death of Moon-men in accidents is proof enough that the Moon is dangerous, that its colonization is a useless fantasy. Why not? It's their excuse for saving money and they can then salve their consciences by investing part of it in Ocean-Deep instead. That's why I said the accident on the Moon had threatened the survival of Luna City even though it killed only twenty people out of nearly a thousand."

"I don't accept your argument. There has been enough money for both for a score of years."

"Not enough money. That's exactly it. Not enough investment to make the Moon self-supporting in all these years, and then they use that lack of self-support against us. Not enough investment to make Ocean-Deep self-supporting either. . . .But now they can give you enough if they cut us out altogether."

"Do you think that will happen?"

"I'm almost sure it will, unless Ocean-Deep shows a statesmanlike concern for man's future."

"How?"

"By refusing to accept additional funds. By not competing with Luna City. By putting the good of the whole race ahead of self-interest."

"Surely you don't expect us to dismantle—"

"You won't have to. Don't you see? Join us in explaining that Luna City is essential, that space exploration is the hope of mankind; that you will wait, retrench, if necessary."

Bergen looked at his wife and raised his eyebrows. She shook her head angrily. Bergen said, "You have a rather romantic view of the PPC, I think. Even if I made noble, self-sacrificing speeches, who's to say they would listen? There's a great deal more involved in the matter of Ocean-Deep than my opinion and my statements. There are economic considerations and public feeling. Why don't you relax, Mr. Demerest? Luna City won't come to an end. You'll receive funds, I'm sure of it. I tell you, I'm sure of it. Now let's break this up—"

"No, I've got to convince you one way or another that I'm serious. If necessary, Ocean-Deep must come to a halt unless the PPC can supply ample funds for both."

Bergen said, "Is this some sort of official mission, Mr. Demerest? Are you speaking for Luna City officially, or just for yourself?"

"Just for myself, but maybe that's enough, Mr. Bergen."

"I don't think it is. I'm sorry, but this is turning out to be unpleasant. I suggest that, after all, you had better return Topside on the first available 'scaphe."

"Not yet! Not yet!" Demerest looked about wildly, then rose unsteadily and put his back against the wall. He was a little too tall for the room and he became conscious of life receding. One more step and he would have gone too far to back out.

He had told them back on the Moon that there would be no use talking, no use negotiating. It was dog-eat-dog for the available funds, and Luna City's destiny must not be aborted; not for Ocean-Deep; not for Earth; no, not for all of Earth, since mankind and the Universe came even before the Earth. Man must outgrow his womb and—

Demerest could hear his own ragged breathing and the inner turmoil of his whirling thoughts. The other two were looking at him with what seemed concern. Annette rose and said, "Are you ill, Mr. Demerest?"

"I am *not* ill. Sit down. I'm a safety engineer and I want to teach you about safety. Sit *down,* Mrs. Bergen."

"Sit down, Annette," said Bergen. "I'll take care of him." He rose and took a step forward.

But Demerest said, "No. Don't you move either. I have something right here. You're too naïve concerning human dangers, Mr. Bergen. You guard against the sea and against mechanical failure and you don't search your human visitors, do you? I have a weapon, Bergen."

Now that it was out and he had taken the final step, from which there was no returning, for he was now dead whatever he did, he was quite calm.

Annette said, "Oh, John," and grasped her husband's arm. "He's—"

Bergen stepped in front of her. "A weapon? Is that what that thing is? Now slowly, Demerest, slowly. There's nothing to get hot over. If you want to talk, we will talk. What is that?"

"Nothing dramatic. A portable laser beam."

"But what do you want to do with it?"

"Destroy Ocean-Deep."

"But you can't, Demerest. You know you can't. There's only so much energy you can pack into your fist and any laser you can hold can't pump enough heat to penetrate the walls."

"I know that. This packs more energy than you think. It's Moon-made and there are some advantages to manufacturing the energy unit in a vacuum. But you're right. Even so, it's designed only for small jobs and requires frequent recharging. So I don't intend to try to cut through a foot-plus of alloy steel. . . . But it will do the job indirectly. For one thing, it will keep you two quiet. There's enough energy in my fist to kill two people."

"You wouldn't kill us," said Bergen evenly. "You have no reason."

"If by that," said Demerest, "you imply that I am an un-reasoning being to be somehow made to understand my madness, forget it. I have every reason to kill you and I *will* kill you. By laser beam if I have to, though I would rather not."

"What good will killing us do you? Make me understand. Is it that I have refused to sacrifice Ocean-Deep funds? I couldn't do anything else. I'm not really the one to make the decision. And if you kill me, that won't help you force the decision in your direction, will it? In fact, quite the contrary. If a Moon-man is a murderer, how will that reflect on Luna City? Consider human emotions on Earth."

There was just an edge of shrillness in Annette's voice as she joined in. "Don't you see there will be people who will say that Solar radiation on the Moon has dangerous effects? That the genetic engineering which has reorganized your bones and muscles has affected mental stability? Consider the word 'lunatic,' Mr. Demerest. Men once believed the Moon brought madness."

"I am not mad, Mrs. Bergen."

"It doesn't matter," said Bergen, following his wife's lead smoothly. "Men will say that you were; that all Moon-men are; and Luna City will be closed down and the Moon itself closed to all further exploration, perhaps forever. Is that what you want?"

"That might happen if they thought I killed you, but they won't. It will be an accident." With his left elbow, Demerest broke the plastic that covered the manual controls.

"I know units of this sort," he said. "I know exactly how it works. Logically, breaking that plastic should set up a warning flash—after all, it might be broken by accident—and then someone would be here to investigate, or better yet, the controls should lock until deliberately released to make sure the break was not merely accidental."

He paused, then said, "But I'm sure no one will come; that no warning has taken place. Your manual system is not fail-safe because in your heart you were sure it would never be used."

"What do you plan to do?" said Bergen.

He was tense, and Demerest watched his knees carefully and said, "If you try to jump toward me, I'll shoot at once, and then keep right on with what I'm doing."

"I think maybe you're giving me nothing to lose."

"You'll lose time. Let me go right on without interference, and you'll have some minutes to keep on talking. You may even be able to talk me out of it. There's my proposal. Don't interfere with me and I will give you your chance to argue."

"But what do you plan to do?"

"This," said Demerest. He did not have to look. His left hand snaked out and closed a contact. "The fusion unit will now pump heat into the air lock and the steam will empty it. It will take a few minutes. When it's done, I'm sure one of those little red-glass buttons will light."

"Are you going to—"

Demerest said, "Why do you ask? You know that I must be intending, having gone this far, to flood Ocean-Deep."

"But why? Damn it, why?"

"Because it will be marked down as an accident. Because your safety record will be spoiled. Because it will be a complete catastrophe and will wipe you out. And PPC will then turn from you, and the glamour of Ocean-Deep will be gone. *We* will get the funds; *we* will continue. If I could bring that to pass in some other way, I would, but the needs of Luna City are the needs of mankind and those are paramount."

"You will die, too," Annette managed to say.

"Of course. Once I am forced to do something like this, would I *want* to live? I'm not a murderer."

"But you will be. If you flood this unit, you will flood all of Ocean-Deep and kill everyone in it—and doom those who are out in their subs to slower death. Fifty men and women—an unborn child—"

"That is not my fault," said Demerest, in clear pain. "I did not expect to find a pregnant woman here, but now that I have, I can't stop because of that."

"But you must stop," said Bergen. "Your plan won't work unless what happens can be shown to be an accident. They'll find you with a beam emitter in your hand and with the manual controls clearly tampered with: Do you think they won't deduce the truth from that?"

Demerest was feeling very tired. "Mr. Bergen, you sound desperate. Listen— When the outer door opens, water under a thousand atmospheres of pressure will enter. It will be a massive battering ram that will destroy and mangle everything in its path. The walls of the Ocean-Deep units will remain but everything inside will be twisted beyond recognition. Human beings will be mangled into shredded tissue and splintered bone, and death will be instantaneous and unfelt. Even if I were to burn you to death with the laser, there would be nothing left to show it had been done, so I won't hesitate, you see. This manual unit will be smashed anyway; anything I can do will be erased by the water."

"But the beam emitter, the laser gun. Even damaged, it will be recognizable," said Annette.

"We use such things on the Moon, Mrs. Bergen. It is a common tool; it is the optical analogue of a jackknife. I could kill you with a jackknive, you know, but one would not deduce that a man carrying a jackknife, or even holding one with the blade open, was necessarily planning murder. He might be whittling. Besides, a Moon-made laser is not a projectile gun. It doesn't have to withstand an internal explosion. It is made of thin metal, mechanically weak. After it is smashed by the waterclap I doubt that it will make much sense as an object."

Demerest did not have to think to make these statements. He had worked them out within himself through months of self-debate back on the Moon.

"In fact," he went on, "how will the investigators ever know what happened here? They will send 'scaphes down to inspect what is left of Ocean-Deep, but how can they get inside without first pumping the water out? They will, in effect, have to build a new Ocean-Deep and that would take—how long? Perhaps, given public reluctance to waste money, they might never do it at all and content themselves with dropping a laurel wreath on the dead walls of the dead Ocean-Deep."

Bergen said, "The men on Luna City will know what you have done. Surely one of them will have a conscience. The truth will be known."

"One truth," said Demerest, "is that I am not a fool. No one on Luna City knows what I planned to do or will suspect what I have done. They sent me down here to negotiate co-operation on the matter of financial grants. I was to argue and nothing more. There's not even a laser-beam emitter missing up there. I put this one together myself out of scrapped parts. . . . And it works. I've tested it."

Annette said slowly, "You haven't thought it through. Do you know what you're doing?"

"I've thought it through. I know what I'm doing. . . . And I know also that you are both conscious of the lit signal. I'm aware of it. The air lock is empty and time's up, I'm afraid."

Rapidly, holding his beam emitter tensely high, he closed another contact. A circular part of the unit wall cracked into a thin crescent and rolled smoothly away.

Out of the corner of his eye, Demerest saw the gaping darkness, but he did not look. A dank salty vapor issued from it; a queer odor of dead steam. He even imagined he could hear the flopping sound of the gathered water at the bottom of the lock.

Demerest said, "In a rational manual unit, the outer door ought to be frozen shut now. With the inner door open, nothing ought to make the outer door open. I suspect, though, that the manuals were put together too quickly at first for that precaution to have been taken, and they were replaced too quickly for that precaution to have been added. And if I need further evidence of that, you wouldn't be sitting there so tensely if you knew the outer door wouldn't open. I need touch one more contact and the waterclap will come. We will feel nothing."

Annette said, "Don't push it just yet. I have one more thing to say. You said we would have time to persuade you."

"While the water was being pushed out."

"Just let me say this. A minute. A *minute*. I said you didn't know what you were doing. You don't. You're destroying the space program, the *space* program. There's more to space than *space*." Her voice had grown shrill.

Demerest frowned. "What are you talking about? Make sense, or I'll end it all. I'm tired. I'm frightened. I want it over."

Annette said, "You're not in the inner councils of the PPC. Neither is my husband. But I am. Do you think because I am a woman that I'm secondary here? I'm not. You, Mr. Demerest, have your eyes fixed on Luna City only. My husband has his fixed on Ocean-Deep. Neither of you knows *anything.*

"Where do you expect to go, Mr. Demerest, if you had all the money you wanted? Mars? The asteroids? The satellites of the gas giants? These are all small worlds; all dry surfaces under a blank sky. It may be generations before we are ready to try for the stars and till then we'd have only pygmy real estate. Is that your ambition?

"My husband's ambition is no better. He dreams of pushing man's habitat over the ocean floor, a surface not much larger in the last analysis than the surface of the Moon and the other pygmy worlds. We of the PPC, on the other hand, want more than either of you, and if you push that button, Mr. Demerest, the greatest dream mankind has ever had will come to nothing."

Demerest found himself interested despite himself, but he said, "You're just babbling." It was possible, he knew, that somehow they had warned others in Ocean-Deep, that any moment someone would cone to interrupt, someone would try to shoot him down. He was, however, staring at the only opening, and he had only to close one contact, without even looking, in a second's movement.

Annette said, "I'm not babbling. You know it took more than rocket ships to colonize the Moon. To make a successful colony possible, men had to be altered genetically and adjusted to low gravity. You are a product of such genetic engineering."

"Well?"

"And might not genetic engineering also help men to greater gravitational pull? What is the largest planet of the Solar System, Mr. Demerest?"

"Jupi—"

"Yes, Jupiter. Eleven times the diameter of the Earth; forty times the diameter of the Moon. A surface a hundred and twenty times that of the Earth in area; sixteen hundred times that of the Moon. Conditions so different from anything we can encounter anywhere on the worlds the size of Earth or less that any scientist of any persuasion would give half his life for a chance to observe at close range."

"But Jupiter is an impossible target."

"Indeed?" said Annette, and even managed a faint smile. "As impossible as flying? Why is it impossible? Genetic engineering could design men with stronger and denser bones, stronger and more compact muscles. The same principles that enclose Luna City against the vacuum and Ocean-Deep against the sea can also enclose the future Jupiter-Deep against its ammoniated surroundings."

"The gravitational field—"

"Can be negotiated by nuclear-powered ships that are now on the drawing board. You don't know that but I do."

"We're not even sure about the depth of the atmosphere. The pressures—"

"The pressures! The *pressures!* Mr. Demerest, look about you. Why do you suppose Ocean-Deep was *really* built? To exploit the ocean? The settlements on the continental shelf are doing that quite adequately. To gain knowledge of the deep-sea bottom? We could do that by 'scaphe easily and we could then have spared the hundred billion dollars invested in Ocean-Deep so far.

"Don't you see, Mr. Demerest, that Ocean-Deep must mean something more than that? The purpose of Ocean-Deep is to devise the ultimate vessels and mechanisms that will suffice to explore and colonize *Jupiter*. Look about you and see the beginnings of a Jovian environment; the closest approach we can come to it on Earth. It is only a faint image of mighty Jupiter, but it's a beginning.

"Destroy this, Mr. Demerest, and you destroy any hope for Jupiter. On the other hand, let us live and we will, together, penetrate and settle the brightest jewel of the Solar System. And long before we can reach the limits of Jupiter, we will be ready for the stars, for the Earth-type planets circling them, *and* the Jupiter-type planets, too. Luna City won't be abandoned, because *both* are necessary for this ultimate aim."

For the moment, Demerest had altogether forgotten about that last button. He said, "Nobody on Luna City has heard of this."

"You haven't. There are those on Luna City who know. If you had told them of your plan of destruction, they would have stopped you. Naturally, we can't make this common knowledge and only a few people anywhere can know. The public supports only with difficulty the planetary projects now in progress. If the PPC is parsimonious it is because public opinion limits its generosity. What do you suppose public opinion would say if they thought we were aiming toward Jupiter? What a super-boondoggle that would be in their eyes. But we continue and what money we can save and make use of we place in the various facets of Project Big World."

"Yes," said Annette. "You know now and I have committed a serious security breach. But it doesn't matter, does it? Since we're all dead and since the project is, too."

"Wait now, Mrs. Bergen."

"If you change your mind now, don't think you can ever

talk about Project Big World. That would end the project just as effectively as destruction here would. And it would end both your career and mine. It might end Luna City and Ocean-Deep, too—so now that you know, maybe it makes no difference anyway. You might just as well push that button."

"I said wait—" Demerest's brow was furrowed and his eyes burned with anguish. "I don't know—"

Bergen gathered for the sudden jump as Demerest's tense alertness wavered into uncertain introspection, but Annette grasped her husband's sleeve.

A timeless interval that might have been ten seconds long followed and then Demerest held out his laser. "Take it," he said. "I'll consider myself under arrest."

"You can't be arrested," said Annette, "without the whole story coming out." She took the laser and gave it to Bergen. "It will be enough that you return to Luna City and keep silent. Till then we will keep you under guard."

Bergen was at the manual controls. The inner door slid shut and after that there was the thunderous waterclap of the water returning into the lock.

Husband and wife were alone again. They had not dared say a word until Demerest was safely put to sleep under the watchful eyes of two men detailed for the purpose. The unexpected waterclap had roused everybody and a sharply bowdlerized account of the incident had been given out.

The manual controls were now locked off and Bergen said, "From this point on, the manuals will have to be adjusted to fail-safe. And visitors will have to be searched."

"Oh, John," said Annette. "I think people are insane. There we were, facing death for us and for Ocean-Deep; just the end of everything. And I kept thinking: I must keep calm; I mustn't have a miscarriage."

"You kept calm all right. You were magnificent. I mean, Project Big World! I never conceived of such a thing, but by—by—*Jove,* it's an attractive thought. It's wonderful."

"I'm sorry I had to say all that, John. It was all a fake, of course. I made it up. Demerest wanted me to make something up really. He wasn't a killer or destroyer; he was, according to his own overheated lights, a patriot, and I suppose he was telling himself he must destroy in order to save—a common enough view among the small-minded. But he *said* he would give us time to talk him out of it and I think he was praying we would manage to do so. He wanted us to think of something that would give him the excuse to save in order to save, and I gave it to him. . . . I'm sorry I had to fool you, John."

"You didn't fool me."

"I didn't?"

"How could you? I knew you weren't a member of PPC."

"What made you so sure of that? Because I'm a woman?"

"Not at all. Because *I'm* a member, Annette, and *that's* confidential. And, if you don't mind, I will begin a move to initiate exactly what you suggested—Project Big World."

"Well!" Annette considered that and slowly smiled. "Well! That's not bad. Women do have their uses."

"Something," said Bergen, smiling also, "I have never denied."

MARS

From the days when telescopes first began to be trained on it, Mars has seemed to be a little Earth. Mars is half the diameter of Earth and has one-tenth the mass. It is half again as far from the Sun as Earth is.

The smallness of Mars means it can only have a thin atmosphere, but it does have one. Its distance from the Sun means it must be cooler than Earth, but there seemed reasons to think that it might not be too cold.

Then, too, Mars has a rotation period of 24.66 days, which is very close to that of Earth, and it has an axial tip of 25.17°, again very close to that of Earth. That means it has Earthlike seasons, each one colder than the corresponding season on Earth, of course, and lasting nearly twice as long because the Martian year is nearly twice as long as ours. Also, because Mars's orbit is a more eccentric ellipse than that of Earth, the seasons on Mars are more unequal in length than those of Earth.

Mars's surface seemed to the nineteenth-century astronomers to be an interlacing of light and dark—which could mean land and sea, respectively—and there was no question but that the planet had ice caps at either pole. On the whole, there were many similarities between Mars and Earth.

According to the favored nineteenth-century theory of the formation of the Solar system, the planets were formed, in order, from the outermost to the innermost as the Sun came into being through the shrinkage of the original cloud of dust and gas. That meant that Mars was older than Earth.

It was easy to suppose that life might have developed on Mars and, having had a longer time to develop on an older planet, would have produced an intelligent civilization surpassing ours.

When Mars made an unusually close approach to Earth in 1877, many telescopes were trained on it, and Giovanni Virginio Schiaparelli reported observing rather thin dark lines on the planet's surface, each connecting two larger dark areas. Schiaparelli called them, in Italian, *canali* ("channels"), the normal name for long thin bodies of water connecting two larger bodies. In English, however, the word was translated as "canals," the name given to human-made waterways.

The very name seemed to imply intelligent life on Mars.

The picture created was that of a small planet slowly losing its water because of the weakness of its gravitational field. The old and technologically advanced civilization on Mars was desperately trying to stave off desiccation by building huge canals to transport needed water from the last planetary reservoir, the ice caps.

Percival Lowell was the most ardent proponent of this viewpoint and wrote a book on the subject in 1894 that attracted much attention. Aware of this ferment on the subject, the science fiction writer H. G. Wells published *The War of the Worlds* in 1898, the first tale of interplanetary warfare. In the book, the Martians, giving up their hopeless struggle to keep Mars viable, decide to emigrate to the lush and watery Earth, taking it over by force if necessary.

From that time on, science fiction writers took it for granted that Mars had native life and native intelligence. The canals were accepted along with the high technology they required. The Martians might be benevolent or they might be evil, but they were there.

Astronomers were not so sure. Lowell represented a minority view, for no other astronomers could see the canals as well as he could, and some couldn't see them at all. What's more, the more closely Mars was studied, the more forbidding its surface seemed. The atmosphere was thinner than had been thought; there was no sign of free oxygen; there was little sign of water outside the ice caps.

Science fiction writers stuck to their guns, however, and the Martian canals were taken as fixtures into the 1950s. In 1938, when Orson Welles did a radio adaptation of *The War of the Worlds,* it proved so realistic that thousands panicked. Few seemed to doubt that there was advanced intelligent life on Mars.

And yet the growing austerity of the astronomical view of Mars was reflected in a few stories in science fiction. "Hop-Friend," published originally in 1962, shows a thin-atmosphered, arid planet—but one that still has intelligent life on it.

A definite decision on the matter of the canals could not be reached, however, until a clearer view of the Martian surface could be obtained than was possible from Earth. Probes were the answer. On July 14, 1965, the probe Mariner 4 passed Mars and sent back twenty photographs of the planet.

There were no canals shown. What was shown were craters, rather like those on the Moon.

In 1969, more advanced probes, Mariners 6 and 7, passed Mars. Definitely no canals—and the atmosphere was thinner, dryer, and colder than even the most pessimistic pre-probe estimates. It seemed that there could not possibly be any form of advanced life on Mars, let alone intelligent life with great engineering ability. The canals seen by Schiaparelli and Lowell were apparently optical illusions.

In 1971, the probe Mariner 9 went into orbit around Mars, and the entire Martian surface was photographed in detail.

There were no canals, but there were enormous volcanoes; one of them, Olympus Mons, was far huger than anything of the sort on Earth. Another record was set by Valles Marineris, a canyon that dwarfed Earth's Grand Canyon to a toothpick scratch. And there were markings that looked precisely like dried river beds.

Could Mars have been wetter and milder in the past, a world of rivers and lakes? Could it be in an ice age of sorts right now, and would it return to a wet, mild climate in the future? The problem is what has happened to the water if it was there in the past, for there is certainly no sign of it now outside the ice caps. One theory is that there is a great deal of water (or, rather, ice) in the subsoil—a kind of planetary permafrost. In this respect, "Hop-Friend's" picture of underground water is interesting. But intelligent life doesn't seem in the cards.

In 1976, the probes Vikings 1 and 2 soft-landed on the Martian surface and tested the soil for signs of microscopic life. The results were ambiguous.

The old Mars of canals and engineers is dead, but there is a new Mars that is just as interesting and will supply a new background and new plots for science fiction writers.

Hop-Friend

TERRY CARR

On the tenth day of the construction job out on the edge of
Syrtis Major they found a Marshie watching them. He might
have been there ever since they'd trucked in their equipment
and thrown up a bubble and temporary toilets, but they never
did find out.

The Marshies flicked in and out of sight so rapidly that
you had to be looking right where they appeared to see them
at all, most of the time. They hopped around like fireflies,
stopping for two seconds or two minutes, standing almost still
with their angular birdlike heads cocked to one side, and then
they'd be gone, turning up almost instantly fifteen feet away,
still with their heads cocked looking at you. They were un-
nerving to most of the Earthmen, and a couple of years back
one nervous kid in Iguana, near the Bald Spot, had taken a
shot at one of them—missed him and burned hell out of one
wall of a building. The Marshies hadn't been around the
Earth towns much since then.

Not that they had ever been especially chummy. The Marshies were partially telepathic and they could manage the
Earth languages well enough, but they seldom bothered. For
the most part they just didn't seem interested. Every now and
then you'd see one of them pause for a minute in the settlements, and maybe he'd say, "Hi, Harry," or "Nice weather
this year," but they never stopped to talk about anything.
The Earthmen had been on the planet for over ten years, but

all the government could tell you about the Marshies was that they had some towns out in the mountains somewhere, they were trisexual, and their lifespan was about thirty years.

Walt Michelson had been wondering about them ever since he'd landed on the planet back with the first wave, when he'd come with his parents. Michelson had been twelve then, busy looking around and asking questions every time his eyes lit on something. When he was fourteen he saw a Marshie—one of them landed right next to him at his brother's funeral and stood completely still for almost ten minutes while the service droned on. It had been out on the flatlands, where the heavy brown dust was sometimes two inches deep and you had to raise your voice to be heard in the thin air. The Marshie had watched the interment rites silently, standing off to one side, and when it had all been over he had looked at Michelson and said "Yes," and disappeared.

Michelson's father had been a building contractor—a pretty good one, successful enough that he could have sent Walt back to Earth by the time he was eighteen. But Walt hadn't wanted to go; all he remembered of Earth was how crowded it was, how many policemen there were, how many laws and taxes and taboos have built up over the centuries, When he'd been on Earth his father hadn't had much money, and that colored his feelings toward the home planet too, but basically he liked Mars because there was *room* here—no walls, real or legislated, to keep a man standing still. So he'd stayed on Mars, and learned the building trades, and he was a foreman this year and would be more next year. He didn't give a damn about Earth.

Now he was working on building a town out here at the base of the hills, on a site which somebody had decided would be an important trade outpost. Some of the drainage from the ice cap reached this area, too, so there might be some chance for agriculture. The city had been planned in detail back at Dry Puget, but nobody had thought that there were any Marshies in the area.

They'd noticed him first by the puffs of dust rising in a line leading from the foothills straight to the building site. The Marshies traveled in a peculiar half-leaping, half-flying fashion, and when they touched down and jumped off again they kicked up small clouds of dust. One of the workmen saw those clouds coming toward them and reported to Michelson, who got his binocs and watched the Marshie coming. He wasn't long in arriving.

He lit right outside the bubble and stood looking for a minute, then disappeared and skipped right in through one of the air locks where they were removing the dirt from the diggings inside. He turned up next to the big shovel for a few seconds, disappeared when one of the men suddenly yelled, reappeared over by the lumber yard next to the foundation work going on in the south quarter, then outside the truck depot, and finally at the door of the contractor's office where Michelson had been going over the drawings for the street layout. Michelson looked up at him and the Marshie cocked his head and stared back.

The Marshie was a faded orange in color, his body covered with a heavy fur through which the powerful muscles showed clearly. His eyes, large and liquid black, were set on the sides of his head, and his nose and mouth were almost indistinguishable under the fur of the face. He had long legs, thin but powerful, giving him a stature of over seven feet; his large brown wings folded down over his back softly like a cloak. He was indistiguishable from any other Marshie that Michelson had ever seen, but that was undoubtedly because the Marshies were so seldom around.

As the Marshie continued to stand silently looking at him Michelson was struck with the humor of the tableau, and he grinned and nodded. "Welcome to our humble diggings," he said.

The Marshie disappeared, leaving two deep footprints in the dirt outside the door where he had kicked off. Michelson got up and went to the door, saw the alien light a couple of times going across the large inner yard, and then he apparently hopped out through the air locks again. Michelson raised his binocs from the strap around his neck, but he was unable to track the Marshies' dust clouds in their erratic jumps out on the flat. They seemed to head toward the hills again, but he couldn't be sure.

Michelson shrugged and turned back to the plans on the desk. The Marshie was no immediate problem to him; if he continued to show up, there might be trouble among the construction workers—the Marshies appeared and disappeared so abruptly that they could upset a whole crew in a few hours—but for the moment Michelson wasn't going to worry about it. He had a more pressing problem.

One of the field men had found that the northeast quarter was right over a large water deposit and it would require some pretty drastic structural modifications or maybe abandoning part of the site altogether. There was bedrock not too far down, and the yearly ice-cap drainage collected there; the water wasn't enough to be useful as a supply for the planned city, but the pocket was large enough to undermine any foundations they might try to put in there.

He'd already checked the specifications and found that any pumping system they could install to periodically drain the pocket would be in a cost bracket making it necessary to get an okay from the builder clear back in Dry Puget. And that could hold up the work long enough to make them miss their deadline. No, there had to be some way to block the seepage before the water got to the pocket, so that it could be drained once and for all.

Damn it, it was just his luck to run into trouble with water on Mars, where that was the last thing you expected. Well, tomorrow he'd get together with a couple of the surveyors and see what could be done.

The Marshie was back the next day, shortly after the sun rose darkly over the low hills. There was so little light at that early hour that no one saw him coming and the first thing they knew of his presence was when he landed for a moment in an air lock and a driver slammed on his brakes to avoid hitting him—which wasn't really necessary, since the Marshie had jumped off again immediately, but a human driver's muscular reactions weren't geared for Marshie pedestrians. The Marshie skipped on in through the interconnecting locks.

He came down beside Michelson as he was going across the yard toward the diggings, and Michelson stopped. He turned and cocked his head at the alien, mocking his stance, and after a moment said, "I'll give you a gate pass if you want."

The Marshie regarded him with his big dark left eye and shook his wings lightly. "Hello, Walt," he said, and skipped off. Michelson shrugged and went on across the yard, but the Marshie came back a minute later, touched down and said, "They aren't so humble," and disappeared again.

Mike Deckinger, who was in charge of the trucks, was nearby and he came over frowning. "He's going to drive us nuts if he keeps that up," he said. "We could tighten up the air lock sequence and maybe keep him out that way."

Michelson shook his head. "That would just down the works. Leave him alone; he's just looking."

"Yeah, but why?" said Deckinger, and walked off.

Harris and Loening, the two surveyors, were waiting for Michelson at the diggings. They were good men, both in their thirties and well trained both on Earth and this planet. Harris was heavyset, with a ruddy, swarthy face and close-cropped black hair; Loening was taller, broad-shouldered, with bony, angular features and dark eyes that seemed to peer out from shadowed caves. Michelson explained the problem to them.

"I want to go outside and see if we can trace the drainage," he concluded. "Find a place where we can dam or re-channel it."

"That'll involve drilling," Loening said.

Michelson raised an eyebrow at him. "Probably. Unless you want to try a dousing rod." Loening grunted disgustedly.

"Well, let's take a walk out there first anyway," Harris said. They started back across the yard toward the north air locks. Since they might be out for some time, they each donned facemasks and picked up small tanks of oxygen before they checked through.

The Marshie hopped through ahead of them.

He passed them in the second lock and was waiting for them when they emerged onto the flat outside. He stood off about twenty feet, ruffling his wings in a way which seemed impatient to Michelson, and skipped back and forth past them as they set off toward the low hills, following the line of the water as closely as it had been traced in the preliminary survey. Loening walked stolidly, his head down and frowning, but Harris didn't seem to pay any attention to the alien. Michelson watched for him as he walked, and thought.

This hop-guy seemed a lot more interested in the construction works than the Marshies had ever been before. What was that he had said back in the compound? "They aren't so humble." What did that mean?

He'd come in from the hills, and the Marshies were supposed to live somewhere in a mountainous area. This one, maybe? Perhaps the Marshies were taking a definite interest in this site because the Earthmen had finally started getting near their own area.

And if so, just what kind of an interest were they taking?

The water had been traced back to the foot of the hills, but no further. On foot in the low Martian gravity the Earthmen made it that far in about half an hour. There was a thin, cold wind out here which cut through their heavy jackets and ruffled Michelson's light hair, but it didn't stir the dust very much. The air on Mars lacked body; once you got used to it you could breathe it well enough if you didn't exert yourself, but if you wanted to smoke a pipe you had to do it when you were inside a bubble or it would go out every time.

They stopped and rested at the base of the first hill, where dry rocks had tumbled down the slope during the ages and collected at the bottom. Loening loosened his pack and swung it off his shoulder to the ground. He nodded up at the rising hills and said, "The first thing to do is scout around there and chart the rock stratifications."

"Do you think the drainage comes through the mountains?" Michelson asked him.

"Might; can't tell offhand. We've been walking on solid rock for a mile or more—that means the water is under rock for a ways out there, and the channel could turn off anywhere. Maybe it skirts the hills; that's one thing I want to check. If the stratifications here show that these hills rose during an upheaval, the chances are that the water channel does go around them."

Michelson nodded. "Well, we can get the preliminary scouting done faster if we split up. I'll try going through the pass up there."

Loening and Harris rose with him, and they set off separately. As Michelson started up the slope, he heard Harris call to him, "If you see our Marshie again, ask him where the hell the water comes from."

Michelson grinned back down at him. "I think I will," he said.

He climbed slowly up the rough slope, now and then cutting in his oxygen supply for a few breaths. The rocks here were bulky and weathered—the kind of weathering that happened on Mars only with the passage of ages. They stood out like silent gray beasts against the morning shadows. Michelson was soon out of sight of their starting point, but he followed the natural pass and made a rough map as he went, noting the rock formations and what he could see of the stratifications. It was all a jumble, as far as he could tell; some of the sheer rocksides seemed to show evidence of having been pushed up as Loening had suggested and others didn't. And the direction of the stratifications varied apparently without pattern. Well, figuring the pattern would be the surveyors' job.

At a small level spot he stopped to rest, and as he sat looking over his rough-sketched map he heard a sound and the Marshie said beside him, "Most of these hills have been here for two million years."

Michelson looked up, carefully registering no outward surprise. "Whose years?" he said. "Yours or mine?"

The Marshie shook his wings and hopped a little way to one side, still regarding him with one dark eye. "We do not count years."

Michelson nodded at him. "Do you have names?"

"No," said the Marshie, and disappeared. Michelson waited for him to show up again, but after a few minutes he shrugged and stood up to go. It looked like there was still a lot of area to be covered up here.

The Marshie landed again. "I am faster than you," he said.

"That's true," Michelson said. He started walking on upward through the rocks. "Do you live near here?"

"Perhaps," said the Marshie. "I am faster than you."

"Near" could mean fifty miles to a Marshie, Michelson reflected. Well, it had been a fair answer then.

"Where does the water come from?" he said.

The Marshie disappeared.

He didn't show up again for the rest of the day. Michelson followed the pass up into the hills for a mile or two, and then he retraced his steps back down to the point of departure. Loening was waiting for him, and Harris returned shortly. They set off again back across the dusty flat to the bubble.

"It's a mess," Loening said. "The rocks vary in age from maybe a couple thousand years to God knows how old, and there are fifty different types. It doesn't tell us much." He ran his fingers through his dry brown hair, frowning.

"Our hop-friend told me they were mostly a couple of million years old," Michelson said. "At least in the area where I was."

"Yeah?" said Harris. "Did he say anything else?"

Michelson shook his head. "I asked him about the water, but he wouldn't answer me; he just shoved off and disappeared. You can't hold a conversation with someone who's liable to be gone at any moment. You get to stuttering."

"I never talked with a Marshie," Harris said. "They're telepathic, aren't they? Maybe they take one look into me and don't like me."

"Don't try to understand them," Loening said over his shoulder as he walked on ahead through the dust. "The only good thing about the damn Marshies is that they stay away from us most of the time."

"I don't know about that," said Michelson, and the three men fell silent, conserving their breath for walking.

But Michelson was thinking about the Marshie. Harris was right—they didn't usually talk with Earthmen. They would hop around and watch interestedly, and sometimes they would say a word or two, usually only enough to acknowledge your existence, but there was no communication between the two species. Yet this one was, comparatively, talking a blue streak. Why?

Michelson was becoming more and more sure that the Marshies had a settlement somewhere nearby. Back in the hills, probably—and Michelson was almost willing to bet that the water drainage ran right through those hills. It figured that the Marshies would settle somewhere where water was handy; on Mars that would be a prime requisite for the Marshies as well as the Earthmen. And if the Marshies were up in those hills, what did they think of the new Earth city being built right on the edge of the flat?

Maybe they hadn't decided yet.

The Marshies, come to think of it, knew a lot more about the Earthmen than they knew about the natives. The Marshies had stayed away from the Earth settlements, watching, and now the Earthmen were accidentally forcing a meeting between them; that must be shaking up the hoppers. And so, apparently, they were taking a final look at the Earthmen; and maybe soon they'd make a decision. He wished he knew what their alternatives were.

They took a landcar out the next day, loaded with a burn-drill. The small red sun was still low over the horizon when they checked through the locks, and they threw a long gray shadow over the dust as they rode toward the hills. There had been no sign of the Marshie yet today, but Michelson was watching for the puffs of dust which would herald his arrival.

They set up the drill half a mile from the hills. It worked on the same principle as their blasters, boring a small hole straight down through the dirt and rock and, by the resistance offered, registering the various strata through which it passed. They found the water fifty feet down, under the layer of rock which formed the floor of the desert here.

They moved on to the base of the hills and again drilled, and again they found the water. Loening drew a straight line on a map of the area, and it passed directly from the building site through the two drilling points. Extended, it would run through the mountains.

"We'll have to take the drill up into the hills," Loening said. "Flex your muscles—it's heavy."

They mounted it on rollers and made the ascent, and when they had got it to the first level spot in the pass they were all puffing with exertion despite the oxygen masks they had donned. They sat and rested while Harris and Loening debated whether to drill here or try moving the drill farther back into the hills. And the Marshie arrived.

He came down the pass in three quick hops and stopped next to the drill, which he regarded for a moment in his cocked-head stance. Then he skipped away and came back a few minutes later, landing next to Michelson.

"It is not a weapon," he said.

"No, it's a drill," Michelson said. "We're looking for water."

"Yes," said the Marshie, and hopped twenty feet back up the pass. There he stood motionless, looking at the Earthmen. Marshies could stand still for hours, completely unmoving, when they felt like it; only the Marshie's liquid-dark eyes moved, flicking from one to another of the Earthmen in turn, and continually back to rest on the drill which sat before them. Harris sat staring back at him, but Leoning coldly ignored his gaze, looking almost sullenly down at his feet. Michelson rose and walked slowly toward the creature.

"We're trying to find the path of the water," he said. "Can you help us?"

The Marshie's head jerked to one side and the big dark eye focused on Michelson. After a moment he said, "I know where the water is."

"We want to dam the water, to keep it from our city," Michelson said. "If you help us, we can be sure we don't divert it from your own use."

The Marshie hopped to one side, paused, and hopped off up the slope out of sight. Michelson waited for several minutes, but he did not return. Michelson shrugged and went back to his companions.

"I think you've frightened him," Loening said. "They don't play our games."

"They haven't so far," Michelson admitted. "But I think they live in these hills, and they're going to have to take notice of that city we're building. It's about time we started co-operating with each other."

"Whether we like it or not?" said Loening.

Michelson nodded. "If that's their attitude—or ours. Personally, I think we might have a lot to offer each other; this could be the first step."

"The Marshies don't *step*," Loening said. "They hop. They skitter around like grasshoppers." His mouth was drawn back in a disgusted grimace. He took a breath and stood up. "Anyway, you can go on talking about cultural exchange with grasshoppers, but I think we'd better lug this drill up a bit further if we want to get anything concrete done today."

The three men began to attach the pulling straps to their shoulders, but before they started their further ascent the Marshie came back. He landed beside them and said immediately, "I can tell you where the water is. You want to be friends."

Michelson dropped the strap and looked at the Marshie, wondering for a moment if the creature was serious. But of course it was useless to try to see what was in a hopper's mind, as Loening had said. At any rate, no matter how difficult it was to communicate with the Marshies, they did not lie.

He turned to Loening and said, "You and Harris take the drill back down to the landcar—the grasshoppers have landed."

He spent hours following the Marshie through the hills, back over five miles into the rocky, desolate terrain. There was silence in those mountains—not just the silence of a thin atmosphere, but the silence of emptiness, of desertion. The gray shadows fell along their path like dull pastel silhouettes, and the Marshie hopped back and forth past Michelson, silent but seemingly impatient. There was an air of excitement about this fur-covered creature—an almost childlike eagerness in his rough, inhuman voice when he occasionally stopped and said, "We will be friends, Walt, when I show you the water."

Well, of course he was interpreting the creature's attitude in his own terms, and it probably didn't make sense. But the Marshie hurried him along the rocky path.

They came down into a small hollow among the rocks, and the Marshie said, "Here is the water." There was an expanse of mud—the heavy brown dust of Mars, with water flowing slowly through it. It covered the floor of this tiny valley, and on its surface Michelson saw a thin green mosslike growth. It was like an expanse of quicksand, like an antiseptic swamp— for there were none of the heavier forms of vegetation of Earth, no insects skimming the surface. Here amid the chill dark rocks of Mars was a branch of the annual drainage of the ice cap, and it seemed pitifully anticlimactic to Michelson.

"You can stop the water here," said the Marshie. "We are friends?"

Michelson looked around him, across the muddy expanse at the hills which rose again immediately beyond. "Your home is back there?" he asked.

"Yes." The Marshie hopped once, twice, twenty feet at a time, and hopped back again. "We are friends?" he said again.

"Of course," Michelson said. And then a thought came to him and he said, "Do you know what friendship is?"

The Marshie's eye regarded him softly for a moment. "We know something of it. But we do not have a word for it."

Michelson was suddenly aware that this small muddy valley was a strangely unimpressive scene for a meeting of races. He felt alone and unimportant standing amid the ages-old rocks of this world with the furry Martian. This was not, after all, his world; he had lived most of his life here, and had come to think of it as his home far more than he thought so of Earth, but here in the quiet gray rock shadows he felt fully for the first time that this desolate world belonged to the hoppers—to the Martians. And without quite realizing what he was doing he cut in his oxygen supply, though he wasn't really short of breath.

The Marshie hopped away without a word, leaving him alone there.

Harris and Loening surveyed the area thoroughly in the days that followed, and Michelson sent some men out to begin construction of a dam there, meanwhile making preparations for draining the waterpocket beneath the city. It kept him busy for several days, and it wasn't until two weeks later, when the dam construction was started, that he began to wonder seriously why the Marshie had not been around again. No one had seen him out at the dam site either.

Michelson took an aircar out to the site soon after and checked the progress of the work there. They had moved machinery in and set up temporary quarters there for the work crew; the area was bustling with activity. Michelson looked at the footprints of the workmen in the Martian dust, heard the noise of the machines and the voices around him, and thought of that silent day when he had stood here alone with the Marshie. Two weeks ago . . . it seemed like months.

He left, and took the aircar up to scout the area. The Marshies' city was supposed to be somewhere farther up the pass; he hoped he could spot it from the air. He flew low, droning through the massive rocky crags, watching the ground through binocs. He had penetrated fifteen miles farther into the mountains and was almost ready to give up when he found it.

The dwellings were cut into the rock, in vertical lines up and down the cliffside. There were perhaps twenty or twenty-five of them, certainly no more. He landed the aircar at the base of those cliffs and approached slowly.

He needn't have bothered; they were empty. Some things had been left behind—a few small objects, delicately carved from stone, some pelts of the Marshies' own fur which had perhaps been used for added warmth during the winter, one or two pieces of what might have been furniture—but the area was definitely deserted. He couldn't tell offhand how long the Marshies had been gone, but he was sure it was no more than two weeks.

He left the dwellings untouched, not even picking up any of the small stone carvings to bring back with him. Perhaps later they could send out a government expedition to catalogue and study what had been left. He walked slowly back to his aircar, looking at the depressions in the floor of the canyon left by the Marshies' footprints.

A fluttering behind him caused him to turn in surprise, and he saw a Marshie regarding him calmly. This could have been the same one, but he seemed a bit more heavily built, his fur somewhat darker.

"Hello," Michelson said. "We are friends?"

The Marshie continued to look silently at him for a moment, his heavy, dark wings folded like shadows around him. Then he said, "Some of us too are insane." And he disappeared with a quick jump and flutter of brown wings.

After a while Michelson turned and continued walking to the aircar, leaving the footprints of his boots behind him in the dust.

ASTEROIDS

The asteroids were discovered by a combination of purposeful-
ness and accident. By the end of the 1700s, astronomers had
noted the regularity with which the planets were spaced in their
orbits about the Sun and had decided that there ought to be one
between the orbits of Mars and Jupiter. A group of astronomers
organized for a systematic search of the heavens, but before
they could begin, Giuseppe Piazzi accidentally discovered
Ceres in the orbital gap. He hadn't been looking for it. The discovery was made on January 1, 1801.

Ceres turned out to be very small, far smaller than Mercury. It
was only 1000 kilometers (600 miles) across, and astronomers
couldn't believe that was all there was in the gap. They continued their search and in the next few years discovered three
more objects in the gap—Pallas, Vesta, and Juno. They were
even smaller than Ceres.

William Herschel suggested they be named "asteroids"
("starlike") because they were so small that, when viewed
through a telescope, their images did not expand into an orb, as
was the case with the other planets, but remained starlike
points.

Eventually additional asteroids were discovered, more and
more and more, until by now over 1800 asteroids have had
their orbits plotted and have been given names. Some of the
nearer ones that have been located are only a couple of kilometers in diameter. The total number of asteroids with diameters

of a kilometer or more has been estimated to be from 40,000 to 100,000. Ceres, the first discovered, remains the largest. Its mass may be as much as 10 percent of the total asteroidal mass.

When the first four asteroids were discovered, Heinrich W. M. Olbers, one of the discoverers, at once suggested that they were fragments of a planet between Mars and Jupiter, a planet which had, for some reason, exploded. This view has never quite lost its popularity, and it is mentioned, for instance, in "Barnacle Bull," which was published in 1960. This view is supported by only a minority of astronomers, however.

After all, even if all the asteroids were imagined to be coalesced into a single body, that body would be even smaller than our Moon, and it is hard to imagine a body of that size, made of ordinary planetary materials, exploding. It seems more likely that the asteroids represent a portion of the original cloud of dust and gas out of which the Solar system was formed that somehow never got to coalesce into a planet. It formed many small bodies instead of one large one perhaps because of the gravitational interference of the too-near giant planet Jupiter.

Throughout the nineteenth century, it was assumed that the asteroids were confined to the "asteroid belt," the region between the orbits of Mars and Jupiter. In 1898, however, Gustav Witt discovered one which had an orbit that carried it inside that of Mars. It could approach Earth within 25 million kilometers (16 million miles), which is closer than the approach of any of the major planets. Witt named the asteroid "Eros," and it was the first of what came to be called the "Earth grazers."

The closest of the Earth grazers so far (if we don't count those small bodies that actually collide with Earth) is Hermes, which was spotted in 1937 and which, it was calculated, might approach within 320,000 kilometers (200,000 miles) of Earth.

Some asteroids approach the Sun surprisingly closely. There are asteroids called "Apollo objects" which approach closer to the Sun than Venus does, and in 1948 Walter Baade discovered

Icarus, which actually moves closer to the Sun than Mercury does.

The Apollo objects have the far end of their orbits in the asteroid belt, but in 1978, the first asteroid was discovered with an orbit that at every point was closer to the Sun than Earth was.

Asteroids with orbits carrying them beyond the other end of the asteroid belt—that is, beyond the orbit of Jupiter—are harder to detect because they tend to be so far away from us.

In 1920, nevertheless, Walter Baade discovered Hidalgo, which moves beyond the orbit of Jupiter and, at its farthest point from the Sun, is nearly as far away from it as the orbit of Saturn is.

An even more startling discovery was made in 1977 by Charles Kowal. He was studying photographic plates in search of distant comets and came across an object that seemed of the correct brightness but proved to be moving unusually slowly as he watched from night to night. He worked out a possible orbit, then searched through all other available photographic plates that might show such an object in various places in its orbit. He came across enough photographs of it to work up a very accurate orbit.

It turned out that Kowal had discovered a good-sized asteroid with an orbit that stretched from a point nearly as close to the Sun as Saturn is to a point nearly as far from the Sun as Uranus is. Kowal called the new object "Chiron."

It may well be that asteroids, while concentrated in the asteroid belt, are to be found in fair abundance throughout the Solar system.

It was taken for granted recently that asteroids were essentially rocky objects, and this is mentioned in "Barnacle Bull." It may not be as simple as all that. About 90 percent of the meteorites that reach Earth's crust are rocky, and 10 percent are nickel-iron. A few, however, are "carbonaceous chondrites," which are black and crumbly and contain light elements and their compounds—including appreciable quantities of water and organic material.

Carbonaceous chondrites are particularly apt to crumble, powder, and burn in the atmosphere. Few survive the trip to Earth's surface.

Out in space, though, the carbonaceous chondrites may be common, and they may be the more common the farther one goes from the Sun.

In the last few years, careful measurements have been made of the albedos of the asteroids, that is, of the fraction of the Sun's light that they reflect. It turns out that most of the asteroids are surprisingly black—as black as carbonaceous chondrites.

Perhaps they *are* carbonaceous chondrites, or objects that have rocky cores and carbonaceous chondrite outer regions. Of the twelve largest asteroids, no less than eight seem to have carbonaceous chondrite surfaces, and that includes Ceres, the largest asteroid.

In that case, while the asteroids might be the prime mines of our future space civilization, they may be even more important as a source of water, organics, and fertilizer for our space settlements than as a source of cement and metals.

Barnacle Bull

POUL ANDERSON (as Winston P. Sanders)

The *Hellik Olav* was well past Mars, acceleration ended, free-falling into the Asteroid Belt on a long elliptical orbit, when the interior radiation count began to rise. It wasn't serious, and worried none of the four men aboard. They had been so worried all along, that a little extra ionization didn't seem to matter.

But as the days passed, the Geigers got still more noisy.

And then the radio quit.

This was bad! No more tapes were being made of signals received—Earth to one of the artificial satellites to Phobos to a cone of space which a rather smug-looking computer insisted held the *Hellik Olav*—for later study by electronics engineers. As for the men, they were suddenly bereft of their favorite programs. Adam Langnes, captain, no longer got the beeps whose distortions gave him an idea of exterior conditions and whose Doppler frequency gave him a check on his velocity. Torvald Winge, astronomer, had no answers to his requests for data omitted from his handbook and computations too elaborate for the ship's digital. Per Helledahl, physicist, heard no more sentimental folk songs nor the recorded babblings of his youngest child. And Erik Bull, engineer, couldn't get the cowboy music sent from the American radio satellite. He couldn't even get the Russians' progressive jazz.

Furthermore, and still more ominous, the ship's transmitter also stopped working.

Helledahl turned from its disassembled guts. Despite all he could do with racks, bags, magnetic boards, he was surrounded by a zero gravity halo of wires, resistances, transistors, and other small objects. His moon face peered through it with an unwonted grimness. "I can find nothing wrong," he said. "The trouble must be outside, in the boom."

Captain Langnes, tall and gaunt and stiff of manner, adjusted his monocle. "I dare say we can repair the trouble," he said. "Can't be too serious, can it?"

"It can like the devil, if the radar goes out too," snapped Helledahl.

"Oh, heavens!" exclaimed Winge. His mild middle-aged features registered dismay. "If I can't maintain my meteorite count, what am I out here for?"

"If we can't detect the big meteorites in time for the autopilot to jerk us off a collision course, you won't be out here very long," said Bull. "None of us will, except as scrap metal and frozen hamburger."

Helledahl winced. "Must you, Erik?"

"Your attitude is undesirable, Herr Bull," Captain Langnes chided. "Never forget, gentlemen, the four of us, crowded into one small vessel for possibly two years, under extremely hazardous conditions, can only survive by maintaining order, self-respect, morale."

"How can I forget?" muttered Bull. "You repeat it every thirty-seven hours and fourteen minutes by the clock." But he didn't mutter very loudly.

"You had best have a look outside, Herr Bull," went on the captain.

"I was afraid it'd come to that," said the engineer dismally. "Hang on, boys, here we go again."

Putting on space armor is a tedious job at best, requiring much assistance. In a cramped air-lock chamber—for lack of another place—and under free fall, it gets so exasperating that one forgets any element of emergency. By the time he was through the outer valve, Bull had invented three new verbal obscenities, the best of which took four minutes to enunciate.

He was a big blocky redhaired and freckle-faced young man, who hadn't wanted to come on this expedition. It was just a miserable series of accidents, he thought. As a boy, standing at a grisly hour on a cliff above the Sognefjord to watch the first Sputnik rise, he had decided to be a spaceship engineer. As a youth, he got a scholarship to the Massachusetts Institute of Technology, and afterward worked for two years on American interplanetary projects. Returning home, he found himself one of the few Norwegians with that kind of experience. But he also found himself thoroughly tired of it. The cramped quarters, tight discipline, reconstituted food and reconstituted air and reconstituted conversation, were bad enough. The innumerable petty nuisances of weightlessness, especially the hours a day spent doing ridiculous exercises lest his very bones atrophy, were worse. The exclusively male companionship was still worse: especially when that all-female Russian satellite station generally called the Nunnery passed within view.

"In short," Erik Bull told his friends, "if I want to take vows of poverty, chastity, and obedience, I'd do better to sign up as a Benedictine monk. I'd at least have something drinkable on hand."

Not that he regretted the time spent, once it was safely behind him. With judicious embroidering, he had a lifetime supply of dinner-table reminiscences. More important, he could take his pick of Earthside jobs. Such as the marine reclamation station his countrymen were building off Svalbard, with regular airbus service to Trondheim and Oslo. *There* was a post!

Instead of which, he was now spinning off beyond Mars, hell for leather into a volume of space that had already swallowed a score of craft without trace.

He emerged on the hull, made sure his lifeline was fast,

and floated a few minutes to let his eyes adjust. A tiny heat-less sun, too brilliant to look close to, spotted puddles of un-diffused glare among coalsack shadows. The stars, unwinking, needle bright, were so many that they swamped the old familiar constellations in their sheer number. He identified several points as asteroids, some twinkling as rotation exposed their irregular surfaces, some so close that their relative motion was visible. His senses did not react to the radiation, which the ship's magnetic field was supposed to ward off from the interior but which sharply limited his stay outside. Bull imagined all those particles zipping through him, each drilling a neat submicroscopic hole, and wished he hadn't.

The much-touted majestic silence of space wasn't evident either. His air pump made too much noise. Also, the suit stank.

Presently he could make sense out of the view. The ship was a long cylinder, lumpy where meteor bumpers protected the most vital spots. A Norwegian flag, painted near the bows, was faded by solar ultraviolet, eroded by microme-teoric impacts. The vessel was old, though basically sound. The Russians had given it to Norway for a museum piece, as a propaganda gesture. But then the Americans had hastily given Norway the parts needed to renovate. Bull himself had spent six dreary months helping do that job. He hadn't been too unhappy about it, though. He liked the idea of his country joining in the exploitation of space. Also, he was Americanized enough to feel a certain malicious pleasure when the *Ivan Pavlov* was rechristened in honor of St. Olav.

However, he had not expected to serve aboard the thing!

"O.K., O.K.," he sneered in English, "hold still, Holy Ole, and we'll have a look at your latest disease."

He drew himself back along the line and waddled forward over the hull in stickum boots. Something on the radio trans-ceiver boom ... what the devil? He bent over. The motion pulled his boots loose. He upended and went drifting off toward Andromeda. Cursing in a lackluster voice, he came back hand over hand. But as he examined the roughened surface he forgot even to be annoyed.

He tried unsuccessfully to pinch himself.

An hour convinced him. He made his laborious way below again. Captain Langnes, who was Navy, insisted that you went "below" when you entered the ship, even in free fall. When his spacesuit was off, with only one frost burn suffered from touching the metal, he faced the others across a cluttered main cabin.

"Well?" barked Helledahl. "What is it?"

"As the lady said when she saw an elephant eating cabbages with what she thought was his tail," Bull answered slowly, "if I told you, you wouldn't believe me."

"Of course I would!" said Langnes. "Out with it!"

"Well, skipper . . . we have barnacles."

A certain amount of chemical and biological apparatus had been brought along to study possible effects of the whatever-it-was that seemed to forbid spacecraft crossing the Asteroid Belt. The equipment was most inadequate, and between them the four men had only an elementary knowledge of its use. But then, all equipment was inadequate in zero gravity, and all knowledge was elementary out here.

Work progressed with maddening slowness. And meanwhile the *Hellik Olav* fell outward and outward, on an orbit which would not bend back again until it was three Astronomical Units from the sun. And the ship was out of communication. And the radar, still functional but losing efficiency all the time, registered an ever thicker concentration of meteorites. And the tween-decks radiation count mounted, slowly but persistently.

"I vote we go home," said Helledahl. Sweat glistened on his forehead, where he sat in his tiny bunk cubicle without touching the mattress.

"Second the motion," said Bull at once. "Any further discussion? I move the vote. All in favor, say '*Ja.*' All opposed, shut up."

"This is no time for jokes, Herr Bull," said Captain Lagnes.

"I quite agree sir. And this trip is more than a joke, it's a farce. Let's turn back!"

"Because of an encrustation on the hull?"

Surprisingly, gentle Torvald Winge supported the skipper with almost as sharp a tone. "Nothing serious has yet happened," he said. "We have now shielded the drive tubes so that the barnacle growth can't advance to them. As for our communications apparatus, we have spare parts in ample supply and can easily repair it once we're out of this fantastic zone. Barnacles can be scraped off the radar arms, as well as the vision parts. What kind of cowards will our people take us for, if we give up at the first little difficulty?"

"Live ones," said Helledahl.

"You see," Bull added, "we're not in such bad shape now, but what'll happen if this continues? Just extrapolate the radiation. I did. We'll be dead men on the return orbit."

"You assume the count will rise to a dangerous level," said Winge. "I doubt that. Time enough to turn back if it seems we have no other hope. But what you don't appreciate, Erik, is the very real, unextrapolated danger of such a course."

"Also, we seem to be on the track of an answer to the mystery—the whole purpose of this expedition," said Langnes. "Given a little more data, we should find out what happened to all the previous ships."

"Including the Chinese?" asked Bull.

Silence descended. They sat in mid-air reviewing a situation which familiarity did nothing to beautify.

Observations from the Martian moons had indicated the Asteroid Belt was much fuller than astronomers had believed. Of course, it was still a rather hard vacuum—but one through which sand, gravel, and boulders went flying with indecent speed and frequency. Unmanned craft were sent in by several nations. Their telemetering instruments confirmed the great density of cosmic debris, which increased as they swung farther in toward the central zone. But then they quit sending. They were never heard from again. Manned ships stationed near the computed orbits of the robot vessels, where these emerged from the danger area, detected objects with radar, panted to match velocities, and saw nothing but common or garden variety meteorites.

Finally the Chinese People's Republic sent three craft with volunteer crews toward the Belt. One ship went off course and landed in the Pacific Ocean near San Francisco. After its personnel explained the unique methods by which they had been persuaded to volunteer, they were allowed to stay. The scientists got good technical jobs, the captain started a restaurant, and the political commissar went on the lecture circuit.

But the other two ships continued as per instructions. Their transmission stopped at about the same distance as the robot radios had, and they were never seen again either.

After that, the big nations decided there was no need for haste in such expensive undertakings. But Norway had just outfitted her own spaceship, and all true Norwegians are crazy. The *Hellik Olav* went out.

Winge stirred. "I believe I can tell you what happened to the Chinese," he said.

"Sure," said Bull. "They stayed in orbit till it was too late. Then the radiation got them."

"No. They saw themselves in our own situation, panicked, and started back."

"So?"

"The meteorites got them."

"Excuse me," said Langnes, obviously meaning it the other way around. "You know better than that, Professor Winge.

The hazard isn't that great. Even at the highest possible density of material, the probability of impact with anything of considerable mass is so low—"

"I am not talking about that, Captain," said the astronomer. "Let me repeat the facts *ab initio,* to keep everything systematic, even if you know most of them already.

"Modern opinion holds that the asteroids, and probably most meteorites throughout the Solar System, really are the remnants of a disintegrated world. I am inclined to suspect that a sudden phase change in its core caused the initial explosion—this can happen at a certain planetary mass—and then Jupiter's attraction gradually broke up the larger pieces. Prior to close-range study, it was never believed the asteroidean planet could have been large enough for this to happen. But today we know it must have been roughly as big as Earth. The total mass was not detectable at a distance, prior to space flight, because so much of it consists of small dark particles. These, I believe, were formed when the larger chunks broke up into lesser ones which abraded and shattered each other in collisions, before gravitational forces spread them too widely apart."

"What has this to do with the mess we're in?" asked Bull.

Winge looked startled. "Why . . . that is—" He blushed. "Nothing, I suppose." To cover his embarrassment, he began talking rapidly, repeating the obvious at even greater length:

"We accelerated from Earth, and a long way beyond, thus throwing ourselves into an eccentric path with a semi-major axis of two Astronomical Units. But this is still an ellipse, and as we entered the danger zone, our velocity gained more and more of a component parallel to the planetary orbits. At our aphelion, which will be in the very heart of the Asteroid Belt, we will be moving substantially with the average meteorite. Relative velocity will be very small, or zero. Hence collisions will be rare, and mild when they do occur. Then we'll be pulled back sunward. By the time we start accelerating under power toward Earth, we will again be traveling at a large angle to the natural orbits. But by that time, also, we will be back out of the danger zone.

"Suppose, however, we decided to turn back at this instant. We would first have to decelerate, spending fuel to kill an outward velocity which the sun would otherwise have killed for us. Then we must accelerate inward. We can just barely afford the fuel. There will be little left for maneuvers. *And .*. we'll be cutting almost perpendicularly across the asteroidal orbits. Their full density and velocity will be directed almost broadside to us.

"Oh, we still needn't worry about being struck by a large object. The probability of that is quite low. But what we will get is the fifteen-kilometer-per-second sandblast of the uncountable small particles. I have been computing the results of my investigations so far, and arrive at a figure for the density of this cosmic sand which is, well, simply appalling. Far more than was hitherto suspected. I don't believe our hull can stand such a prolonged scouring, meteor bumpers or no."

"Are you certain?" gulped Helledahl.

"Of course not," said Winge testily. "What is certain, out here? I believe it highly probable, though. And the fact that the Chinese never came back would seem to lend credence to my hypothesis."

The barnacles had advanced astoundingly since Bull last looked at them. Soon the entire ship would be covered, except for a few crucial places toilfully kept clean.

He braced his armored self against the reactive push of his cutting torch. It was about the only way to get a full-grown barnacle loose. The things melded themselves with the hull. The flame drowned the sardonic stars in his vision but illuminated the growths.

They looked quite a bit like the Terrestrial marine sort. Each humped up in a hard conoidal shell of blackish brown material. Beneath them was a layer of excreted metal, chiefly ferrous, plated onto the aluminum hull.

I'd hate to try landing through an atmosphere, thought Bull. Of course, that wouldn't be necessary. We would go into orbit around Earth and call for someone to lay alongside and take us off . . . But heading back sunward, we'll have one sweet time controlling internal temperature . . . No, I can simply slap some shiny paint on. That should do the trick. I'd have to paint anyway, to maintain constant radiation characteristics when micrometeorites are forever scratching our metal. Another chore. Space flight is nothing but one long round of chores. The next poet who recites in my presence an ode to man's conquest of the universe can take that universe—every galaxy and every supernova through every last long light-year—and put . . .

If we get home alive.

He tossed the barnacle into a metal canister for later study. It was still red hot, and doubtless the marvelously intricate organism within the shell had suffered damage. But the details of the lithophagic metabolism could be left for professional biologists to figure out. All they wanted aboard Holy Ole was enough knowledge to base a decision on.

Before taking more specimens, Bull made a circuit of the hull. There were many hummocks on it, barnacles growing upon barnacles. The foresection had turned into a hill of shells, under which the radio transceiver boom lay buried. Another could be built when required for Earth approach. The trouble was, with the interior radiation still mounting—while a hasty retreat seemed impossible—Bull had started to doubt he ever would see Earth again.

He scrubbed down the radar, then paused to examine the spot where he had initially cut off a few dozen samples. New ones were already burgeoning on the ferroplate left by their predecessors—little fellows with delicate glasslike shells which would soon grow and thicken, becoming incredibly tough. Whatever that silicate material was, study of it should repay Terrestrial industry. Another bonanza from the Asteroid Belt, the modern Mother Lode.

"Ha!" said Bull.

It had sounded very convincing. The proper way to exploit space was not to mine the planets, where you must grub deep in the crust to find a few stingy ore pockets, then spend fabulous amounts of energy hauling your gains home. No, the asteroids had all the minerals man would ever need, in developing his extraterrestrial colonies and on Earth herself. Freely available minerals, especially on the metallic asteroids from the core of the ancient planet. Just land and help yourself. No elaborate apparatus needed to protect you from your environment. Just the spaceship and space armor you had to have anyway. No gravitational well to back down into and climb back out of. Just a simple thrust of minimum power.

Given free access to the asteroids, even a small nation like Norway could operate in space, with all the resulting benefits to her economy, politics, and prestige. And there was the *Hellik Olav,* newly outfitted, with plenty of volunteers— genuine ones—for an exploratory mission, and to hell with the danger.

"Ha!" repeated Bull.

He had been quite in favor of the expedition, provided somebody else went. But he was offered a berth and made the mistake of telling his girl.

"Ohhhh, Erik!" she exclaimed, enormous-eyed.

After six months in space helping to rig and test the ship, Bull could have fallen in love with the *Sea Hag.* However, this had not been necessary. When he had returned to Earth, swearing a mighty oath never to set foot above the stratosphere again, he met Marta. She was small and blond and deliciously shaped. She adored him right back. The only flaw he could find in her was a set of romantic notions about the starry universe and the noble Norwegian destiny therein.

"Oh, oh," he said, recognizing the symptoms. In haste: "Don't get ideas, now. I told you I'm a marine reclamation man, from here on forever."

"But this, darling! This chance! To be one of the conquerors! To make your name immortal!"

"The trouble is, I'm still mortal myself."

"The service you can do—to our country!"

"Uh, apart from everything else, do you realize that, uh, even allowing for acceleration under power for part of the distance, I'd be gone for more than two years?"

"I'll wait for you."

"But—"

"Are you *afraid,* Erik?"

"Well, no. But—"

"Think of the Vikings! Think of Fridtjof Nansen! Think of Roald Amundsen!"

Bull dutifully thought of all these gentlemen. "What about them?" he asked.

But it was a light summer night, and Marta couldn't imagine any true Norwegian refusing such a chance for deathless glory, and one thing sort of led to another. Before he recovered his wits, Bull had accepted the job.

There followed a good deal of work up in orbit, readying the ship, and a shakedown cruise lasting some weeks. When he finally got pre-departure leave, Bull broke every known traffic law and a few yet to be invented, on the way to Marta's home. She informed him tearfully that she was so sorry and she hoped they would always be good friends, but she had been seeing so little of him and had met someone else but she would always follow his future career with the greatest interest. The someone else turned out to be a bespectacled writer who had just completed a three-volume novel about King Harold Hardcounsel (1015–1066). Bull didn't remember the rest of his furlough very clearly.

A shock jarred through him. He bounced from the hull, jerked to a halt at the end of his lifeline, and waited for the dizziness to subside. The stars leered.

"Hallo! Hallo, Erik! Are you all right?"

Bull shook his head to clear it. Helledahl's voice, phoned across the lifeline, was tinny in his earphones. "I think so. What happened?"

"A small meteorite hit us, I suppose. It must have had an abnormal orbit to strike so hard. We can't see any damage from inside, though. Will you check the outer hull?"

Bull nodded, though there was no point in doing so. After he hauled himself back, he needed a while to find the spot of impact. The pebble had collided near the waist of the ship, vaporizing silicate shell material to form a neat little crater in a barnacle hummock. It hadn't quite penetrated to the ferroplate. A fragment remained, trapped between the rough lumps.

Bull shivered. Without that overgrowth, the hull would have been pierced. Not that that mattered greatly in itself. There was enough patching aboard to repair several hundred such holes. But the violence of impact was an object lesson. Torvald Winge was almost certainly right. Trying to cut straight across the Asteroid Belt would be as long a chance as men had ever taken. The incessant bombardment of particles, mostly far smaller than this but all possessing a similar speed, would wear down the entire hull. When it was thin enough to rip apart under stress, no meteor bumpers or patches would avail.

His eyes sought the blue-green glint of Earth, but couldn't find it among so many stars. You know, he told himself, I don't even mind the prospect of dying out here as much as I do the dreariness of it. If we turned around now, and somehow survived, I'd be home by Christmas. I'd only have wasted one extra year in space, instead of more than three—counting in the preparations for this arduous cruise. I'd find me a girl, no, a dozen girls. And a hundred bottles. I'd make up for that year in style, before settling down to do work I really enjoy.

But we aren't likely to survive, if we turn around now.

But how likely is our survival if we keep going—with the

radiation shield failing us? And an extra two years on Holy Ole? I'd go nuts!

Judas priest! Was ever a man in such an ugly situation?

Langnes peered at the sheaf of papers in his hand. "I have drafted a report of our findings with regard to the, ah, space barnacles," he said. "I would like you gentlemen to criticize it as I read aloud. We have now accounted for the vanishing of the previous ships—"

Helledahl mopped his brow. Tiny beads of sweat broke loose and glittered in the air. "That doesn't do much good if we also vanish," he pointed out.

"Quite," Langnes looked irritated. "Believe me, I am more than willing to turn home at once. But that is impracticable, as Professor Winge has shown and the unfortunate Chinese example has confirmed."

"I say it's just as impracticable to follow the original orbit," declared Bull.

"I understand you don't like it here," said Winge, "but really, courting an almost certain death in order to escape two more years of boredom seems a trifle extreme."

"The boredom will be all the worse, now that we don't have anything to work toward," said Bull.

The captain's monocle glared at him. "Ahem!" said Langnes. "If you gentlemen are quite through, may I have the floor?"

"Sure," said Bull. "Or the wall or the ceiling, if you prefer. Makes no difference here."

"I'll skip the preamble of the report and start with our conclusions. 'Winge believes the barnacles originated as a possibly mutant life form on the ancient planet before it was destroyed. The slower breakup of the resulting superasteroidal masses gave this life time to adapt to spatial conditions. The organism itself is not truly protoplasmic. Instead of water, which would either boil or freeze in vacuo at this distance from the sun, the essential liquid is some heavy substance we have not been able to identify except as an aromatic compound.' "

"Aromatic is too polite," said Bull, wrinkling his nose. The air purifiers had still not gotten all the chemical stench out.

Langnes proceeded unrelenting: " 'The basic chemistry does remain that of carbon, of proteins, albeit with an extensive use of complex silicon compounds. We theorize the life cycle as follows. The adult form ejects spores which drift freely through space. Doubtless most are lost, but such wastefulness is characteristic of nature on Earth, too. When a spore does chance on a meteorite or an asteroid it can use, it develops rapidly. It requires silicon and carbon, plus traces of other elements; hence it must normally flourish only on stony meteorites, which are, however, the most abundant sort. Since the barnacle's powerful pseu-denzymatic digestive processes—deriving their ultimate energy from sunlight—also extract metals where these exist, it must eliminate same, which it does by laying down a plating, molecule by molecule, under its shell. Research into the details of this process should interest both biologists and metallurgists.

" 'The shell serves a double function. To some extent, it protects against ionizing radiation of solar or cosmic origin. Also, being a nonconductor, it can hold a biologically generated static charge, which will cause nearby dust to drift down upon it. Though this is a slow method of getting the extra nourishment, the barnacle is exceedingly long-lived, and can adjust its own metabolic and reproductive rates to the exigencies of the situation. Since the charge is not very great, and he himself is encased in metal, a spaceman notices no direct consequences.

" 'One may well ask why this life form has never been observed before. First, it is doubtless confined to the Asteroid Belt, the density of matter being too low elsewhere. We have established that it is poisoned by water and free oxygen, so no spores could survive on any planet man has yet visited, even if they did drift there. Second, if a meteorite covered with such barnacles does strike an atmosphere, the surface vaporization as it falls will destroy all evidence. Third, even if barnacle-crusted meteorites have been seen from spaceships, they look superficially like any other stony objects. No one has captured them for closer examination.' "

He paused to drink water from a squeeze bottle. "Hear, hear," murmured Bull, pretending the captain stood behind a lectern.

"That's why the unmanned probe ships never were found," said Helledahl. "They may well have been seen, more or less on their predicted orbits, but they weren't recognized."

Langnes nodded. "Of course. That comes next in the report. Then I go on to say: 'The reason that radio transmission ceased in the first place is equally obvious. Silicon components are built into the boom, as part of a transistor system. The barnacles ate them.

" 'The observed increase in internal irradiation is due to the plating of heavy metals laid down by the barnacles. First, the static charges and the ferromagnetic atoms interfere with the powerful external magnetic fields which are generated to divert ions from the ship. Second, primary cosmic rays coming through that same plating produce showers of secondary particles.

" 'Some question may be raised as to the explosive growth rate of barnacles on our hull, even after all the silicon available in our external apparatus had been consumed. The answer involves consideration of vectors. The ordinary member of the Asteroid Belt, be it large or small, travels in an orbit roughly parallel to the orbits of all other members. There are close approaches and occasional collisions, but on the whole, the particles are thinly scattered by Terrestrial standards, isolated from each other. Our ship, however, is slanting across those same orbits, thus exposing itself to a veritable rain of bodies, ranging in size from microscopic to sand granular.

Even a single spore, coming in contact with our hull, could multiply indefinitely.'"

"That means we're picking up mass all the time," groaned Bull. "Which means we'll accelerate slower and get home even later than I'd feared."

"Do you think we'll get home at all?" fretted Helledahl. "We can expect the interference with our radiation shield, and the accumulation of heavy atoms, to get worse all the time. Nobody will ever be able to cross the Belt!"

"Oh, yes, they will," said Captain Langnes. "Ships must simply be redesigned. The magnetic screens must be differently heterodyned, to compensate. The radio booms must be enclosed in protective material. Or perhaps—"

"I know," said Bull in great weariness. "Perhaps antifouling paint can be developed. Or spaceships can be careened, God help us. Oh, yes. All I care about is how we personally get home. I can't modify our own magnetic generators. I haven't the parts or the tools, even if I knew precisely how. We'll spin on and on, the radiation worse every hour, till—"

"Be quiet!" snapped Langnes.

"The Chinese turned around, and look what happened to them," underlined Winge. "We must try something different, however hopeless it too may look."

Bull braced his heavy shoulders. "See here, Torvald," he growled, "what makes you so sure the Chinese did head back under power?"

"Because they were never seen again. If they had been on the predicted orbit, or even on a completed free-fall ellipse, one of the ships watching for them in the neighborhood of Earth would have— Oh."

"Yes," said Bull through his teeth. "Would have seen them? How do you know they weren't seen? I think they were. I think they plugged blindly on as they'd been ordered to, and the radiation suddenly started increasing on a steep curve—as you'd expect, when a critical point of fouling up was passed. I think they died, and came back like comets, sealed into spaceships so crusted they looked like ordinary meteorites!"

The silence thundered.

"So we may as well turn back," said Bull at last. "If we don't make it, our death'll be a quicker and cleaner one than those poor devils had."

Again the quietude. Until Captain Langnes shook his head. "No. I'm sorry, gentlemen. But we go on."

"What?" screamed Helledahl.

The captain floated in the air, a ludicrous parody of officerlike erectness. But there was an odd dignity to him all the same.

"I'm sorry," he repeated. "I have a family too, you know. I would turn about if it could be done with reasonable safety. But Professor Winge has shown that that is impossible. We would die anyhow—and our ship would be a ruin, a few bits of worn and crumpled metal, all our results gone. If we proceed, we can prepare specimens and keep records which will be of use to our successors. Us they will find, for we can improvise a conspicuous feature on the hull that the barnacles won't obliterate."

He looked from one to another.

"Shall we do less for our country's honor than the Chinese did for theirs?" he finished.

Well, if you put it that way, thought Bull, yes.

But he couldn't bring himself to say it aloud. Maybe they all thought the same, including Langnes himself, but none was brave enough to admit it. The trouble with us moral cowards, thought Bull, is that we make heroes of ourselves.

I suppose Marta will shed some pretty, nostalgic tears when she gets the news. Ech! It's bad enough to croak out here; but if that bluestocking memorializes me with a newspaper poem about my Viking spirit—

Maybe that's what we should rig up on the hull, so they

won't ignore this poor barnacled derelict as just another flying boulder. Make the Holy Ole into a real, old-fashioned, Gokstad type ship. Dragon figurehead, oars, sail—shields hung along the side—hey, yes! Imagine some smug Russian on an Earth satellite, bragging about how his people were the first into space—and then along comes this Viking ship—

I think I'll even paint the shields. A face on each one, with its tongue out and a thumb to its nose—

Holy hopping Ole!

"Shields!" roared Bull.

"What?" said Langnes through the echoes.

"We're shielded! We can turn back! Right now!"

When the hubbub had died down and a few slide rule calculations had been made, Bull addressed the others.

"It's really quite simple," he said. "All the elements of the answer were there all the time. I'm only surprised that the Chinese never realized it; but then, I imagine they used all their spare moments for socialist self-criticism.

"Anyhow, we know our ship is a space barnacle's paradise. Even our barnacles have barnacles. Why? Because it picks up so much sand and gravel. Now what worried us about heading straight home was not an occasional meteorite big enough to punch clear through the skin of the ship—we've patching to take care of that—no, we were afraid of a sandblast wearing the entire hull paper thin. But we're protected against precisely that danger! The more such little particles that hit us, the more barnacles we'll have. They can't be eroded away, because they're alive. They renew themselves from the very stuff that strikes them. Like a stone in a river, worn away by the current, while the soft moss is always there.

"We'll get back out of the Belt before the radiation level builds up to anything serious. Then, if we want to, we can chisel off the encrustation. But why bother, really? We'll soon be home."

"No argument there." Langnes smiled.

"I'll go check the engines prior to starting up," said Bull. "Will you and Torvald compute us an Earthward course?"

He started for the doorway, paused, and added slowly, "Uh, I kind of hate to say this, but those barnacles are what will really make the Asteroid Belt available to men."

"What?" said Helledahl.

"Sure," said Bull. "Simple. Naturally, we'll have to devise protection for the radio, and redesign the radiation screen apparatus, as the skipper remarked. But under proper control, the barnacles make a self-repairing shield against sandblast. It shouldn't be necessary to go through the Belt on these tedious elliptical orbits. The space miners can take hyperbolic paths, as fast as they choose, in any direction they please.

"I," he finished with emphasis, "will not be among them."

"Where will you be?" asked Winge.

But Erik Bull was already headed aft to his work. A snatch of song, bawled from powerful lungs, came back to the others. They all knew English, but it took them a moment to get the drift.

> " 'Who's that knocking at my door?'
> Said the fair young maiden.
> 'Oh, it's only me, from over the sea,'
> Said Barnacle Bill the sailor.
> 'I've sailed the seas from shore to shore,
> I'll never sail the seas no more.
> Now open up this blank-blank door!'
> Said Barnacle Bill the sailor."

JUPITER

By 1700, it was quite clear that Jupiter was a giant. It could not look so large in the telescope at the distance it was determined to be if it weren't.

The statistics are awesome. Its diameter is 11.2 times that of the Earth; its area is 125 times that of the Earth; its volume is 1400 times that of the Earth.

Jupiter is made up largely of light materials rather than of rock and metal as Earth is, so it is only a quarter as dense as Earth is. Even so, it has 318.4 times the mass of the Earth, and a gravitational field with an intensity to match.

To be sure, Jupiter is only a planet and it is a pygmy compared to the Sun, possessing only 1/1040 the mass of the Sun. If, however, we leave the Sun out of it, then Jupiter alone makes up 70 percent of all the mass of the Solar system. All the other planets, satellites, asteroids, meteors, and comets *put together* make up 30 percent.

Jupiter has four large satellites, Moon-sized or better, and at least nine smaller ones. No other planet has so magnificent or far-flung a planetary system—which is not surprising.

Despite all this, we don't see Jupiter—not its solid surface. What we see are clouds. These clouds are whipped into gales and hurricanes of unimaginable intensity, largely because of Jupiter's rapid rotation. Despite its huge size it makes one turn in 9 hours and 55 minutes as compared to Earth's 24 hours. A point on Jupiter's equator travels at a speed of 45,000 kilometers (28,000 miles) per hour, 27 times as fast as a point on Earth's equator travels.

As a result we see the clouds smeared out horizontally, and this gives Jupiter the appearance of a striped planet.

It is not exclusively striped, however. There is one vast hurricane that has apparently been raging without stop for a long period of time. It produces the Great Red Spot, a reddish oval that was first noted in 1664. This is about 45,000 kilometers (30,000 miles) long and 13,000 kilometers (8000 miles) wide. The Earth could be dropped into that hurricane funnel without touching its sides.

In the nineteenth century, there was one school of thought which suggested that Jupiter had not yet had time to lose its store of heat, so that it was incandescent—a kind of miniature Sun. Its satellites were too far from the Sun to receive much heat (they, and Jupiter, were 779 million kilometers, or 483 million miles from the Sun—5.2 times the distance of the Earth from the Sun) but, by this way of thinking, would be warmed instead by Jupiter and might, in that way, be warm enough to bear life. Science fiction stories were written on that basis well into the 1930s.

Temperature readings of the visible cloud surface with the sophisticated instruments of the twentieth century yielded, however, a figure of $-135°C$. Jupiter might be hot underneath its cloud layer, but the heat emerging out of that frigid region was negligible and would not serve to warm the satellites, which would therefore have surfaces that could only be frozen wastelands.

And what did go on under the atmosphere?

It was to be assumed that Jupiter's atmosphere was deep, since otherwise its low density could not be accounted for. Measurements in the 1930s and afterward showed that it was largely hydrogen and helium, with an admixture of ammonia and methane.

It was naturally assumed that somewhere under the atmosphere was a solid surface, a world with continents and oceans.

It would be a horrible world, though, for the ocean was likely to be liquid ammonia and the continents might be largely ice. Both would be under an atmospheric pressure equal to a million times that of our atmosphere and would be subjected to winds of incredible fury.

It is a world such as this which is described in "Bridge," which was first published in 1952.

On March 2, 1972, however, the first Jupiter probe, Pioneer 10, was launched and on December 3, 1973, it reached its goal, passing only 135,000 kilometers (85,000 miles) from Jupiter's surface.

The first thing it discovered was that Jupiter had a magnetosphere (belts of electrically charged particles outside its atmosphere) that was both far more voluminous and far more densely charged than Earth's was.

Mercury, Venus, Mars, and our Moon have no magnetospheres to speak of, and even Earth's magnetosphere is not energetic enough to prevent astronauts from passing through. Jupiter's magnetosphere is deadly, however, and encloses three of the four large satellites. Unless fundamental advances are made in shielding strategies, this may mean that Jupiter and its three inner large satellites may simply be unreachable by anything but unmanned probes.

Furthermore, it would appear that the assumption of a sizable solid core must be put aside. Earlier suggestions of an almost entirely hydrogen planet now look good.

At best, there would seem to be only a tiny rocky core, and perhaps none at all. Jupiter would seem to be essentially a ball of hot liquid hydrogen. Ordinarily, liquid hydrogen boils at only 20 degrees above absolute zero, but under the enormous pressures within Jupiter, it reaches far higher temperatures. Near the center of Jupiter, in fact, it may be compressed into solid "metallic hydrogen," a form capable of conducting an electric current.

At 950 kilometers (600 miles) below the visible cloud surface, the temperature is 3600°C. At 2900 kilometers (1800 miles) below the surface it is 10,000°C. At 24,000 kilometers (15,000 miles) below the surface, it is 20,000°C. At the very center of Jupiter, it is 54,000°C.

There is no doubt that the world of "Bridge" does not exist, but there may be something else. In the uppermost layers of the planet, where the temperatures are mild and equable, there is water, ammonia, methane, colored ammonia hydrosulfide, and so on.

It is out of molecules such as these that life formed on Earth more than 3 billion years ago, and life may have formed in the Jovian ocean similarly, drawing its energy from gigantic electric storms rather than from Sunlight. Life forms may float in the vast planetary ocean, lifting in upward-rising currents toward cooler temperatures and sinking in downward-falling currents toward warmer ones, swimming against the current to avoid becoming too cold or too hot, or shifting from an upward-rising current to a downward-falling one, or vice-versa, in order to keep temperature at the proper figure.

We won't know until we send a probe down into Jupiter's atmosphere.

And, oh, yes, Voyager 1 in 1979, spotted a thin ring of debris around Jupiter, active volcanoes on satellite Io, surface cracks on Europa, craters on Ganymede and Callisto. There is still so much to learn.

Bridge

JAMES BLISH

I

A screeching tornado was rocking the Bridge when the alarm sounded; it was making the whole structure shudder and sway. This was normal and Robert Helmuth barely noticed it. There was always a tornado shaking the Bridge. The whole planet was enswathed in tornadoes, and worse.

The scanner on the foreman's board had given 114 as the sector of the trouble. That was at the northwestern end of the Bridge, where it broke off, leaving nothing but the raging clouds of ammonia crystals and methane, and a sheer drop thirty miles to the invisible surface. There were no ultraphone "eyes" at that end which gave a general view of the area—in so far as any general view was possible—because both ends of the Bridge were incomplete.

With a sigh Helmuth put the beetle into motion. The little car, as flat-bottomed and thin through as a bedbug, got slowly under way on ball-bearing races, guided and held firmly to the surface of the Bridge by ten close-set flanged rails. Even so, the hydrogen gales made a terrific sirenlike shrieking between the edge of the vehicle and the deck, and the impact of the falling drops of ammonia upon the curved roof was as heavy and deafening as a rain of cannon balls. As a matter of fact, they weighed almost as much as cannon balls here, though they were not much bigger than ordinary raindrops.

Every so often, too, there was a blast, accompanied by a dull orange glare, which made the car, the deck, and the Bridge itself buck savagely.

These blasts were below, however, on the surface. While they shook the structure of the Bridge heavily, they almost never interfered with its functioning, and could not, in the very nature of things, do Helmuth any harm. Had any real damage ever been done, it would never have been repaired. There was no one on Jupiter to repair it.

The Bridge, actually, was building itself. Massive, alone, and lifeless, it grew in the black deeps of Jupiter.

The Bridge had been well planned. From Helmuth's point of view almost nothing could be seen of it, for the beetle tracks ran down the center of the deck, and in the darkness and perpetual storm even ultrawave-assisted vision could not penetrate more than a few hundred yards at the most. The width of the Bridge was eleven miles; its height, thirty miles; its length, deliberately unspecified in the plans, fifty-four miles at the moment—a squat, colossal structure, built with engineering principles, methods, materials, and tools never touched before—

For the very good reason that they would have been impossible anywhere else. Most of the Bridge, for instance, was made of ice: a marvelous structural material under a pressure of a mlllion atmospheres, at a temperature of -94°C. Under such conditions, the best structural steel is a friable talclike powder, and aluminum becomes a peculiar transparent substance that splits at a tap.

Back home, Helmuth remembered, there had been talk of starting another Bridge on Saturn, and perhaps still later on Uranus, too. But that had been politicians' talk. The Bridge was almost five thousand miles below the visible surface of Jupiter's atmosphere, and its mechanisms were just barely manageable. The bottom of Saturn's atmosphere had been sounded at 16,878 miles, and the temperature there was below -150°C. There, even pressure-ice would be immovable

and could not be worked with anything except itself. And as
for Uranus . . .

As far as Helmuth was concerned, Jupiter was quite bad
enough.

The beetle crept within sight of the end of the Bridge and
stopped automatically. Helmuth set the vehicle's eyes for
highest penetration and examined the nearby beams.

The great bars were as close-set as screening. They had to
be in order to support even their own weight, let alone the
weight of the components of the Bridge, the whole webwork
was flexing and fluctuating to the harpist-fingered gale, but
it had been designed to do that. Helmuth could never help
being alarmed by the movement, but habit assured him that
he had nothing to fear from it.

He took the automatics out of the circuit and inched the
beetle forward manually. This was only Sector 113, and the
Bridge's own Wheatstone-bridge scanning system—there was
no electronic device anywhere on the Bridge, since it was impossible to maintain a vacuum on Jupiter—said that the trouble was in Sector 114. The boundary of Sector 114 was still
fully fifty feet away.

It was a bad sign. Helmuth scratched nervously in his red
beard. Evidently there was really cause for alarm—real
alarm, not just the deep, grinding depression which he always
felt while working on the Bridge. Any damage serious enough
to halt the beetle a full sector short of the trouble area was
bound to be major.

It might even turn out to be the disaster which he had felt
lurking ahead of him ever since he had been made foreman of
the Bridge—that disaster which the Bridge itself could not
repair, sending man reeling home from Jupiter in defeat.

The secondaries cut in and the beetle stopped again. Grim-
ly, Helmuth opened the switch and sent the beetle creeping
across the invisible danger line. Almost at once, the car tilted
just perceptibly to the left, and the screaming of the winds

between its edges and the deck shot up the scale, sirening in and out of the soundless-dogwhistle range with an eeriness that set Helmuth's teeth on edge. The beetle itself fluttered and chattered like an alarm-clock hammer between the surface of the deck and the flanges of the tracks.

Ahead there was still nothing to be seen but the horizontal driving of the clouds and the hail, roaring along the length of the Bridge, out of the blackness into the beetle's fanlights, and onward into blackness again toward the horizon no eye would ever see.

Thirty miles below, the fusillade of hydrogen explosions continued. Evidently something really wild was going on on the surface. Helmuth could not remember having heard so much activity in years.

There was a flat, especially heavy crash, and a long line of fuming orange fire came pouring down the seething atmosphere into the depths, feathering horizontally like the mane of a Lippizaner horse, directly in front of Helmuth. Instinctively, he winced and drew back from the board, although that stream of flame actually was only a little less cold than the rest of the streaming gases, far too cold to injure the Bridge.

In the momentary glare, however, he saw something—an upward twisting of shadows, patterned but obviously unfinished, fluttering in silhouette against the hydrogen cataract's lurid light.

The end of the Bridge.

Wrecked.

Helmuth grunted involuntarily and backed the beetle away. The flare dimmed; the light poured down the sky and fell away into the raging sea below. The scanner clucked with satisfaction as the beetle recrossed the line into Zone 113.

He turned the body of the vehicle 180°, presenting its back to the dying torrent. There was nothing further that he could do at the moment on the Bridge. He scanned his control

board—a ghost image of which was cast across the scene on
the Bridge—for the blue button marked *Garage*, punched it
savagely, and tore off his helmet.

Obediently, the Bridge vanished.

II

Dillon was looking at him.

"Well?" the civil engineer said. "What's the matter, Bob?
Is it bad?"

Helmuth did not reply for a moment. The abrupt transition
from the storm-ravaged deck of the Bridge to the quiet, plac-
id air of the control shack on Jupiter V was always a shock.
He had never been able to anticipate it, let alone become ac-
customed to it; it was worse each time, not better.

He put the helmet down carefully in front of him and got
up, moving carefully upon shaky legs, feeling implicit in his
own body the enormous pressures and weights his guiding intelligence had just quitted. The fact that the gravity on the
foreman's deck was as weak as that of most of the habitable
asteroids only made the contrast greater and his need for
caution in walking more extreme.

He went to the big porthole and looked out. The unworn,
tumbled, monotonous surface of airless Jupiter V looked almost homey after the perpetual holocaust of Jupiter itself.
But there was an overpowering reminder of that holocaust—
for through the thick quartz, the face of the giant planet
stared at him, across only 112,600 miles; a sphere-section oc-
cupying almost all of the sky except the near horizon. It was
crawling with color, striped and blotched with the eternal
frigid, poisonous storming of its atmosphere, spotted with the
deep planet-sized shadows of farther moons.

Somewhere down there, six thousand miles below the
clouds that boiled in his face, was the Bridge. The Bridge was
thirty miles high and eleven miles wide and fifty-four miles

long—but it was only a sliver, an intricate and fragile arrangement of ice crystals beneath the bulging, racing tornadoes.

On Earth, even in the West, the Bridge would have been the mightiest engineering achievement of all history, could the Earth have borne its weight at all. But on Jupiter, the Bridge was as precarious and perishable as a snowflake. "Bob?" Dillon's voice asked. "You seem more upset than usual. Is it serious?" Helmuth turned. His superior's worn young face, lantern-jawed and crowned by black hair already beginning to gray at the temples, was alight both with love for the Bridge and the consuming ardor of the responsibility he had to bear. As always, it touched Helmuth, and reminded him that the implacable universe had, after all, provided one warm corner in which human beings might huddle together.

"Serious enough," he said, forming the words with difficulty against the frozen inarticulateness Jupiter forced upon him. "But not fatal, as far as I could see. There's a lot of hydrogen vulcanism on the surface, especially at the northwest end, and it looks like there must have been a big blast under the cliffs. I saw what looked like the last of a series of fireballs."

Dillon's face relaxed while Helmuth was talking, slowly, line by engraved line. "Oh. Just a flying chunk, then."

"I'm almost sure that's what it was. The cross-drafts are heavy now. The Spot and the STD are due to pass each other sometime next week, aren't 'they? I haven't checked, but I can feel the difference in the storms."

"So the chunk got picked up and thrown through the end of the Bridge. A big piece?"

Helmuth shrugged. "That end is all twisted away to the left, and the deck is burst to flinders. The scaffolding is all gone, too, of course. A pretty big piece, all right, Charity—two miles through at a minimum."

Dillon sighed. He, too, went to the window and looked out.

Helmuth did not need to be a mind reader to know what he was looking at. Out there, across the stony waste of Jupiter V plus 112,600 miles of space, the South Tropical Disturbance was streaming toward the great Red Spot, and would soon overtake it. When the whirling funnel of the STD—more than big enough to suck three Earths into deep freeze—passed the planetary island of sodium-tainted ice which was the Red Spot, the Spot would follow it for a few thousand miles, at the same time rising closer to the surface of the atmosphere.

Then the Spot would sink again, drifting back toward the incredible jet of stress fluid which kept it in being—a jet fed by no one knew what forces at Jupiter's hot, rocky 22,000-mile core, under 16,000 miles of eternal ice. During the entire passage, the storms all over Jupiter became especially violent; and the Bridge had been forced to locate in anything but the calmest spot on the planet, thanks to the uneven distribution of the few permanent land masses.

Helmuth watched Dillon with a certain compassion, tempered with mild envy. Charity Dillon's unfortunate given name betrayed him as the son of a hangover, the only male child of a Witness family which dated back to the great Witness Revival of 2003. He was one of the hundreds of government-drafted experts who had planned the Bridge, and he was as obsessed by the Bridge as Helmuth was—but for different reasons.

Helmuth moved back to the port, dropping his hand gently upon Dillon's shoulder. Together they looked at the screaming straw yellows, brick reds, pinks, oranges, browns, even blues and greens that Jupiter threw across the ruined stone of its innermost satellite. On Jupiter V, even the shadows had color.

Dillon did not move. He said at last, "Are you pleased, Bob?"

"Pleased?" Helmuth said in astonishment. "No. It scares me white; you know that. I'm just glad that the whole Bridge didn't go."

"You're quite sure?" Dillon said quietly.

Helmuth took his hand from Dillon's shoulder and returned to his seat at the central desk. "You've no right to needle me for something I can't help," he said, his voice even lower than Dillon's. "I work on Jupiter four hours a day—not actually, because we can't keep a man alive for more than a split second down there—but my eyes and my ears and my mind are there, on the Bridge, four hours a day. Jupiter is not a nice place. I don't like it. I won't pretend I do."

"Spending four hours a day in an environment like that over a period of years—well, the human mind instinctively tries to adapt, even to the unthinkable. Sometimes I wonder how I'll behave when I'm put back in Chicago again. Sometimes I can't remember anything about Chicago except vague generalities, sometimes I can't even believe there is such a place as Earth—how could there be, when the rest of the universe is like Jupiter, or worse?"

"I know," Dillon said. "I've tried several times to show you that isn't a very reasonable frame of mind."

"I know it isn't. But I can't help how I feel. No, I don't think the Bridge will last. It can't last; it's all wrong. But I don't *want* to see it go. I've just got sense enough to know that one of these days Jupiter is going to sweep it away."

He wiped an open palm across the control boards, snapping all the toggles "Off" with a sound like the fall of a double-handful of marbles on a pane of glass. "Like that, Charity! And I work four hours a day, every day, on the Bridge. One of these days, Jupiter is going to destroy the Bridge. It'll go flying away in little flinders into the storms. My mind will be there, supervising some puny job, and my mind will go flying away along with my mechanical eyes and ears—still trying to adapt to the unthinkable, tumbling away into the winds and the flames and the rains and the darkness and the pressure and the cold."

"Bob, you're deliberately running away with yourself. Cut it out. Cut it out, I say!"

Helmuth shrugged, putting a trembling hand on the edge of the board to steady himself. "All right. I'm all right, Charity. I'm here, aren't I? Right here on Jupiter V, in no danger, in no danger at all. The bridge is 112,600 miles away from here. But when the day comes that the Bridge is swept away—

"Charity, sometimes I imagine you ferrying my body back to the cozy nook it came from, while my soul goes tumbling and tumbling through millions of cubic miles of poison. All right, Charity, I'll be good. I won't think about it out loud; but you can't expect me to forget it. It's on my mind; I can't help it, and you should know that."

"I do," Dillon said, with a kind of eagerness. "I do, Bob. I'm only trying to help, to make you see the problem as it is. The Bridge isn't really that awful, it isn't worth a single nightmare."

"Oh, it isn't the Bridge that makes me yell out when I'm sleeping," Helmuth said, smiling bitterly. "I'm not that ridden by it yet. It's while I'm awake that I'm afraid the Bridge will be swept away. What I sleep with is a fear of myself."

"That's a sane fear. You're as sane as any of us," Dillon insisted, fiercely solemn. "Look, Bob. The Bridge isn't a monster. It's a way we've developed for studying the behavior of materials under specific conditions of temperature, pressure, and gravity. Jupiter isn't Hell, either; it's a set of conditions. The Bridge is the laboratory we set up to work with those conditions."

"It isn't going anywhere. It's a bridge to no place."

"There aren't many *places* on Jupiter," Dillon said, missing Helmuth's meaning entirely. "We put the Bridge on an island in the local sea because we needed solid ice we could sink the caissons in. Otherwise, it wouldn't have mattered where we put it. We could have floated it on the sea itself, if we hadn't wanted to fix it in order to measure storm velocities and such things."

"I know that," Helmuth said.

"But, Bob, you don't show any signs of understanding it. Why, for instance, should the Bridge *go* any place? It isn't even, properly speaking, a bridge at all. We only call it that because we used some bridge engineering principles in building it. Actually, it's much more like a travelling crane—an extremely heavy-duty overhead rail line. It isn't going anywhere because it hasn't any place interesting to go, that's all. We're extending it to cover as much territory as possible, and to increase its stability, not to span the distance between places. There's no point to reproaching it because it doesn't span a real gap—between, say, Dover and Calais. It's a bridge to knowledge, and that's far more important. Why can't you see that?"

"I can see that; that's what I was talking about," Helmuth said, trying to control his impatience. "I have as much common sense as the average child. What I was trying to point out is that meeting colossalness with colossalness—out here—is a mug's game. It's a game Jupiter will always win, without the slightest effort. What if the engineers who built the Dover–Calais bridge had been limited to broomstraws for their structural members? They could have got the bridge up somehow, sure, and made it strong enough to carry light traffic on a fair day. But what would you have had left of it after the first winter storm came down the Channel from the North Sea? The whole approach is idiotic!"

"All right," Dillon said reasonably. "You have a point. Now you're being reasonable. What better approach have you to suggest? Should we abandon Jupiter entirely because it's too big for us?"

"No," Helmuth said. "Or maybe, yes. I don't know. I don't

have any easy answer. I just know that this one is no answer at all—it's just a cumbersome evasion."

Dillon smiled. "You're depressed, and no wonder. Sleep it off, Bob, if you can—you might even come up with that answer. In the meantime—well, when you stop to think about it, the surface of Jupiter isn't any more hostile, inherently, than the surface of Jupiter V, except in degree. If you stepped out of this building naked, you'd die just as fast as you would on Jupiter. Try to look at it that way."

Helmuth, looking forward into another night of dreams, said, "That's the way I look at it now."

III

There were three yellow "Critical" signals lit on the long gang board when Helmuth passed through the gang deck on the way back to duty. All of them, as usual, were concentrated on Panel 9, where Eva Chavez worked.

Eva, despite her Latin name—such once-valid tickets no longer meant anything among Earth's uniformly mixed-race population—was a big girl, vaguely blond, who cherished a passion for the Bridge. Unfortunately, she was apt to become enthralled by the sheer Cosmicness of it all, precisely at the moments when cold analysis and split-second decisions were most crucial.

Helmuth reached over her shoulder, cut her out of the circuit except as an observer, and donned the co-operator's helmet. The incomplete new shoals caisson sprang into being around him. Breakers of boiling hydrogen seethed seven hundred feet up along its slanted sides—breakers that never subsided, but simply were torn away into flying spray.

There was a spot of dull orange near the top of the north face of the caisson, crawling slowly toward the pediment of the nearest truss. Catalysis—

Or cancer, as Helmuth could not help but think of it. On

this bitter, violent monster of a planet, even the tiny specks of calcium carbide were deadly. At these wind velocities, such specks imbedded themselves in everything; and at fifteen million pounds per square inch, pressure ice catalyzed by sodium took up ammonia and carbon dioxide, building proteinlike compounds in a rapid, deadly chain of decay:

$$H^2NCHCO°HNCHCO°HNCHCO°HN\ldots$$
$$\quad\mid\qquad\qquad\mid\qquad\qquad\mid$$
$$CaO\qquad\quad Ca\qquad\quad Ca$$
$$\qquad\qquad\qquad HNCHCO°HNCHCO°HNCHCO°HN\ldots$$
$$\qquad\qquad\qquad\quad\mid\qquad\qquad\mid\qquad\qquad\mid$$
$$\qquad\qquad\qquad\quad CaO\qquad\quad Ca\qquad\quad Ca$$
$$\qquad\qquad\qquad\qquad\qquad HNCHCO°HNCHCO°HN\ldots$$

For a second, Helmuth watched it grow. It was, after all, one of the incredible possibilities the Bridge had been built to study. On Earth, such a compound, had it occurred at all, might have grown porous, bony, and quite strong. Here, under nearly eight times the gravity, the molecules were forced to assemble in strict aliphatic order, but in cross section their arrangement was hexagonal, as if the stuff would become an aromatic compound if it only could. Even here it was moderately strong in cross section—but along the long axis it smeared like graphite, the calcium atoms readily surrendering their valence hold on one carbon atom to grab hopefully for the next one in line—

No stuff to hold up the piers of humanity's greatest engineering project. Perhaps it was suitable for the ribs of some Jovian jellyfish, but in a Bridge caisson, it was cancer.

There was a scraper mechanism working on the edge of the lesion, flaking away the shearing aminos and laying down new ice. In the meantime, the decay of the caisson face was working deeper. The scraper could not possibly get at the core of the trouble—which was not the calcium carbide dust, with which the atmosphere was charged beyond redemption, but was instead one imbedded sodium speck which was taking no part in the reaction—fast enough to extirpate it. It could barely keep pace with the surface spread of the disease.

And laying new ice over the surface of the wound was worthless. At this rate, the whole caisson would slough away and melt like butter within an hour under the weight of the Bridge above it.

Helmuth sent the futile scraper aloft. Drill for it? No—too deep already, and location unknown.

Quickly he called two borers up from the shoals below, where constant blasting was taking the foundation of the caisson deeper and deeper into Jupiter's dubious "soil." He drove both blind fire-snouted machines down into the lesion.

The bottom of that sore turned out to be forty-five meters within the immense block. Helmuth pushed the red button all the same.

The borers blew up, with a heavy, quite invisible blast, as they had been designed to do. A pit appeared on the face of the caisson.

The nearest truss bent upward in the wind. It fluttered for a moment, trying to resist. It bent farther.

Deprived of its major attachment, it tore free suddenly and went whirling away into the blackness. A sudden flash of lightning picked it out for a moment, and Helmuth saw it dwindling like a bat with torn wings being borne away by a cyclone.

The scraper scuttled down into the pit and began to fill it with ice from the bottom. Helmuth ordered down a new truss and a squad of scaffolders. Damage of this order took time to repair. He watched the tornado tearing ragged chunks from the edges of the pit until he was sure that the catalysis had stopped. Then, suddenly, prematurely, dismally tired, he took off the helmet.

He was astounded by the white fury that masked Eva's big-boned, mildly pretty face.

"You'll blow the Bridge up yet, won't you?" she said, evenly, without preamble. "Any pretext will do!"

Baffled, Helmuth turned his head helplessly away; but that was no better. The suffused face of Jupiter peered swollenly through the picture-port, just as it did on the foreman's desk.

He and Eva and Charity and the gang and the whole of satellite V were falling forward toward Jupiter; their uneventful cooped-up lives on Jupiter V were utterly unreal compared to the four hours of each changeless day spent on Jupiter's ever-changing surface. Every new day brought their minds, like ships out of control, closer and closer to that gaudy inferno.

There was no other way for a man—or a woman—on Jupiter V to look at the giant planet. It was simple experience, shared by all of them, that planets do not occupy four-fifths of the whole sky, unless the observer is himself up there in that planet's sky, falling, falling faster and faster—

"I have no intention," he said tiredly, "of blowing up the Bridge. I wish you could get it through your head that I want the Bridge to stay up—even though I'm not starry-eyed to the point of incompetence about the project. Did you think that rotten spot was going to go away by itself when you'd painted it over? Didn't you know that—"

Several helmeted masked heads nearby turned blindly toward the sound of his voice. Helmuth shut up. Any distracting conversation or activity was taboo down here in the gang room. He motioned Eva back to duty.

The girl donned her helmet obediently enough, but it was plain from the way her normally full lips were thinned that she thought Helmuth had ended the argument only in order to have the last word.

Helmuth strode to the thick pillar which ran down the central axis of the shack, and mounted the spiraling cleats toward his own foreman's cubicle. Already he felt in anticipation the weight of the helmet upon his own head.

Charity Dillon, however, was already wearing the helmet; he was sitting in Helmuth's chair.

Charity was characteristically oblivious of Helmuth's entrance. The Bridge operator must learn to ignore, to be utterly unconscious of anything happening around his body except the inhuman sounds of signals; must learn to heed only those senses which report something going on thousands of miles away.

Helmuth knew better than to interrupt him. Instead, he watched Dillon's white bladelike fingers roving with blind sureness over the controls.

Dillon, evidently, was making a complete tour of the Bridge—not only from end to end, but up and down, too. The tally board showed that he had already activated nearly two-thirds of the ultraphone eyes. That meant that he had been up all night at the job; had begun it immediately after last talking to Helmuth.

Why?

With a thrill of unfocused apprehension, Helmuth looked at the foreman's jack, which allowed the operator here in the cubicle to communicate with the gang when necessary, and which kept him aware of anything said or done at gang boards.

It was plugged in.

Dillon sighed suddenly, took the helmet off, and turned.

"Hello, Bob," he said. "Funny about this job. You can't see, you can't hear, but when somebody's watching you, you feel a sort of pressure on the back of your neck. ESP, maybe. Ever felt it?"

"Pretty often, lately. Why the grand tour, Charity?"

"There's to be an inspection," Dillon said. His eyes met Helmuth's. They were frank and transparent. "A mob of Western officials coming to see that their eight billion dollars isn't being wasted. Naturally, I'm a little anxious to see that they find everything in order."

"I see," Helmuth said. "First time in five years, isn't it?"

"Just about. What was that dust-up down below just now? Somebody—you, I'm sure, from the drastic handiwork involved—bailed Eva out of a mess, and then I heard her talk about your wanting to blow up the Bridge. I checked the area when I heard the fracas start, and it did seem as if she had let things go rather far, but— What was it all about?" Dillon ordinarily hadn't the guile for cat-and-mouse games, and he had never looked less guileful than now.

Helmuth said carefully, "Eva was upset, I suppose. On the subject of Jupiter we're all of us cracked by now, in our different ways. The way she was dealing with the catalysis didn't look to me to be suitable—a difference of opinion, resolved in my favor because I had the authority, Eva didn't. That's all."

"Kind of an expensive difference, Bob. I'm not niggling by nature, you know that. But an incident like that while the commission is here—"

"The point is," Helmuth said, "are we to spend an extra ten thousand, or whatever it costs to replace a truss and reinforce a caisson, or are we to lose the whole caisson—and as much as a third of the whole Bridge along with it?"

"Yes, you're right there, of course. That could be explained, even to a pack of senators. But—it would be difficult to have to explain it very often. Well, the board's yours, Bob. You could continue my spot check, if you've time."

Dillon got up. Then he added suddenly, as if it were forced out of him, "Bob, I'm trying to understand your state of mind. From what Eva said, I gather that you've made it fairly public. I . . . I don't think it's a good idea to infect your fellow workers with your own pessimism. It leads to sloppy work. I know that regardless of your own feelings you won't countenance sloppy work, but one foreman can do only so much. And you're making extra work for yourself—not for me, but for yourself—by being openly gloomy about the Bridge.

"You're the best man on the Bridge, Bob, for all your grousing about the job, and your assorted misgivings. I'd hate to see you replaced."

"A threat, Charity?" Helmuth said softly.

"*No.* I wouldn't replace you unless you actually went nuts, and I firmly believe that your fears in that respect are groundless. It's a commonplace that only sane men suspect their own sanity, isn't it?"

"It's a common misconception. Most psychopathic obsessions begin with a mild worry."

Dillon made as if to brush that subject away. "Anyhow, I'm not threatening; I'd fight to keep you here. But my say-so only covers Jupiter V; there are people higher up on Ganymede, and people higher yet back in Washington—and in this inspecting commission.

"Why don't you try to look on the bright side for a change? Obviously the Bridge isn't ever going to inspire you. But you might at least try thinking about all those dollars piling up in your account every hour you're on this job, and about the bridges and ships and who knows what-all that you'll be building, at any fee you ask, when you get back down to Earth. All under the magic words 'One of the men who built the Bridge on Jupiter'!" Charity was bright red with embarrassment and enthusiasm.

Helmuth smiled. "I'll try to bear it in mind, Charity," he said. "When is this gaggle of senators due to arrive?"

"They're on Ganymede now, taking a breather. They came directly from Washington without any routing. I suppose they'll make a stop at Callisto before they come here. They've something new on their ship, I'm told, that lets them flit about more freely than the usual uphill transport can."

An icy lizard suddenly was resting in Helmuth's stomach, coiling and coiling but never settling itself. The room blurred. The persistent nightmare was suddenly almost upon him—already.

"Something . . . new?" he echoed, his voice as flat and noncommittal as he could make it. "Do you know what it is?"

"Well, yes. But I think I'd better keep quiet about it until—"

"Charity, nobody on this deserted rock heap could possibly be a Soviet spy. The whole habit of 'security' is idiotic out here. Tell me now and save me the trouble of dealing with senators; or tell me at least that you know I know. *They have antigravity!* Isn't that it?"

One word from Dillon, and the nightmare would be real.

"Yes," Dillon said. "How did you know? Of course, it couldn't be a complete gravity screen by any means. But it seems to be a good long step toward it. We've waited a long time to see that dream come true— But you're the last man in the world to take pride in the achievement, so there's no sense exulting about it to you. I'll let you know when I get a definite arrival date. In the meantime, will you think about what I said before?"

"Yes. I will." Helmuth took the seat before the board.

"Good. With you, I have to be grateful for small victories. Good trick, Bob."

"Good trick, Charity."

IV

Instead of sleeping—for now he knew that he was really afraid—he sat up in the reading chair in his cabin. The illuminated microfilm pages of a book flipped by across the surface of the wall opposite him, timed precisely to the reading rate most comfortable for him, and he had several weeks' worry-conserved alcohol and smoke rations for ready consumption.

But Helmuth let his mix go flat, and did not notice the book, which had turned itself on, at the page where he had abandoned it last, when he had fitted himself into the chair. Instead, he listened to the radio.

There was always a great deal of ham radio activity in the Jovian system. The conditions were good for it, since there was plenty of power available, few impeding atmosphere layers, and those thin, no Heaviside layers, and few official and no commercial channels with which the hams could interfere.

And there were plenty of people scattered about the satellites who needed the sound of a voice.

". . . Anybody know whether the senators are coming here? Doc Barth put in a report a while back on a fossil plant he found here, at least he thinks it was a plant. Maybe they'd like a look at it."

"They're supposed to hit the Bridge team next." A strong voice, and the impression of a strong transmitter wavering in and out; that would be Sweeney on Ganymede. "Sorry to throw the wet blanket, boys, but I don't think the senators are interested in our rock balls for their own lumpy selves. We could only hold them here three days."

Helmut thought grayly, *Then they've already left Callisto.*

"Is that you, Sweeney? Where's the Bridge tonight?"

"Dillon's on duty," a very distant transmitter said. "Try to raise Helmuth, Sweeney."

"Helmuth, Helmuth, you gloomy beetle gooser! Come in, Helmuth!"

"Sure, Bob, come in and dampen us."

Sluggishly, Helmuth reached out to take the mike where it lay clipped to one arm of the chair. But the door to his room opened before he had completed the gesture.

Eva came in. She said, "Bob, I want to tell you something."

"His voice is changing!" the voice of the Callisto operator said. "Ask him what he's drinking, Sweeney!"

Helmuth cut the radio out. The girl was freshly dressed— in so far as anybody dressed in anything on Jupiter V—and Helmuth wondered why she was prowling the decks at this hour, halfway between her sleep period and her trick. Her hair was hazy against the light from the corridor, and she looked less mannish than usual. She reminded him a little of the way she had looked when they first met.

"All right," he said. "I owe you a mix, I guess. Citric, sugar and the other stuff is in the locker—you know where it is. Shot cans are there, too."

The girl shut the door and sat down on the bunk with a free litheness that was almost grace, but with a determination which Helmuth knew meant that she had just decided to do something silly for all the right reasons.

"I don't need a drink," she said. "As a matter of fact, lately I've been turning my lux-R's back to the common pool. I suppose you did that for me—by showing me what a mind looked like that is hiding from itself."

"Eva, stop sounding like a tract. Obviously, you've advanced to a higher, more Jovian plane of existence, but won't you still need your metabolism? Or have you decided that vitamins are all-in-the-mind?"

"Now, you're being superior. Anyhow, alcohol isn't a vitamin. And I didn't come to talk about that. I came to tell you something I think you ought to know."

"Which is?"

She said, "Bob, I mean to have a child here."

A bark of laughter, part sheer hysteria and part exasperation, jackknifed Helmuth into a sitting position. A red arrow bloomed on the far wall, obediently marking the paragraph which supposedly he had reached in his reading, and the page vanished.

"Women!" he said, when he could get his breath back. "Really, Evita, you make me feel much better. No environment can change a human being much, after all."

"Why should it?" she said suspiciously. "I don't see the joke. Shouldn't a woman want to have a child?"

"Of course she should," he said, settling back. The flipping pages began again. "It's quite ordinary. All women want to have children. All women dream of the day they can turn a child out to play in an airless rock garden, to pluck fossils and get quaintly starburned. How cozy to tuck the little blue body back into its corner that night, promptly at the sound of the trick-change bell! Why, it's as natural as Jupiter light— as Earthian as vacuum-frozen apple pie."

He turned his head casually away. "As for me, though, Eva, I'd much prefer that you take your ghostly little pretext out of here."

Eva surged to her feet in one furious motion. Her fingers grasped him by the beard and jerked his head painfully around again.

"You reedy male platitude!" she said in a low grinding voice. "How you could see almost the whole point and make so little of it— *Women*, is it? So you think I came creeping in here, full of humbleness, to settle our technical differences."

He closed his hand on her wrist and twisted it away. "What else?" he demanded, trying to imagine how it would feel to stay reasonable for five minutes at a time with these Bridge robots. "None of us need bother with games and excuses. We're here, we're isolated, we were all chosen because, among other things, we were judged incapable of forming permanent emotional attachments, and capable of such alliances as we found attractive without going unbalanced when the attraction diminished and the alliance came unstuck. None of us have to pretend that our living arrangements would keep us out of jail in Boston, or that they have to involve any Earth-normal excuses."

She said nothing. After a while he asked gently, "Isn't that so?"

"Of course it's so. Also it has nothing to do with the matter."

"It doesn't? How stupid do you think I am? *I* don't care whether or not you've decided to have a child here, if you really mean what you say."

She was trembling with rage. "You really don't, too. The decision means nothing to you."

"Well, if I liked children, I'd be sorry for the child. But as it happens, I can't stand children. In short, Eva as far as I'm concerned you can have as many as you want, and to me you'll *still* be the worst operator on the Bridge."

"I'll bear that in mind," she said. At this moment she seemed to have been cut from pressure ice. "I'll leave you something to charge your mind with, too, Robert Helmuth. I'll leave you sprawled here under your precious book—what is Madame Bovary to you, anyhow, you unadventurous turtle?—to think about a man who believes that children must always be born into warm cradles, a man who thinks that men have to huddle on warm worlds or they won't survive. A man with no ears, no eyes, scarcely any head. A man in terror, a man crying Mamma! *Mamma!* all the stellar days and nights long!"

"Parlor diagnosis!"

"Parlor labeling. Good trick, Bob. Draw your warm woolly blanket in tight about your brains, or some little sneeze of sense might creep in, and impair your—efficiency!"

The door closed sharply after her.

A million pounds of fatigue crashed down without warning on Helmuth's brain, and he fell back into the reading chair with a gasp. The roots of his beard ached, and Jupiters bloomed and wavered away before his closed eyes.

He struggled once, and fell asleep.

Instantly he was in the grip of the dream.

It started, as always, with commonplaces, almost realistic enough to be a documentary filmstrip—except for the appalling sense of pressure and the distorted emotional significance with which the least word, the smallest movement was invested.

It was the sinking of the first caisson of the Bridge. The actual event had been bad enough. The job demanded enough exactness of placement to require that manned ships enter Jupiter's atmosphere itself: a squadron of twenty of the most powerful ships ever built, with the five-million-ton asteroid, trimmed and shaped in space, slung beneath them in an immense cat's cradle.

Four times that squadron had disappeared beneath the

clouds; four times the tense voices of pilots and engineers had muttered in Helmuth's ears; four times there were shouts and futile orders and the snapping of cables and someone screaming endlessly against the eternal howl of the Jovian sky.

It had cost, altogether, nine ships and 231 men, to get one of five laboriously shaped asteroids planted in the shifting slush that was Jupiter's surface. Helmuth had helped to supervise all five operations, counting the successful one, from his desk on Jupiter V; but in the dream he was not in the control shack, but instead on shipboard, in one of the ships that was never to come back—

Then, without transition, but without any sense of discontinuity either, he was on the Bridge itself. Not *in absentia,* as the remote guiding intelligence of a beetle, but in person, in an ovular tanklike suit the details of which would never come clear. The high brass had discovered antigravity, and had asked for volunteers to man the Bridge. Helmuth had volunteered.

Looking back on it in the dream, he did not understand why he had volunteered. It had simply seemed expected of him, and he had not been able to help it, even though he had known what it would be like. He belonged on the Bridge, though he hated it—he had been doomed to go there, from the first.

And there was . . . something wrong . . . with the antigravity. The high brass had asked for its volunteers before the scientific work had been completed. The present antigravity fields were weak, and there was some basic flaw in the theory. Generators broke down after only short periods of use, burned out unpredictably, sometimes only moments after testing up without a flaw—like vacuum tubes in waking life.

That was what Helmuth's set was about to do. He crouched inside his personal womb, above the boiling sea, the clouds raging about him, lit by a plume of hydrogen flame, and waited to feel his weight suddenly become eight times greater than normal. He knew what would happen to him then. It happened.

Helmuth greeted morning on Jupiter V with his customary scream.

V

The ship that landed as he was going on duty did nothing to lighten the load on his heart. In shape it was not distinguishable from any of the long-range cruisers which ran the legs of the Moon-Mars-Belt-Ganymede trip. But it grounded its huge bulk with less visible expenditure of power than one of the little intersatellary boats.

That landing told Helmuth that his dream was well on its way to coming true. If the high brass had had a real antigravity, there would have been no reason why the main jets should have been necessary at all. Obviously, what had been discovered was some sort of partial screen, which allowed a ship to operate with far less jet action than was normal, but which still left it subject to a sizable fraction of the universal stress of space.

Nothing less than complete and completely controllable antigravity would do on Jupiter.

He worked mechanically, noting that Charity was not in evidence. Probably he was conferring with the senators, receiving what would be for him the glad news.

Helmuth realized suddenly that there was nothing left for him to do now but to cut and run.

There could certainly be no reason why he should have to re-enact the entire dream helplessly, event for event, like an actor committed to a play. He was awake now, in full control of his own senses, and still at least partially sane. The man in the dream had volunteered—but that man would not be Robert Helmuth. Not any longer.

While the senators were here, he would turn in his resignation. Direct, over Charity's head.

"Wake up, Helmuth," a voice from the gang deck snapped

suddenly. "If it hadn't been for me, you'd have run yourself off the end of the Bridge. You had all the automatic stops on that beetle cut out."

Helmuth reached guiltily and more than a little too late for the controls. Eva had already run his beetle back beyond the danger line.

"Sorry," he mumbled. "Thanks, Eva."

"Don't thank me. If you'd actually been in it, I'd have let it go. Less reading and more sleep is what I recommend for you, Helmuth."

"Keep your recommendations to yourself," he snapped.

The incident started a new and even more disturbing chain of thought. If he were to resign now, it would be nearly a year before he could get back to Chicago. Antigravity or no antigravity, the senators' ship would have no room for unexpected passengers. Shipping a man back home had to be arranged far in advance. Space had to be provided, and a cargo equivalent of the weight and space requirements he would take up on the return trip had to be deadheaded out to Jupiter.

A year of living in the station on Jupiter V without any function—as a man whose drain on the station's supplies no longer could be justified in terms of what he did. A year of living under the eyes of Eva Chavez and Charity Dillon and the other men and women who still remained Bridge operators, men and women who would not hesitate to let him know what they thought of his quitting.

A year of living as a bystander in the feverish excitement of direct personal exploration of Jupiter. A year of watching and hearing the inevitable deaths—while he alone stood aloof, privileged, and useless. A year during which Robert Helmuth would become the most hated living entity in the Jovian system.

And, when he got back to Chicago and went looking for a job—for his resignation from the Bridge gang would automatically take him out of government service—he would be asked why he left the Bridge at the moment when work on the Bridge was just reaching its culmination.

He began to understand why the man in the dream had volunteered.

When the trick-change bell rang, he was still determined to resign, but he had already concluded bitterly that there were, after all, other kinds of hells besides the one on Jupiter.

He was returning the board to neutral as Charity came up the cleats. Charity's eyes were snapping like a skyful of comets. Helmuth had known that they would be.

"Senator Wagoner wants to speak to you, if you're not too tired, Bob," he said. "Go ahead; I'll finish up here."

"He does?" Helmuth frowned. The dream surged back upon him. *NO.* They would not rush him any faster than he wanted to go. "What about, Charity? Am I suspected of un-Western activities? I suppose you've told them how I feel."

"I have," Dillon said, unruffled. "But we're agreed that you may not feel the same after you've talked to Wagoner. He's in the ship, of course. I've put out a suit for you at the lock." Charity put the helmet over his head, effectively cutting himself off from further conversation, or from any further consciousness of Helmuth at all.

Helmuth stood looking at him a moment. Then, with a convulsive shrug, he went down the cleats.

Three minutes later, he was plodding in a spacesuit across the surface of Jupiter V, with the vivid bulk of Jupiter splashing his shoulders with color.

A courteous Marine let him through the ship's air lock and deftly peeled him out of the suit. Despite a grim determination to be uninterested in the new antigravity and any possible consequence of it, he looked curiously about as he was conducted up toward the bow.

But the ship was like the ones that had brought him from Chicago to Jupiter V—it was like any spaceship: there was nothing in it to see but corridor walls and stairwells, until you arrived at the cabin where you were needed.

Senator Wagoner was a surprise. He was a young man, no more than sixty-five at most, not at all portly, and he had the keenest pair of blue eyes that Helmuth had ever seen. He received Helmuth alone in his own cabin—a comfortable cabin as spaceship accommodations go, but neither roomy nor luxurious. He was hard to match up with the stories Helmuth had been hearing about the current Senate, which had been involved in scandal after scandal of more than Roman proportions.

Helmuth looked around. "I thought there were several of you" he said.

"There are, but I didn't want to give you the idea that you were facing a panel," Wagoner said, smiling. "I've been forced to sit in on most of these endless loyalty investigations back home, but I can't see any point in exporting such religious ceremonies to deep space. Do sit down, Mr. Helmuth. There are drinks coming. We have a lot to talk about."

Stiffly, Helmuth sat down.

"Dillon tells me," Wagoner said, leaning back comfortably in his own chair, "that your usefulness to the Bridge is about at an end. In a way, I'm sorry to hear that, for you've been one of the best men we've had on any of our planetary projects. But, in another way, I'm glad. It makes you available for something much bigger, where we need you much more."

"What do you mean by that?"

"I'll explain in a moment. First, I'd like to talk a little about the Bridge. Please don't feel that I'm quizzing you, by the way. You're at perfect liberty to say that any given question is none of my business, and I'll take no offense and hold no grudge. Also, 'I hereby disavow the authenticity of any tape or other tapping of which this statement may be a part.' In short, our conversation is unofficial, highly so."

"Thank you."

"It's to my interest; I'm hoping that you'll talk freely to me. Of course my disavowal means nothing, since such formal statements can always be excised from a tape; but later on I'm going to tell you some things you're not supposed to know, and you'll be able to judge by what I say then that anything you say to me is privileged. Okay?"

A steward came in silently with drinks, and left again. Helmuth tasted his. As far as he could tell, it was exactly like many he had mixed for himself back in the control shack, from standard space rations. The only difference was that it was cold, which Helmuth found startling, but not unpleasant after the first sip. He tried to relax. "I'll do my best," he said.

"Good enough. Now: Dillon says that you regard the Bridge as a monster. I've examined your dossier pretty closely, and I think perhaps Dillon hasn't quite the gist of your meaning. I'd like to hear it straight from you."

"I don't think the Bridge is a monster," Helmuth said slowly. "You see, Charity is on the defensive. He takes the Bridge to be conclusive evidence that no possible set of adverse conditions ever will stop man for long, and there I'm in agreement with him. But he also thinks of it as Progress personified. He can't admit—you asked me to speak my mind, Senator—that the West is a decadent and drying culture. All the other evidence that's available shows that it is. Charity likes to think of the Bridge as giving the lie to that evidence."

"The West hasn't many more years," Wagoner agreed, astonishingly. "Still and all, the West has been responsible for some really towering achievements in its time. Perhaps the Bridge could be considered as the last and mightiest of them all."

"Not by me," Helmuth said. "The building of gigantic projects for ritual purposes—doing a thing for the sake of doing it—is the last act of an already dead culture. Look at the pyramids in Egypt for an example. Or an even more idiotic and more enormous example, bigger than anything human beings have accomplished yet, the laying out of the 'Diagram of Power' over the whole face of Mars. If the Martians had put all that energy into survival instead, they'd probably be alive yet."

"Agreed," Wagoner said.

"All right. Then maybe you'll also agree that the essence of a vital culture is its ability to defend itself. The West has beaten off the Soviets for a century now—but as far as I can see, the Bridge is the West's 'Diagram of Power', its pyramids, or what have you. All the money and the resources that went into the Bridge are going to be badly needed, *and won't be there,* when the next Soviet attack comes."

"Which will be very shortly, I'm told," Wagoner said, with complete calm. "Furthermore, it will be successful, and in part it will be successful for the very reasons you've outlined. For a man who's been cut off from the Earth for years, Helmuth, you seem to know more about what's going on down there than most of the general populace does."

"Nothing promotes an interest in Earth like being off it," Helmuth said. "And there's plenty of time to read out here." Either the drink was stronger than he had expected, or the senator's calm concurrence in the collapse of Helmuth's entire world had given him another shove toward nothingness; his head was spinning.

Wagoner saw it. He leaned forward suddenly, catching Helmuth flat-footed. *"However,"* he said, "it's difficult for me to agree that the Bridge serves, or ever did serve, a ritual purpose. The Bridge served a huge practical purpose which is now fulfilled—the Bridge, as such, is now a defunct project."

"Defunct?" Helmuth repeated faintly.

"Quite. Of course we'll continue to operate it for a while, simply because you can't stop a process of that size on a dime, and that's just as well for people like Dillon who are emotionally tied up in it. You're the one person with any authority in the whole station who has already lost enough interest in the Bridge to make it safe for me to tell you that it's being abandoned."

"But why?"

"Because," Wagoner went on quietly, "the Bridge has now given us confirmation of a theory of stupendous importance—so important, in my opinion, that the imminent fall of the West seems like a puny event in comparison. A confirmation, incidentally, which contains in it the seeds of ultimate destruction for the Soviets, whatever they may win for themselves in the next fifty years or so."

"I suppose," Helmuth said, puzzled, "that you mean antigravity?"

For the first time, it was Wagoner's turn to be taken aback. "Man," he said at last, "do you know *everything* I want to tell you? I hope not, or my conclusions will be mighty suspicious. Surely Charity didn't tell you we had antigravity; I strictly enjoined him not to mention it."

"No, the subject's been on my mind," Helmuth said. "But I certainly don't see why it should be so world-shaking, any more than I see how the Bridge helped to bring it about. I thought it had been developed independently, for the further exploitation of the Bridge, and would step up Bridge operation, not discontinue it."

"Not at all. Of course, the Bridge has given us information in thousands of different categories, much of it very valuable indeed. But the one job that *only* the Bridge could do was that of confirming, or throwing out, the Blackett-Dirac equations."

"Which are?"

"A relationship between magnetism and the spinning of a massive body—that much is the Dirac part of it. The Blackett Equation seemed to show that the same formula also applied to gravity. If the figures we collected on the magnetic field strength of Jupiter forced us to retire the Dirac equations, then none of the rest of the information we've gotten from the Bridge would have been worth the money we spent to get it. On the other hand, Jupiter was the only body in the solar system available to us which was big enough in all relevant respects to make it possible for us to test those equations at all. They involve quantities of enormous orders of magnitudes.

"And the figures show that Dirac was right. *They also show that Blackett was right.* Both magnetism *and* gravity are phenomena of rotation.

"I won't bother to trace the succeeding steps, because I think you can work them out for yourself. It's enough to say that there's a drive generator on board this ship which is the complete and final justification of all the hell you people on the Bridge gang have been put through. The gadget has a long technical name, but the technies who tend it have already nicknamed it the 'spindizzy,' because of what it does to the magnetic moment of any atom—*any* atom—within its field.

"While it's in operation, it absolutely refuses to notice any atom outside its own influence. Furthermore, it will notice no other strain or influence which holds good beyond the borders of that field. It's so snooty that it has to be stopped down to almost nothing when it's brought close to a planet, or it won't let you land. But in deep space . . . well, it's impervious to meteors and such trash, of course; it's impervious to gravity; and—it hasn't the faintest interest in any legislation about top speed limits."

"You're kidding," Helmuth said.

"Am I, now? The ship came to Ganymede directly from Earth. It did it in a little under two hours, counting maneuvering time."

Helmuth took a defiant pull at his drink. "This thing really has no top speed at all?" he said. "How can you be sure of that?"

"Well, we can't," Wagoner admitted. "After all, one of the unfortunate things about general mathematical formulas is that they don't contain cut-off points to warn you of areas where they don't apply. Even quantum mechanics is somewhat subject to that criticism. However, we expect to know pretty soon just how fast the spindizzy can drive an object, if there is any limit. We expect you to tell us."

"I?"

"Yes, Helmuth, you. The coming debacle on Earth makes it absolutely imperative for us—the West—to get interstellar expeditions started at once. Richardson Observatory, on the Moon, has two likely-looking systems picked out already—one at Wolf 359, another at 61 Cygni—and there are sure to be hundreds of others where Earthlike planets are highly probable. We want to scatter adventurous people, people with a thoroughly indoctrinated love of being free, all over this part of the galaxy, if it can be done.

"Once they're out there, they'll be free to flourish, with no interference from Earth. The Soviets haven't the spindizzy yet, and even after they steal it from us, they won't dare allow it to be used. It's too good and too final an escape route.

"What we want you to do—now I'm getting to the point, you see—is to direct this exodus. You've the intelligence and the cast of mind for it. Your analysis of the situation on Earth confirms that, if any more confirmation were needed. And—there's no future for you on Earth now."

"You'll have to excuse me," Helmuth said firmly. "I'm in no condition to be reasonable now; it's been more than I could digest in a few moments. And the decision doesn't entirely rest with me, either. If I could give you an answer in ... let me see ... about three hours. Will that be soon enough?"

"That'll be fine," the senator said.

"And so, that's the story," Helmuth said.

Eva remained silent in her chair for a long time. "One thing I don't understand," she said at last. "Why did you come to me? I'd have thought that you'd find the whole thing terrifying."

"Oh, it's terrifying, all right," Helmuth said with quiet exultation. "But terror and fright are two different things, as

've just discovered. We were both wrong, Evita. I was wrong
in thinking that the Bridge was a dead end. You were wrong
in thinking of it as an end in itself."

"I don't understand you."

"All right, let's put it this way: The work the Bridge was
doing was worthwhile, as I know now—so I was wrong in being frightened of it, in calling it a bridge to nowhere.

"But you no more saw where it was going than I, and you
made the Bridge the be-all and end-all of your existence.

"Now there's a place to go to; in fact there are places—
hundreds of places. They'll be Earthlike places. Since the Soviets are about to win Earth, those places will be more Earthlike than Earth itself, for the next century or so at least!"

She said, "Why are you telling me this? Just to make
peace between us?"

"I'm going to take on this job, Evita, if you'll go along?"

She turned swiftly, rising out of the chair with a marvelous
fluidity of motion. At the same instant, all the alarm bells in
the station went off at once, filling every metal cranny with a
jangle of pure horror.

"Posts!" the speaker above Eva's bed roared in a distorted,
gigantic version of Charity Dillon's voice. *"Peak storm overload! The STD is now passing the Spot. Wind velocity has
already topped all previous records, and part of the land
mass has begun to settle. This is an A-1 overload emergency."*

Behind Charity's bellow, the winds of Jupiter made a spectrum of continuous insane shrieking. The Bridge was re-
sponding with monstrous groans of agony. There was another
sound, too, an almost musical cacophony of sharp percussive
tones, such as a dinosaur might make pushing its way
through a forest of huge steel tuning forks. Helmuth had never heard that sound before, but he knew what it was.

The deck of the Bridge was splitting up the middle.

After a moment more, the uproar dimmed, and the speaker
said, in Charity's normal voice, "Eva, you too, please. Ac-

knowledge, please. This is it. Unless everybody comes on duty at once, the Bridge may go down within the next hour."

"Let it," Eva responded quietly.

There was a brief startled silence, and then a ghost of a human sound. The voice was Senator Wagoner's, and the sound just might have been a chuckle.

Charity's circuit clicked out.

The mighty death of the Bridge continued to resound in the little room.

After a while, the man and the woman went to the window, and looked past the discarded bulk of Jupiter at the near horizon, where there had always been visible a few stars.

SATURN

Saturn is only the second-largest planet in the Solar system, and it is rather dwarfed by Jupiter.

Its diameter is only 0.85 that of Jupiter; its surface area only 0.72 that of Jupiter. Its volume is only 0.61 times that of Jupiter.

It is less dense than Jupiter, too. In fact, it is the least dense object in the Solar system as far as we know. Its average density is only 0.71 grams per cubic centimeter, only about an eighth as dense as Earth is and about half as dense as Jupiter is. Saturn is actually less dense than water is.

As a result Saturn is only 0.30 times as massive as Jupiter is—less than a third. It's not a very good second-largest. Although smaller than Jupiter, it doesn't manage to turn more quickly. Its period of rotation is 10.23 hours—23 minutes longer than Jupiter's is.

Moreover, whereas Jupiter has four large satellites, Saturn has only one—Titan. (Saturn also has nine small satellites, however.)

To be sure, Titan is the most voluminous satellite in the Solar system. It is 4.65 times as voluminous as our Moon and 1.37 times as voluminous as Jupiter's largest satellite, Ganymede.

However, Titan is low in density, as Saturn is, so its mass doesn't quite live up to its volume. It is 2.9 times as massive as the Moon, but only 0.94 times as massive as Ganymede.

Yet in one respect Saturn is unparalleled—by Jupiter or by any other body we know. Some of the material which would ordinarily have coalesced into satellites, as the Saturnian system was formed, was close enough to the planet to be so strongly influenced by tidal effects as to have been unable to coalesce. It remained a thick scattering of relatively small particles that spread throughout a circular orbit about Saturn. In other words, there are systems of rings about the planet that make it the most beautiful sight one can see in a telescope.

In the early days when the telescopes were unable to make out distant things clearly (Saturn is 1428 million kilometers, or 886 million miles from the Sun—or 1.8 times as far from the Sun as Jupiter is) the rings were a puzzle. Galileo, in 1610, was unable to make out clearly what he was seeing, for instance.

It was not till 1655 that Christiaan Huygens finally realized there were rings around Saturn. It was two more centuries before James Clerk Maxwell showed conclusively that, by gravitational theory, the rings could neither be solid nor liquid, but had to be a collection of small discrete objects.

Our knowledge of Saturn has not progressed much in the last century. We have discovered a couple of satellites, the most recent being Janus (discovered in 1967 by Audouin Dolfuss), which is closest to the planet and is just outside the limits of the ring system. Janus is not mentioned in "Saturn Rising," which was published in 1961, but nothing else in the story has been outdated.

Titan, on which the final scene of "Saturn Rising" is laid, is an interesting world. In 1944, Gerard Peter Kuiper detected an atmosphere about Titan and found it to consist of methane. What's more, it is a substantial atmosphere, very likely denser than that of Mars. Titan is the only satellite in the Solar system and the smallest body of any kind known to possess an atmosphere.

Methane can build up into more complex organic molecules, and it may be these that give Titan its distinctly orange color. Titan may conceivably have a gasoline ocean and may have built up some life forms. It will take probe observations of the right sort, including a soft landing, to tell us what Titan is really like.

At the moment of writing, no probe has reached Saturn. Pioneer 11 is on the way, however. It is the second Jupiter probe (which confirmed the findings of Pioneer 10), and it is scheduled to pass Saturn on September 1, 1979.

The logical guess is that it will show Saturn to be a little sister of Jupiter. Saturn will have a magnetic field that is neither as large nor as intense as that of Jupiter. Saturn will also be essentially a ball of liquid hydrogen, but it will not be as hot as Jupiter.

Saturn Rising

ARTHUR C. CLARKE

Yes, that's perfectly true. I met Morris Perlman when I was about twenty-eight. I met thousands of people in those days, from presidents downward.

When we got back from Saturn, everybody wanted to see us, and about half the crew took off on lecture tours. I've always enjoyed talking (don't say you haven't noticed it), but some of my colleagues said they'd rather go to Pluto than face another audience. Some of them did.

My beat was the Midwest, and the first time I ran into Mr. Perlman—no one ever called him anything else, certainly never "Morris"—was in Chicago. The agency always booked me into good, but not too luxurious, hotels. That suited me; I liked to stay in places where I could come and go as I pleased without running a gauntlet of liveried flunkies, and where I could wear anything within reason without being made to feel a tramp. I see you're grinning; well, I was only a kid then, and a lot of things have changed.

It's all a long time ago now, but I must have been lecturing at the University. At any rate, I remember being disappointed because they couldn't show me the place where Fermi started the first atomic pile—they said that the building had been pulled down forty years before, and there was only a plaque to mark the spot. I stood looking at it for a while, thinking of all that had happened since that far-off day in 1942. I'd been born, for one thing; and atomic power had

214

taken me out to Saturn and back. *That* was probably something that Fermi and Co. never thought of, when they built their primitive latticework of uranium and graphite.

I was having breakfast in the coffee shop when a slightly built middle-aged man dropped into the seat on the other side of the table. He nodded a polite "Good morning," then gave a start of surprise as he recognized me. (Of course, he'd planned the encounter, but I didn't know it at the time.)

"This is a pleasure!" he said. "I was at your lecture last night. How I envied you!"

I gave a rather forced smile; I'm never very sociable at breakfast, and I'd learned to be on my guard against the cranks, bores, and enthusiasts who seemed to regard me as their legitimate prey. Mr. Perlman, however, was not a bore—though he was certainly an enthusiast, and I suppose you could call him a crank.

He looked like any average fairly prosperous businessman, and I assumed that he was a guest like myself. The fact that he had attended my lecture was not surprising; it had been a popular one, open to the public, and of course well advertised over press and radio.

"Ever since I was a kid," said my uninvited companion, "Saturn has fascinated me. I know exactly when and how it all started. I must have been about ten years old when I came across those wonderful paintings of Chesley Bonestell's, showing the planet as it would look from its nine moons. I suppose you've seen them?"

"Of course," I answered. "Though they're half a century old, no one's beaten them yet. We had a couple aboard the *Endeavour,* pinned on the plotting table. I often used to look at the pictures and then compare them with the real thing."

"Then you know how I felt, back in the nineteen fifties. I used to sit for hours trying to grasp the fact that this incredible object, with its silver rings spinning around it, wasn't just some artist's dream, but actually existed—that it was a world, in fact, ten times the size of Earth."

"At that time I never imagined that I could see this wonderful thing for myself; I took it for granted that only the astronomers, with their giant telescopes, could ever look at such sights. But then, when I was about fifteen, I made another discovery—so exciting that I could hardly believe it."

"And what was that?" I asked. By now I'd become reconciled to sharing breakfast; my companion seemed a harmless enough character, and there was something quite endearing about his obvious enthusiasm.

"I found that any fool could make a high-powered astronomical telescope in his own kitchen, for a few dollars and a couple of weeks work. It was a revelation; like thousands of other kids, I borrowed a copy of Ingalls' *Amateur Telescope Making* from the public library, and went ahead. Tell me—have *you* ever built a telescope of your own?"

"No: I'm an engineer, not an astronomer. I wouldn't know how to begin the job."

"It's incredibly simple, if you follow the rules. You start with two disks of glass, about an inch thick. I got mine for fifty cents from a ship chandler's; they were porthole glasses that were of no use because they'd been chipped around the edges. Then you cement one disk to some flat, firm surface—I used an old barrel standing on end.

"Next you have to buy several grades of emery powder, starting from coarse, gritty stuff and working down to the finest that's made. You lay a pinch of the coarsest powder between the two disks, and start rubbing the upper one back and forth with regular strokes. As you do so, you slowly circle around the job.

"You see what happens? The upper disk gets hollowed out by the cutting action of the emery powder and as you walk around, it shapes itself into a concave spherical surface. From time to time you have to change to a finer grade of powder, and make some simple optical tests to check that your curve's right.

"Later still, you drop the emery and switch to rouge, until

at last you have a smooth polished surface that you can hardly credit you've made yourself. There's only one more step, though that's a little tricky. You still have to silver the mirror, and turn it into a good reflector. This means getting some chemicals made up at the drugstore, and doing exactly what the book says.

"I can still remember the kick I got when the silver film began to spread like magic across the face of my little mirror. It wasn't perfect, but it was good enough, and I wouldn't have swapped it for anything on Mount Palomar.

"I fixed it at one end of a wooden plank; there was no need to bother about a telescope tube, though I put a couple of feet of cardboard round the mirror to cut out stray light. For an eyepiece I used a small magnifying lens I'd picked up in a junk store for a few cents. Altogether, I don't suppose the telescope cost more than five dollars—though that was a lot of money to me when I was a kid.

"We were living then in a run-down hotel my family owned on Third Avenue. When I'd assembled the telescope I went up on the roof and tried it out, among the jungle of TV antennas that covered every building in those days. It took me a while to get the mirror and eyepiece lined up, but I hadn't made any mistakes and the thing worked. As an optical instrument it was probably lousy—after all, it was my first attempt—but it magnified at least fifty times and I could hardly wait until nightfall to try it on the stars.

"I'd checked with the almanac, and knew that Saturn was high in the east after sunset. As soon as it was dark I was up on the roof again, with my crazy contraption of wood and glass propped between two chimneys. It was late fall, but I never noticed the cold, for the sky was full of stars—and they were all mine.

"I took my time setting the focus as accurately as possible, using the first star that came into the field. Then I started hunting for Saturn, and soon discovered how hard it was to locate anything in a reflecting telescope that wasn't properly mounted. But presently the planet shot across the field of view, I nudged the instrument a few inches this way and that—and there it was.

"It was tiny, but it was perfect. I don't think I breathed for a minute; I could hardly believe my eyes. After all the pictures, here was the reality. It looked like a toy hanging there in space, with the rings slightly open and tilted toward me. Even now, forty years later, I can remember thinking, It looks so *artificial*—like something for a Christmas tree! There was a single bright star to the left of it, and I knew that was Titan."

He paused, and for a moment we must have shared the same thoughts. For to both of us Titan was no longer merely the largest moon of Saturn—a point of light known only to astronomers. It was the fiercely hostile world upon which *Endeavour* had landed, and where three of my crewmates lay in lonely graves, farther from their homes than any of Mankind's dead had ever rested before.

"I don't know how long I stared, straining my eyes and moving the telescope across the sky in jerky steps as Saturn rose above the city. I was a billion miles from New York; but presently New York caught up with me.

"I told you about our hotel; it belonged to my mother, but my father ran it—not very well. It had been losing money for years, and all through my boyhood there had been continuous financial crises. So I don't want to blame my father for drinking; he must have been half crazy with worry most of the time. And I had quite forgotten that I was supposed to be helping the clerk at the reception desk.

"So Dad came looking for me, full of his own cares and knowing nothing about my dreams. He found me stargazing on the roof.

"He wasn't a cruel man—he couldn't have understood the study and patience and care that had gone into my little telescope, or the wonders it had shown me during the short time I had used it. I don't hate him any more, but I'll remember all my life the splintering crack of my first and last mirror as it smashed against the brickwork."

There was nothing I could say. My initial resentment at this interruption had long since changed to curiosity. Already I sensed that there was much more to this story than I'd heard so far, and I'd noticed something else. The waitress was treating us with an exaggerated deference—only a little of which was directed at me.

My companion toyed with the sugar bowl while I waited in silent sympathy. By this time I felt there was some bond between us, though I did not know exactly what it was.

"I never built another telescope," he said. "Something else broke, besides that mirror—something in my heart. Anyway, I was much too busy. Two things happened that turned my life upside down. Dad walked out on us, leaving me the head of the family. And then they pulled down the Third Avenue El."

He must have seen my puzzled look, for he grinned across the table at me.

"Oh, you wouldn't know about that. But when I was a kid, there was an elevated railroad down the middle of Third. It made the whole area dirty and noisy; the Avenue was a slum district of bars, pawnshops, and cheap hotels—like ours. All that changed when the El went; land values shot up, and we were suddenly prosperous. Dad came back quickly enough, but it was too late; I was running the business. Before long I started moving across town—then across country. I wasn't an absent-minded stargazer any more, and I gave Dad one of my smaller hotels, where he couldn't do much harm.

"It's forty years since I looked at Saturn, but I've never forgotten that one glimpse, and last night your photographs brought it all back. I just wanted to say how grateful I am."

He fumbled in his wallet and pulled out a card.

"I hope you'll look me up when you're in town again; you can be sure I'll be there if you give any more lectures. Good luck—and I'm sorry to have taken so much of your time."

Then he was gone, almost before I could say a word. I glanced at the card, put it away in my pocket, and finished my breakfast, rather thoughtfully.

When I signed my check on the way out of the coffee shop I asked, "Who was that gentleman at my table? The boss?"

The cashier looked at me as if I were mentally retarded.

"I suppose you *could* call him that, sir," she answered. "Of course he owns this hotel, but we've never seen him here before. He always stays at the Ambassador, when he's in Chicago."

"And does he own *that?*" I said, without too much irony, for I'd already suspected the answer.

"Why, yes. As well as—" and she rattled off a whole string of others, including the two biggest hotels in New York.

I was impressed, and also rather amused, for it was now obvious that Mr. Perlman had come here with the deliberate intention of meeting me. It seemed a roundabout way of doing it; I knew nothing, then, of his notorious shyness and secretiveness. From the first, he was never shy with me.

Then I forgot about him for five years. (Oh, I should mention that when I asked for my bill, I was told I didn't have one.) During those five years, I made my second trip.

We knew what to expect this time, and weren't going completely into the unknown. There were no more worries about fuel, because all we could ever use was waiting for us on Titan; we just had to pump its methane atmosphere into our tanks, and we'd made our plans accordingly. One after another, we visited all the nine moons; and then we went into the rings.

There was little danger, yet it was a nerve-racking experience. The ring system is very thin, you know—only about twenty miles in thickness. We descended into it slowly and cautiously, after having matched its spin so that we were moving at exactly the same speed. It was like stepping onto a carousel 170,000 miles across.

But a ghostly kind of carousel, because the rings aren't solid and you can look right through them. Close up, in fact, they're almost invisible; the billions of separate particles that make them up are so widely spaced that all you see in your immediate neighborhood are occasional small chunks, drifting very slowly past. It's only when you look into the distance that the countless fragments merge into a continuous sheet, like a hailstorm that sweeps around Saturn forever.

That's not *my* phrase, but it's a good one. For when we brought our first piece of genuine Saturnian ring into the air lock, it melted down in a few minutes into a pool of muddy water. Some people think it spoils the magic to know that the rings—or ninety per cent of them—are made of ordinary ice. But that's a stupid attitude; they would be just as wonderful, and just as beautiful, if they were made of diamond.

When I got back to Earth, in the first year of the new century, I started off on another lecture tour—only a short one, for now I had a family and wanted to see as much of them as possible. This time I ran into Mr. Perlman in New York, when I was speaking at Columbia and showing our movie, "Exploring Saturn." (A misleading title that, since the nearest we'd been to the planet itself was about 20,000 miles. No one dreamed, in those days, that men would ever go down into the turbulent slush which is the closest thing Saturn has to a surface.)

Mr. Perlman was waiting for me after the lecture. I didn't recognize him, for I'd met about a million people since our last encounter. But when he gave his name, it all came back, so clearly that I realized he must have made a deep impression on my mind.

Somehow he got me away from the crowd; though he disliked meeting people in the mass, he had an extraordinary knack of dominating any group when he found it necessary— and then clearing out before his victims knew what had happened. Though I saw him in action scores of times, I never knew exactly how he did it.

At any rate, half an hour later we were having a superb dinner in an exclusive restaurant (his, of course). It was a wonderful meal, especially after the chicken and ice cream of the lecture circuit, but he made me pay for it. Metaphorically, I mean.

Now all the facts and photos gathered by the two expeditions to Saturn were available to everyone, in hundreds of reports and books and popular articles. Mr. Perlman seemed to have read all the material that wasn't too technical; what he wanted from me was something different. Even then, I put his interest down to that of a lonely, aging man, trying to recapture a dream that had been lost in youth. I was right; but that was only a fraction of the whole picture.

He was after something that all the reports and articles failed to give. What did it *feel* like, he wanted to know, to wake up in the morning and see that great, golden globe with its scudding cloud belts dominating the sky? And the rings themselves—what did they do to your mind when they were so close that they filled the heavens from end to end?

You want a poet, I said—not an engineer. But I'll tell you this; however long you look at Saturn, and fly in and out among its moons, you can never quite believe it. Every so often you find yourself thinking, It's all a dream—a thing like that *can't* be real. And you go to the nearest viewport—and there it is, taking your breath away.

You must remember that, altogether apart from our nearness, we were able to look at the rings from angles and vantage points that are quite impossible from Earth, where you always see them turned toward the sun. We could fly into their shadow, and then they would no longer gleam like silver—they would be a faint haze, a bridge of smoke across the stars.

And most of the time we could see the shadow of Saturn lying across the full width of the rings, eclipsing them so completely that it seemed as if a great bite had been taken out of them. It worked the other way, too; on the day side of the planet, there would always be the shadow of the rings running like a dusky band parallel to the Equator and not far from it.

Above all—though we did this only a few times—we could

rise high above either pole of the planet and look down upon the whole stupendous system, so that it was spread out in plan beneath us. Then we could see that instead of the four visible from Earth, there were at least a dozen separate rings, merging one into the other. When we saw this, our skipper made a remark that I've never forgotten. "This," he said—and there wasn't a trace of flippancy in the words—"is where the angels have parked their halos."

All this, and a lot more, I told Mr. Perlman in that little but oh-so-expensive restaurant just south of Central Park. When I'd finished, he seemed very pleased, though he was silent for several minutes. Then he said, about as casually as you might ask the time of the next train at your local station: "Which would be the best satellite for a tourist resort?"

When the words got through to me, I nearly choked on my hundred-year-old brandy. Then I said, very patiently and politely (for after all, I'd had a wonderful dinner), "Listen, Mr. Perlman. You know as well as I do that Saturn is nearly a billion miles from Earth—more than that, in fact, when we're on opposite sides of the sun. Someone worked out that our round-trip tickets averaged seven and a half million dollars apiece—and, believe me, there was no first-class accommodation on *Endeavour I* or *II.* Anyway, no matter how much money he had, no one could book a passage to Saturn. Only scientists and space crews will be going there, for as far ahead as anyone can imagine."

I could see that my words had absolutely no effect; he merely smiled, as if he knew some secret hidden from me.

"What you say is true enough *now,*" he answered, "but I've studied history. And I understand people—that's my business. Let me remind you of a few facts.

"Two or three centuries ago, almost all the world's great tourist centers and beauty spots were as far away from civilization as Saturn is today. What did—oh, Napoleon, let's say—know about the Grand Canyon, Victoria Falls, Hawaii, Mount Everest? And look at the South Pole; it was reached for the first time when my father was a boy—but there's been a hotel there for the whole of your lifetime.

"Now it's starting all over again. *You* can appreciate only the problems and difficulties, because you're too close to them. Whatever they are, men will overcome them, as they've always done in the past.

"For wherever there's something strange or beautiful or novel, people will want to see it. The rings of Saturn are the greatest spectacle in the known universe: I've always guessed so, and now you've convinced me. Today it takes a fortune to reach them, and the men who go there must risk their lives. So did the first men who flew—but now there are a million passengers in the air every second of the day and night.

"The same thing is going to happen in space. It won't happen in ten years, maybe not in twenty. But twenty-five is all it took, remember, before the first commercial flights started to the moon. I don't think it will be as long for Saturn.

"I won't be around to see it—but when it happens, I want people to remember me. So—where should we build?"

I still thought he was crazy, but at last I was beginning to understand what made him tick. And there was no harm in humoring him, so I gave the matter careful thought.

"Mimas is too close," I said, "and so are Enceladus and Tethys." (I don't mind telling you, those names were tough after all that brandy.) "Saturn just fills the sky, and you think it's falling on top of you. Besides, they aren't solid enough—they're nothing but overgrown snowballs. Dione and Rhea are better—you get a magnificent view from both of them. But all these inner moons are so tiny; even Rhea is only eight hundred miles across, and the others are much smaller.

"I don't think there's any real argument; it will have to be Titan. That's a man-sized satellite—it's a lot bigger than *our* moon, and very nearly as large as Mars. There's a reasonable gravity too—about a fifth of Earth's—so your guests won't be floating all over the place. And it will always be a major refueling point because of its methane atmosphere, which should be an important factor in your calculations. Every ship that goes out to Saturn will touch down there."

"And the outer moons?"

"Oh, Hyperion, Japetus, and Phoebe are much too far away. You have to look hard to see the rings at all from Phoebe! Forget about them. Stick to good old Titan. Even if the temperature is two hundred below zero, and ammonia snow isn't the sort of stuff you'd want to ski on."

He listened to me very carefully, and if he thought I was making fun of his impractical, unscientific notions he gave no sign of it. We parted soon afterward—I don't remember anything more of that dinner—and then it must have been fifteen years before we met again. He had no further use for me in all that time; but when he wanted me, he called.

I see now what he had been waiting for; his vision had been clearer than mine. He couldn't have guessed, of course, that the rocket would go the way of the steam engine within less than a century—but he knew *something* better would come along, and I think he financed Saunderson's early work on the Paragravity Drive. But it was not until they started building fusion plants that could warm up a hundred square miles of a world as cold as Pluto that he got in contact with me again.

He was a very old man, and dying. They told me how rich he was, and I could hardly believe it. Not until he showed me the elaborate plans and the beautiful models his experts had prepared with such remarkable lack of publicity.

He sat in his wheelchair like a wrinkled mummy, watching my face as I studied the models and blueprints. Then he said, "Captain, I have a job for you. . . ."

So here I am. It's just like running a spaceship, of course—many of the technical problems are identical. And by this time I'd be too old to command a ship, so I'm very grateful to Mr. Perlman.

There goes the gong. If the ladies are ready, I suggest we walk down to dinner through the Observation Lounge.

Even after all these years, I still like to watch Saturn rising—and tonight it's almost full.

URANUS

Uranus is the first planet to have been discovered in modern times. William Herschel spotted it in 1781 and promptly became the most famous astronomer in the world.

Uranus, like Jupiter and Saturn, is a "gas giant," but it is distinctly smaller than the other two. The diameter of Uranus is 45,000 kilometers (29,000 miles) which is only one third that of Jupiter. Its surface area is only one-tenth that of Jupiter and its volume is only one-thirtieth that of Jupiter. (Lest we lose our sense of proportion, however, Uranus is still large in comparison to Earth. It has 47 times the volume of Earth.)

Uranus has a system of five satellites, but none of them is really large.

One real curiosity about the planet is that the axis of rotation is tipped much more than that of Earth or Mars, for instance. It is tilted 97.9°, or slightly more than a right angle. This means that Uranus rotates on its side, so to speak. Its satellites remain in the equatorial plane of Uranus, so instead of moving right and left with respect to the Sun, they move up and down.

No one knows just why Uranus is tipped to this extent.

This is virtually all we know about Uranus almost to the present day. It is, after all, at an average distance of 2872 million kilometers (1782 million miles) from the Sun. It is twice as far from the Sun as Saturn is, four times as far as Jupiter is. It is quite small and dim in our telescopes compared to Jupiter and Saturn, and there is little to be made out.

What we do know today about the planet is accurately portrayed in "The Snowbank Orbit"—which was first published in 1962—with one exception.

Even without the help of a probe, the 1970s sprang a breathtaking surprise on astronomers.

In 1973, astronomical calculations showed that Uranus would move in front of a certain 9th magnitude star on March 10, 1977. On that day, James L. Elliot and associates from Cornell University observed the occultation from an airplane that took them high enough to minimize the distorting and obscuring effects of the lower atmosphere.

The notion was to observe just how the starlight was affected as Uranus reached the star and began to encroach upon it. The starlight would penetrate Uranus's upper atmosphere and would, in this way, yield information about its atmospheric temperature, pressure, and composition.

But some time before Uranus reached the star, the starlight suddenly dimmed for about seven seconds and brightened. Then, as Uranus approached still closer, there were several more brief episodes of dimming, for a second each. Uranus eventually passed in front of the star, and as the planet moved away on the other side there was the same dimming of starlight in reverse.

Something in Uranus's vicinity was obscuring the star. It could not be an ordinary set of satellites. With so many dimmings on both sides of the planet, it had to be a ring system. Uranus has a series of thin rings, one inside the other; the total number is now thought to be nine.

Why did it take so long to discover them? The Uranian rings are very narrow and very sparsely populated; much narrower and much more sparsely populated than Saturn's rings are. In addition, Uranus's rings are twice as far away from the Sun and from us. The light reflected from Uranus's rings is weakened by distance sixteen times as much as the light reflected from Saturn's rings.

Finally, whereas the material making up Saturn's rings is icy and reflects a great deal of light, the material making up Uranus's rings is dark, and reflects very little.

All told, Uranus's rings may reflect as little as 1/3,000,000 as much light as Saturn's rings do, so it is no wonder that it took so long to detect them.

Still, from this point on, no science fiction story dealing with Uranus can fail to mention the rings.

The Snowbank Orbit

FRITZ LEIBER

The pole stars of the other planets cluster around Polaris and Octans, but Uranus spins on a snobbishly different axis between Aldebaran and Antares. The Bull is her coronet and the Scorpion her footstool. Dear blowzy old bitch-planet, swollen and pale and cold, mad with your Shakespearean moons, white-mottled as death from Venerean Plague, spinning on your side like a poisoned pregnant cockroach, rolling around the sun like a fat drunken floozie with green hair rolling on the black floor of an infinite barroom, what a sweet last view of the Solar System you are for a cleancut young spaceman. . . .

Grunfeld chopped that train of thought short. He was young, and the First Interstellar War had snatched him up and now it was going to pitch him and twenty other Joes out of the System on a fast curve breaking around Uranus—and so what! He shivered to get a little heat and then applied himself to the occulted star he was tracking through *Prospero*'s bridge telescope. The star was a twentieth planetary diameter into Uranus, the crosslines showed—a glint almost lost in pale green. That meant its light was bulleting 1600 miles deep through the seventh planet's thick hydrogen atmosphere, unless he were seeing the star on a mirage trajectory—and at least its depth agreed with the time since rim contact.

At 2000 miles he lost it. That should mean 2000 miles plus

of hydrogen soup above the methane ocean, an America-wide layer of gaseous gunk for the captain to play the mad hero in with the fleet.

Grunfeld didn't think the captain wanted to play the mad hero. The captain hadn't gone space-simple in any obvious way like Croker and Ness. And he wasn't, like Jackson, a telepathy-racked visionary entranced by the Enemy. Worry and responsibility had turned the captain's face into a skull which floated in Grunfeld's imagination when he wasn't actually seeing it, but the tired eyes deep-sunk in the dark sockets were still cool and perhaps sane. But because of the worry the captain always wanted to have the last bit of fact bearing on the least likely maneuver, and two pieces of evidence were better than one. Grunfeld found the next sizable star due to occult. Five-six minutes to rim contact. He floated back a foot from the telescope, stretching out his thin body in the plane of the ecliptic—strange how he automatically assumed that orientation in free fall! He blinked and blinked, then rested his eyes on the same planet he'd been straining them on.

The pale greenish bulk of Uranus was centered in the big bridge spaceshield against the black velvet dark and bayonet-bright stars, a water-splotched and faded chartreuse tennis ball on the diamond-spiked bed of night. At eight million miles she looked half the width of Luna seen from Earth. Her whitish equatorial bands went from bottom to top, where Grunfeld knew, they were spinning out of sight at three miles a second—a gelid waterfall that he imagined tugging at him with ghostly green gangrenous fingers and pulling him over into a hydrogen Niagara.

Half as wide as Luna. But in a day she'd overflow the port as they whipped past her on a new miss and in another day she'd be as small as this again, but behind them, sunward having altered their outward course by some small and as yet unpredictable angle, but no more able to slow *Prospero* and her sister ships or turn them back at their 100 miles a second than the fleet's solar jets could operate at this chilly distance from Sol. G'by, fleet. G'by, C.C.Y. spaceman.

Grunfeld looked for the pale planet's moons. Miranda and Umbriel were too tiny to make disks, but he distinguished Ariel four diameters above the planet and Oberon a dozen below. Spectral sequins. If the fleet were going to get a radio signal from any of them, it would have to be Titania, occulted now by the planet and the noisy natural static of her roiling hydrogen air and seething methane seas—but it had always been only a faint hope that there were survivors from the First Uranus Expedition.

Grunfeld relaxed his neck and let his gaze drift down across the curving star-bordered forward edge of *Prospero*'s huge mirror and the thin jutting beams of the pot lattice arm to the dim red-lit gauges below the spaceshield.

Forward Skin Temperature seven degrees Kelvin. Almost low enough for helium to crawl, if you had some helium. *Prospero*'s insulation, originally designed to hold out solar heat, was doing a fair job in reverse.

Aft (sunward) Skin Temperature 75 degrees Kelvin. Close to that of Uranus' sunlit face. Check.

Cabin Temperature 43 degrees Fahrenheit. Brr! The captain was a miser with the chem fuel remaining. And rightly . . . if it were right to drag out life as long as possible in the empty icebox beyond Uranus.

Gravities of Acceleration zero. Many other zeros.

The four telltales for the fleet unblinkingly glowed dimmest blue—one each for *Caliban, Snug, Moth,* and *Starveling,* following *Prospero* in the astern on slave automatic—though for months inertia had done all five ships' piloting. Once the buttons had been green, but they'd wiped that color off the boards because of the Enemy.

The gauges still showed their last maximums. Skin 793 Kelvin, Cabin 144 Fahrenheit, Gravs 3.2. All of them hit almost a year ago, when they'd been acing past the sun. Grunfeld's gaze edged back to the five bulbous pressure suits, once more rigidly upright in their braced racks, that they'd been wearing during that stretch of acceleration inside the orbit of Mercury. He started. For a moment he'd thought he saw the dark-circled eyes of the captain peering between two of the bulging black suits. Nerves! The captain had to be in his cabin, readying alternate piloting programs for Copperhead.

Suddenly Grunfeld jerked his face back toward the spaceshield—so violently that his body began very slowly to spin in the opposite direction. This time he'd thought he saw the Enemy's green flashing near the margin of the planet—bright green, viridian, far vivider than that of Uranus herself. He drew himself to the telescope and feverishly studied the area. Nothing at all. Nerves again. If the Enemy were much nearer than a light-minute, Jackson would esp it and give warning. The next star was still three minutes from rim contact. Grunfeld's mind retreated to the circumstances that had brought *Prospero* (then only *Mercury One*) out here.

II

When the First Interstellar War erupted, the pioneer fleets of Earth's nations had barely pushed their explorations beyond the orbit of Saturn. Except for the vessels of the International Meteor Guard, spaceflight was still a military enterprise of America, Russia, England, and the other megapowers.

During the first months the advantage lay wholly with the slim black cruisers of the Enemy, who had an antigravity which allowed them to hover near planets without going into orbit; and a frightening degree of control over light itself. Indeed, their principal weapon was a tight beam of visible light, a dense photonic stiletto with an effective range of several Jupiter-diameters in vacuum. They also used visible light, in the green band, for communication as men use radio, sometimes broadcasting it and sometimes beaming it loosely in strange abstract pictures that seemed part of their language. Their gravity-immune ships moved by reaction to photonic jets the tightness of which rendered them invisible except near the sun, where they tended to ionize electronically dirty volumes of space. It was probably this effective invisibility, based on light control, which allowed them to penetrate the Solar System as deep as Earth's orbit undetected, rather than any power of travel in time or subspace, as was first assumed. Earthmen could only guess at the physical appearance of the Enemy, since no prisoners were taken on either side.

Despite his impressive maneuverability and armament, the Enemy was oddly timid about attacking live planets. He showed no fear of the big gas planets, in fact hovering very close to their turgid surfaces, as if having some way of fueling from them.

Near Terra the first tactic of the black cruisers, after destroying Lunostrovok and Circumluna, was to hover behind the moon, as though sharing its tide-lockedness—a circumstance that led to a sortie by Earth's Combined Fleet, England and Sweden excepted.

At the wholly disastrous Battle of the Far Side, which was visible in part to naked-eye viewers on Earth, the Combined Fleet was annihilated. No Enemy ship was captured, boarded, or seriously damaged—except for one which, apparently by a fluke, was struck by a fission-headed antimissile and proceeded after the blast to "burn," meaning that it suffered a slow and puzzling disintegration, accompanied by a dazzling rainbow display of visible radiation. This was before the "stupidity" of the Enemy with regard to small atomic missiles was noted, or their allergy to certain radio wave bands, and also before Terran telepaths began to claim cloudy contact with Enemy minds.

Following Far Side, the Enemy burst into activity, harrying Terran spacecraft as far as Mercury and Saturn, though still showing great caution in maneuver and making no direct attacks on planets. It was as if a race of heavily armed marine creatures should sink all ocean-going ships or drive them to harbor, but make no assaults beyond the shore line. For a full year Earth, though her groundside and satellite rocket-yards were furiously busy, had no vehicle in deep space—with one exception.

At the onset of the War a fleet of five mobile bases of the U.S. Space Force were in Orbit to Mercury, where it was intended they take up satellite positions prior to the prospecting and mineral exploitation of the small sun-blasted planet. These five ships, each with a skeleton five-man crew, were essentially Ross-Smith space stations with a solar drive, assembled in space and intended solely for space-to-space flight inside Earth's orbit. A huge paraboloid mirror, its diameter four times the length of the ship's hull, superheated at its focus the hydrogen which was ejected as a plasma at high exhaust velocity. Each ship likewise mounted versatile radio-radar equipment on dual lattice arms and carried as ship's launch a two-man chemical fuel rocket adaptable as a fusion-headed torpedo.

After Far Side, this "tin can" fleet was ordered to bypass Mercury and, tacking on the sun, shape an orbit for Uranus, chiefly because that remote planet, making its 84-year circuit of Sol, was currently on the opposite side of the sun to the four inner planets and the two nearer gas giants Jupiter and Saturn. In the empty regions of space the relatively defenseless fleet might escape the attention of the Enemy.

However, while still accelerating into the sun for maximum boost, the fleet received information that two Enemy cruisers were in pursuit. The five ships cracked on all possible speed, drawing on the solar drive's high efficiency near the sun and expending all their hydrogen and most material capable of being vaporized, including some of the light-metal hydrogen storage tanks—like an old steamer burning her cabin furniture and the cabins themselves to win a race. Gradually the curving course that would have taken years to reach the outer planet flattened into a hyperbola that would make the journey in 200 days.

In the asteroid belt the pursuing cruisers turned aside to join in the crucial Battle of the Trojans with Earth's largely new-built, more heavily and wisely armed Combined Fleet— a battle that proved to be only a prelude to the decisive Battle of Jupiter.

Meanwhile the five-ship fleet sped onward, its solar drive quite useless in this twilight region even if it could have scraped together the needed boilable ejectant mass to slow its flight. Weeks became months. The ships were renamed for the planet they were aimed at. At least the fleet's trajectory had been truly set.

Almost on collision course it neared Uranus, a mystery-cored ball of frigid gas 32,000 miles wide coasting through space across the fleet's course at a lazy four miles a second. At this time the fleet was traveling at 100 miles a second. Beyond Uranus lay only the interstellar night, into which the fleet would inevitably vanish.

Unless, Grunfeld told himself . . . unless the fleet shed its velocity by ramming the gaseous bulk of Uranus. This idea of atmospheric braking on a grand scale had sounded possible at first suggestion, half a year ago—a little like a man falling off a mountain or from a plane and saving his life by dropping into a great thickness of feathery new-fallen snow.

Supposing her solar jet worked out here and she had the reaction mass, *Prospero* could have shed her present velocity in five hours, decelerating at a comfortable one G.

But allowing her 12,000 miles of straight-line travel through Uranus' frigid soupy atmosphere—and that might be dipping very close to the methane seas blanketing the planet's hypothetical mineral core—*Prospero* would have two minutes in which to shed her velocity.

Two minutes—at 150 Gs.

Men had stood 40 and 50 Gs for a fractional second.

But for two minutes . . . Grunfeld told himself that the only surer way to die would be to run into a section of the Enemy fleet. According to one calculation the ship's skin would melt by heat of friction in 90 seconds, despite the low temperature of the abrading atmosphere.

The star Grunfeld had been waiting for touched the hazy rim of Uranus. He drifted back to the eyepiece and began to follow it in as the pale planet's hydrogen muted its diamond brilliance.

III

In the aft cabin, lank hairy-wristed Croker pinned another blanket around black Jackson as the latter shivered in his trance. Then Croker turned on a small light at the head of the hammock.

"Captain won't like that," plump, pale Ness observed tranquilly from where he floated in womb position across the cabin. "Enemy can feel a candle of *our* light, captain says, ten million miles away." He rocked his elbows for warmth and his body wobbled in reaction like a pollywog's.

"And Jackson hears the Enemy think ... and Heimdall hears the grass grow," Croker commented with a harsh manic laugh. "Isn't an Enemy for a billion miles, Ness." He launched aft from the hammock. "We haven't spotted their green since Saturn orbit. There's nowhere for them."

"There's the far side of Uranus," Ness pointed out. "That's less than ten million miles now. Eight. A bare day. They could be there."

"Yes, waiting to bushwack us as we whip past on our way to eternity," Croker chuckled as he crumpled up against the aft port, shedding momentum. "That's likely, isn't it, when they didn't have time for us back in the Belt?" He scowled at the tiny white sun, no bigger a disk than Venus, but still with one hundred times as much light as the full moon pouring from it—too much light to look at comfortably. He began to button the inner cover over the port.

"Don't do that," Ness objected without conviction.

"There's not much heat in it but there's some." He hugged his elbows and shivered. "I don't remember being warm since Mars orbit."

"The sun gets on my nerves," Croker said. "It's like looking at an arc light through a pinhole. It's like a high, high jail light in a cold concrete yard. The stars are highlights on the barbed wire." He continued to button out the sun.

"You ever in jail?" Ness asked. Croker grinned.

With the tropism of a fish, Ness began to paddle toward the little light at the head of Jackson's hammock, flicking his hands from the wrists like flippers. "I got one thing against the sun," he said quietly. "It's blanketing out the radio. I'd like us to get one more message from Earth. We haven't tried rigging our mirror to catch radio waves. I'd like to hear how we won the battle of Jupiter."

"If we won it," Croker said.

"Our telescopes show no more green around Jove," Ness reminded him. "We counted 27 rainbows on Enemy cruisers 'burning.' Captain verified the count."

"Repeat: if we won it." Croker pushed off and drifted back toward the hammock. "If there was a real victory message they'd push it through, even if the sun's in the way and it takes three hours to catch us. People who win, shout."

Ness shrugged as he paddled. "One way or the other, we should be getting the news soon from Titania station," he said. "They'll have heard."

"If they're still alive and there ever was a Titania Station," Croker amended, backing air violently to stop himself as he neared the hammock. "Look, Ness, we know that the First Uranus Expedition arrived. At least they set off their flares. But that was three years before the War and we haven't any idea of what's happened to them since and if they ever managed to set up housekeeping on Titania—or Ariel or Oberon or even Miranda or Umbriel. At least if they built a station could raise Earth I haven't been told. Sure thing *Prospero* hasn't heard anything . . . and we're getting close."

"I won't argue," Ness said. "Even if we raise 'em, it'll just be hello-goodby with maybe time between for a battle report."

"And a football score and a short letter from home, ten seconds per man as the station fades." Croker frowned and added, "If Captain had cottoned to my idea, two of us at any rate could have got off this express train at Uranus."

"Tell me how," Ness asked drily.

"How? Why, one of the ship's launches. Replace the fusion-head with the cabin. Put all the chem fuel in the tanks instead of divvying it between the ship and the launch."

"I haven't got the brain for math Copperhead has, but I can subtract," Ness said, referring to *Prospero*'s piloting robot. "Fully fueled, one of the launches has a max velocity change in free-fall of 30 miles per second. Use it all in braking and you've only taken 30 from 100. The launch is still going past Uranus and out of the system at 70 miles a second."

"You didn't hear all my idea," Croker said. "You put piggyback tanks on your launch and top them off with the fuel from the other four launches. Then you've 100 miles of braking *and* a maneuvering reserve. You only need to shed 90 miles, anyway. Ten miles a second's the close circum-Uranian velocity. Go into circum-Uranian orbit and wait for Titania to send their jeep to pick you up. Have to start the maneuver four hours this side of Uranus, though. Take that long at 1 G to shed it."

"Cute," Ness conceded. "Especially the jeep. But I'm glad just the same we've got 70 per cent of our chem fuel in our ships' tanks instead of the launches. We're on such a bull's-eye course for Uranus—Copperhead really pulled a miracle plotting our orbit—that we may need a sidewise shove to miss her. If we slapped into that cold hydrogen soup at our 100 mps—"

Croker shrugged. "We still could have dropped a couple of us," he said.

"Captain's got to look after the whole fleet," Ness said.

"You're beginning to agitate, Croker, like you was Grunfeld—or the captain himself."

"But if Titania Station's alive, a couple of men dropped off would do the fleet some good. Stir Titania up to punch a message through to Earth and get a really high-speed retrieve-and-rescue ship started out after us. *If* we've won the War."

"But Titania Station's dead or never was, not to mention its jeep. And we've lost the Battle of Jupiter. You said so yourself," Ness asserted owlishly. "Captain's got to look after the whole fleet."

"Yeah, so he kills himself fretting and the rest of us die of old age in the outskirts of the Solar System. Join the Space Force and See the Stars! Ness, do you know how long it'd take us to reach the nearest star—except we aren't headed for her—at our 100 mps? Eight thousand years!"

"That's a lot of time to kill," Ness said. "Let's play chess."

Jackson sighed and they both looked quickly at the dark unlined face above the cocoon, but the lips did not flutter again, or the eyelids. Croker said, "Suppose he knows what the Enemy looks like?"

"I suppose," Ness said. "When he talks about them it's as if he was their interpreter. How about the chess?"

"Suits. Knight to King Bishop Three."

"Hmm. Knight to King Knight Two, Third Floor."

"Hey, I meant flat chess, not three-D," Croker objected.

"That thin old game? Why, I no sooner start to get the position really visualized in my head than the game's over."

"I don't want to start a game of three-D with Uranus only eighteen hours away."

Jackson stirred in his hammock. His lips worked. "They ..." he breathed. Croker and Ness instantly watched him. "They ..."

"I wonder if he is really inside the Enemy's mind?" Ness said.

"He thinks he speaks for them," Croker replied and the

next instant felt a warning touch on his arm and looked sideways and saw dark-circled eyes in a skull-angular face under a battered cap with a tarnished sunburst. Damn, thought Croker, how does the captain always know when Jackson's going to talk?"

"They are waiting for us on the other side of Uranus," Jackson breathed. His lips trembled into a smile and his voice grew a little louder, though his eyes stayed shut. "They're welcoming us, they're our brothers." The smile died. "But they know they got to kill us, they know we got to die."

The hammock with its tight-swathed form began to move past Croker and he snatched at it. The captain had pushed off from him for the hatch leading forward.

Grunfeld was losing the new star at 2200 miles into Uranus when he saw the two viridian flares flashing between it and the rim. Each flash was circled by a fleeting bright green ring, like a mist halo. He thought he'd be afraid when he saw that green again, but what he felt was a jolt of excitement that made him grin. With it came a touch on his shoulder. He thought, The captain always knows.

"Ambush," he said. "At least two cruisers."

He yielded the eyepiece to the captain. Even without the telescope he could see those incredibly brilliant green flickers. He asked himself if the Enemy was already gunning for the fleet through Uranus.

The blue telltales for *Caliban* and *Starveling* began to blink.

"They've seen it too," the captain said. He snatched up the mike and his next words rang through the *Prospero*.

"Rig ship for the snowbank orbit! Snowbank orbit with stinger! Mr. Grunfeld, raise the fleet."

Aft, Croker muttered, "Rig our shrouds, don't he mean? Rig shrouds and firecrackers mounted on Fourth of July rockets."

Ness said, "Cheer up. Even the longest strategic withdrawal in history has to end some time."

IV

Three quarters of a day later Grunfeld felt a spasm of futile fear and revolt as the pressure suit closed like a thick-fleshed carnivorous plant on his drugged and tired body. Relax, he told himself. Fine thing if you cooked up a fuss when even Croker didn't. He thought of forty things to recheck. Relax, he repeated—the work's over; all that matters is in Copperhead's memory tanks now, or will be as soon as the captain's suited up.

The suit held Grunfeld erect, his arms at his sides—the best attitude, except he was still facing forward, for taking high G, providing the ship herself didn't start to tumble. Only the cheekpieces and visor hadn't closed in on his face—translucent hand-thick petals as yet unfolded. He felt the delicate firm pressure of built-in fingertips monitoring his pulses and against his buttocks the cold smooth muzzles of the jet hypodermics that would feed him metronomic drugs during the high-G stretch and stimulants when they were in free-fall again. When.

He could swing his head and eyes just enough to make out the suits of Croker and Ness to either side of him and their profiles wavy through the jutting misty cheekpieces. Ahead to the left was Jackson—just the back of his suit, like a black snowman standing at attention, pale-olive-edged by the great glow of Uranus. And to the right the captain, his legs suited but his upper body still bent out to the side as he checked the monitor of his suit with its glowing blue button and the manual controls that would lie under his hands during the maneuver.

Beyond the captain was the spaceshield, the lower quarter of it still blackness and stars, but the upper three-quarters filled with the onrushing planet's pale mottled green that now had the dulled richness of watered silk. They were so close that the rim hardly showed curvature. The atmosphere must have a steep gradient, Grunfeld thought, or they'd already be feeling decel. That stuff ahead looked more like water than any kind of air. It bothered him that the captain was still half out of his suit.

There should be action and shouted commands, Grunfeld thought, to fill up these last tight-stretched minutes. Last orders to the fleet, port covers being cranked shut, someone doing a countdown on the firing of their torpedo. But the last message had gone to the fleet minutes ago. Its robot pilots were set to follow *Prospero* and imitate, nothing else. And all the rest was up to Copperhead. Still . . .

Grunfeld wet his lips. "Captain," he said hesitantly. "Captain?"

"Thank you, Grunfeld." He caught the edge of the skull's answering grin. "We are beginning to hit hydrogen," the quiet voice went on. "Forward skin temperature's up to 9 K."

Beyond the friendly skull, a great patch of the rim of Uranus flared bright green. As if that final stimulus had been needed, Jackson began to talk dreamily from his suit.

"They're still welcoming us and grieving for us. I begin to get it a little more now. Their ship's one thing and they're another. Their ship is frightened to death of us. It hates us and the only thing it knows to do is to kill us. They can't stop it, they're even less than passengers . . ."

The captain was in his suit now. Grunfeld sensed a faint throbbing and felt a rush of cold air. The cabin refrigeration system had started up, carrying cabin heat to the lattice arms. Intended to protect them from solar heat, it would now do what it could against the heat of friction.

The straight edge of Uranus was getting hazier. Even the fainter stars shone through, spangling it. A bell jangled and the pale green segment narrowed as the steel meteor panels began to close in front of the spaceshield. Soon there was only a narrow vertical ribbon of green—*bright* green as it narrowed to a thread—then for a few seconds only blackness except for the dim red and blue beads and semicircles, just beyond the captain, of the board. Then the muted interior cabin lights glowed on.

Jackson droned: "They and their ships come from very far away, from the edge. If this is the continuum, they come from the . . . discontinuum, where they don't have stars but something else and where gravity is different. Their ships came from the edge on a gust of fear with the other ships, and our brothers came with it though they didn't want to . . ."

And now Grunfeld thought he began to feel it—the first faint thrill, less than a cobweb's tug, of *weight*.

The cabin wall moved sideways. Grunfeld's suit had begun to revolve slowly on a vertical axis.

For a moment he glimpsed Jackson's dark profile—all five suits were revolving in their framework. They locked into position when the men in them were facing aft. Now at least retinas wouldn't pull forward at high-G decel, or spines crush through thorax and abdomen.

The cabin air was cold on Grunfeld's forehead. And now he was sure he felt weight—maybe five pounds of it. Suddenly aft was *up*. It was as if he were lying on his back on the spaceshield.

A sudden snarling roar came through his suit from the beams bracing it. He lost weight, then regained it and a little more besides. He realized it was their torpedo taking off, to skim by Uranus in the top of the atmosphere and then curve inward the little their chem fuel would let them, homing toward the Enemy. He imaged its tiny red jet over the great gray-green glowing plain. Four more would be taking off from the other ships—the fleet's feeble sting. Like a bee's, just one, in dying.

The cheekpieces and foreheadpiece of Grunfeld's suit began to close on his face like layers of pliable ice.

Jackson called faintly, "*Now* I understand. Their ship—" His voice was cut off.

Grunfeld's ice-mask was tight shut. He felt a small surge of vigor as the suit took over his breathing and sent his lungs a gush of high-oxy air. Then came a tingling numbness as the suit field went on, adding an extra prop against decel to each molecule of his body.

But the weight was growing. He was on the moon now . . . now on Mars . . . now back on Earth . . .

The weight was stifling now, crushing—a hill of invisible sand. Grunfeld saw a black pillow hanging in the cabin above him aft. It had red fringe around it. It grew.

There was a whistling and shaking. Everything lurched torturingly, the ship's jets roared, everything recovered, or didn't.

The black pillow came down on him, crushing out sight, crushing out thought.

The universe was a black tingling, a limitless ache floating in a large black infinity. Something drew back and there was a dry fiery wind on numb humps and ridges—the cabin air on his face, Grunfeld decided, then shivered and started at the thought that he was alive and in free-fall. His body didn't feel like a mass of internal hemorrhages. Or did it?

He spun slowly. It stopped. Dizziness? Or the suits revolving forward again? If they'd actually come through—

There was a creaking and cracking. The ship contracting after frictional heating?

There was a faint stink like ammonia and formaldehyde mixed. A few Uranian molecules forced past plates racked by turbulence?

He saw dim red specks. The board? Or last flickers from ruined retinas? A bell jangled. He waited, but he saw nothing. Blind? Or the meteor guard jammed? No wonder if it were. No wonder if the cabin lights were broken.

The hot air that had dried his sweaty face rushed down the front of his body. Needles of pain pierced him as he slumped forward out of the top of his opening suit.

Then he saw the horizontal band of stars outlining the top of the spaceshield and below it the great field of inky black, barely convex upward. *That must*, he realized, *be the dark side of Uranus.*

Pain ignored, Grunfeld pushed himself forward out of his suit and pulled himself past the captain's to the spaceshield.

The view stayed the same, though broadening out: stars above, a curve-edged velvet black plain below. They were orbiting.

A pulsing, color-changing glow from somewhere showed him twisted stumps of the radio lattices. There was no sign of the mirror at all. It must have been torn away, or vaporized completely, in the fiery turbulence of decel.

New Maxs showed on the board: Cabin Temperature 214, F, Skin Temperature 907 K. Gravs 87.

Then in the top of the spacefield, almost out of vision, Grunfeld saw the source of the pulsing glow: two sharp-ended ovals flickering brightly all colors against the pale starfields, like the dead fish phosphorescing.

"The torps got to 'em," Croker said, pushed forward beside Grunfeld to the right.

"I did find out at the end," Jackson said quietly from the left, his voice at last free of the trance tone. "The Enemy ships weren't ships at all. They were (there's no other word for it) space animals. We've always thought life was a prerogative of planets, that space was inorganic. But you can walk miles through the desert or sail leagues through the sea before you notice life and I guess space is the same. Anyway the Enemy was (what else can I call 'em?) space whales. Inertialess space whales from the discontinuum. Space whales that ate hydrogen (that's the only way I know to say it) and spat light to move and fight. The ones I talked to, our brothers, were just their parasites."

"That's crazy," Grunfeld said. "All of it. A child's picture."

"Sure it is," Jackson agreed.

From beyond Jackson, Ness, punching buttons, said, "Quiet."

The radio came on thin and wailing with static: "Titania Station calling fleet. We have jeep and can orbit in to you. The *two* Enemy are dead—the last in the System. Titania Station calling fleet. We have jeep fueled and set to go—"

Fleet? thought Grunfeld. He turned back to the board. The first and last blue telltales still glowed for *Caliban* and *Starveling*. Breathe a prayer, he thought, for *Moth* and *Snug*.

Something else shone on the board, something Grunfeld knew had to be wrong. Three little words: SHIP ON MANUAL.

The black rim of Uranus ahead suddenly brightened along its length, which was very slightly bowed, like a section of a giant new moon. A bead formed toward the center, brightened, and then all at once the jailyard sun had risen and was glaring coldly through its pinhole into their eyes.

They looked away from it. Grunfeld turned around.

The austere light showed the captain still in his pressure suit, only the head fallen out forward, hiding the skull features. Studying the monitor box of the captain's suit, Grunfeld saw it was set to inject the captain with power stimulants as soon as the Gravs began to slacken from their max.

He realized who had done the impossible job of piloting them out of Uranus.

But the button on the monitor, that should have glowed blue, was as dark as those of *Moth* and *Snug*.

Grunfeld thought, Now he can rest.

NEPTUNE

The discovery of Neptune is one of the great dramatic stories of science. Once Uranus was discovered, its orbit was calculated, and it was expected that Uranus would follow that orbit. It would have to if Newton's law of gravitation was correct, and astronomers were sure it was.

Uranus did *not* follow the orbit, however, but deviated very slightly. One possibility was that there was an unknown planet beyond Uranus whose gravitational attraction was not taken into account in calculating Uranus's orbit. Two astronomers, John Couch Adams and Urbain J. J. Leverrier, independently calculated where the unknown planet ought to be in the sky if it were to have the proper effect on Uranus.

The spot was observed and the planet was found and named "Neptune."

Neptune is virtually Uranus's twin except for being considerably farther from the Sun. Neptune is, on the average, 4501 million kilometers (2792 million miles) from the Sun, or 1.6 times as far from the Sun as Uranus is. It is just a shade smaller than Uranus, and has a volume only 0.91 times that of Uranus. It is, however, distinctly denser than Uranus is, so that Neptune is 1 1/6 times as massive as Uranus. Neptune is the third most massive planet.

It may be, judging from Neptune's density, that it is the least gassy of the four "gas giants" and that it has a sizable rocky core. We can only guess; we don't know. In fact, we know very little about the planet other than the facts I've just stated. It is a small, dim, and featureless globe even in large telescopes, and we will have to wait for probes to learn more. Nor have we made any startling discoveries from our Earth-based studies comparable to those of the rings of Uranus.

Neptune has two satellites, one of them a large one, Triton, and the other one, Nereid, a small one with a very eccentric orbit. Nereid seems surely to be a captured asteroid, which indicates that, even as far from the Sun as Neptune is, there are asteroids to be found and captured. (Saturn's outermost satellite, Phoebe, is also very likely a captured asteroid, as are Jupiter's eight outermost satellites.)

The picture of Neptune in "One Sunday in Neptune" is in accord with what we know today; it was first published in 1969.

However, since it was written before the first landings on the Moon, it is a little too sanguine about the occurrence of life in the Solar system. We already know, for instance, that life does not exist on the Moon and Venus, and very likely doesn't on Mars.

One Sunday in Neptune

ALEXEI PANSHIN

Ben Wiseman and I were the first people to land on Neptune, but he doesn't talk to me anymore. He thinks I betrayed him.

The assignment to Triton Base, an opportunity for me, was for him simply one final dead end. I couldn't yet see the limits of my life, but he could see the limits of his. His life was thin, and he had a hunger for recognition.

He was a man of sudden enthusiasm, haphazardly produced. He knew next to nothing about biology, but having a great deal of time to stare at the green bulk of Neptune in our sky, he had conceived the idea that there was life on the planet, and he had become convinced that if he proved it he would have the automatic security of a place in the reference library. His theory was lent a certain force by the fact that we had found life already on our own Moon, on Venus and Mars, on Jupiter, Saturn and Uranus, and even on Ganymede. Not on Mercury—too small, too close, too hot. Not on Pluto—too small, too far, too cold. But the odds seemed good to him, and the list of names he would join short enough to give him the feeling of being distinguished.

"Life is insistent," Ben said. "Life is persistent."

He approached me because he had no one else. He was an extremely difficult man. At the age of thirty-five, he still hadn't discovered the basic principles of social dealing. On first acquaintance he was too close too quickly. Then he took anything less than total reciprocation as betrayal. The more favorable your initial response to him, the greater wound he felt when he was inevitably betrayed. He had no friends, of course.

I betrayed him early in our acquaintance, something I was unaware of until he told me. After that he was always stiff and generally guarded, but since he found me no worse than the general run of humanity, and since the company on Triton numbered only twenty, he used me to talk to. I was willing to talk to him, and in this case I was willing to listen.

Triton, Neptune's major satellite, is a good substantial base. It comes close to being the largest moon in the Solar System, and it is two fingers larger than Mercury. It's the last comfortable footing for men in the Solar System, and the obvious site for a major base.

With Operation Springboard complete and our first starship on its way to a new green and pleasant land, major activity had ceased at Triton Base. We twenty were there to maintain and monitor. Some of us, like me, were there because we were bright young men with futures. Some, like Ben Wiseman, were there because no one else would have them.

But in general life was a bore. Maintenance is a bore. Monitoring is a bore. Even the skies are dull. Neptune is there, big and green. Uranus can be found if you look for it. But the Sun is only a distant candle flame flickering palely in the night and the inner planets are impossible to see. You feel very alone out there.

I was interested in Ben's suggestion. Mike Marshall, our leader, had dropped the morale problem on me in one of his fits of delegation, and since I was bored myself I was in favor of any project that might give us something to do on Sundays.

I said, "This is a good idea, Ben. There's one problem, though. We don't have the equipment for an assault like that. You know how tight the budget is, too. I could ask Mike."

"Don't ask Mike!"

"Well, I'd have to ask Mike. And he could ask. But I don't think we'd get what we have to have."

"But it's much simpler than that," Ben said. "The Uranus bathyscaphe is still on Titania. It's old, of course, but there is no reason it couldn't be used here. The two planets are practically twins. Opposition is coming up. The bathyscaphe could be brought here for almost nothing. I thought you could requisition it through your department."

That was Ben for you. A very strange man. I think he supposed that I would very quietly requisition the bathyscaphe that had been used to probe the atmosphere ocean of Uranus, and just not say anything to Mike. Then he and I would slip quietly over to Neptune on our weekends. If he could have obtained and operated the machine by himself, I'm sure he would have preferred that.

"If the equipment is still on Titania, we may be able to get it," I said. "I'll ask Mike when I take up department operations with him tomorrow."

"Don't ask Mike."

"Look, Ben. If you want this at all, it has to go through Mike. There's no other way. You know that."

"No," he said. "Just forget the whole thing. I'm sorry I brought the subject up."

Ben was jealous of his ideas. If they passed through too many hands, they lost their savor for him. This was a good idea, or so it seemed to me, but he would prefer to let it lapse than to have the rest of our little colony involved.

I talked to Mike the next day. Mike was another odd one. At some previous time, he may have had drive, but he no longer cared very deeply. He delegated as much responsibility as he possibly could. He worked erratically. And he greeted my proposal with no great interest.

"Who cares if we find life on Neptune? We already know that ammonia-methane worlds can support life, and none of it has been very interesting after the novelty wears off."

"That's true," I said, "but do you suppose I care one way or the other if we find another strange kind of minnow? The important thing is that it would give as many of us as turned out to be interested something constructive to do. It's a project I could enjoy."

"Do you think anybody else would?" Mike asked. "How many first landings have there been? If you count everything, there must have been fifty or sixty. Who remembers them all? Who cares?"

"The point isn't whether anybody else would be interested," I said. "This isn't for outsiders. Mike, this morning I got out of my chair and I found that my rear end had gone to sleep. I want something to do."

It took argument, but Mike finally agreed to find out if the bathyscaphe was available. It turned out to be, and it arrived at Triton Base aboard ship some seven months later. That wasn't so very long. We didn't have anything else to do. We didn't have anywhere else to go.

Ben, of course, was hopping mad, mostly with me. I'd stolen his idea. I'd ruined his idea. I'd betrayed his trust. I'd spoiled things.

"It's the last time I ever tell you anything," he said. As he had said more than once before.

The project turned out to be far more of a success than I had ever anticipated. Our job was to keep contact with the starship, which we did adequately, and to keep a large, empty house in order, which we did inadequately. Not that anybody cared.

After the bathyscaphe arrived, however, schedules started being observed. People cared whether or not they were relieved on time. There was less dust in corners, less dirt on people. Minor illness fell off dramatically. And my rear end stopped going to sleep on me. Even Mike, of all people, became interested.

It was all very much like the boat you built in your basement when you were fourteen. It was what we did in our spare time. It was the Project.

Ben was in and Ben was out. Ben worked sometimes and sometimes he didn't. He didn't feel the venture was quite his anymore, but he couldn't bring himself to stay away. So even he wound up involved.

Everybody else cared a lot. There was work to do. The bathyscaphe had to be overhauled completely. That took a lot of spare time. And when we were done, there was every prospect of even more spare time being whiled away in months and months of exploration.

Like all the outer planets except Pluto, which is a misplaced moon, Neptune is a gassy giant. At one time, it was expected to have a layer of ice and a rocky core beneath its atmosphere. In fact, however, it has no solid surface. It's all atmosphere, a murky green sea of hydrogen and helium and methane and ammonia. There are clouds and snowstorms, but no place to put your feet. More than anything else, it is like the oceans of Earth, and the vehicle we intended to use to explore its unknown depths was a fantastic cross between a dirigible and the bathyscaphes of Piccard and his successors. Neptune was no well-tended garden, safe and comfortable, but in fact it was more easily accessible than are Earth's hostile ocean deeps with their incredible pressures.

The planet was only a step away from us on Triton, closer than the Moon is to Earth. It was possible for the bathyscaphe to reach Neptune under its own power, but not for it to return up the gravity well. Consequently we decided to use a mother ship, like a tender for a helmet diver, that would drop the bathyscaphe and then recover it. In a way I was sorry because I found the idea of a hydrogen-filled balloon chugging its way through space amusing.

In time, we were ready to make our first probe. The question then became one of who would be the two of us to go first. It was a painful question. Should it be settled by rank? Should it be settled by amount of work contributed? Should it be settled by lot? As the day of readiness came closer, the issue became more acute. Each method of choice had its champions. By and large we were polite about the subject, but there was one fistfight between Arlo Harlow, who had worked particularly hard, and Sperry Donner, who was second-in-command, which was terminated when both participants discovered they actually had no particular enthusiasm for fistfighting.

Mike finally settled the issue. The first trip would be Ben and me because we were responsible. After that, it would be alphabetically by pairs. He told me later that he had been intending to be strictly alphabetical, but that would have thrown Ben into the last pair, which was one problem, and would have made Ben the partner of Roy Wilimczyk, which was another.

"This seemed the best solution," he said. "If anybody can cope with him, it's you."

"Thank you," I said, and he understood that I didn't mean it.

Ben was frankly mellow that week—mellow for Ben. This means that about forty percent of the time he was his obnoxious ingratiating self instead of his normal obnoxious uningratiating self. He even forgave me.

Finally, on a Sunday that was as brisk and bright and sunny as a day ever gets on Triton, four of us set off toward the great green cotton candy boulder that filled a full ten degrees of sky. Ben and I didn't wait to see it grow. Long before the ship was in a parking orbit, Ben and I were in the cabin of the bathyscaphe and the whole was enclosed in a drop capsule.

I was piloting our machine. Ben was to supervise the monitoring equipment that would record our encounters with the planet.

We weren't lowered over the side in the tradition of Earth's oceans. We were popped out like a watermelon seed. We were strapped in and blind. I had my finger on the manual switch and had no need to trigger it. The rockets did what rockets do. The drop capsule peeled away automatically.

Then when our lights came on, we were deep in a green murk. It wasn't of a consistency. There were winds or eddies, call them whichever you choose. Our lights probed ahead.

Sometimes we could see for considerable distances—yards. Often we could only see a few feet. We had the additional eyes of radar which looked in circles about us and saw nothing except once what I took to be an ammonia snowstorm and avoided. Other sensors listened to the sound of the planet, took its temperature and pulse. Its temperature was very, very cold. Its pulse was slow and steady.

I feathered my elevators and found that the bathyscaphe worked as I had been assured that it did. The turboprops drove us steadily through the green. I was extremely glad to have my instruments. They told me I was right-side up, a fact I would not otherwise have known. And they kept me connected to our mother ship.

"I hope you are keeping in mind why we are here," Ben said.

"I am," I said. "However, until we know the planet better, I think one place will be about as likely as the next. I haven't seen any whale herds yet."

"No," said Ben, "but it doesn't mean they're not out there. They may simply be shy. After all, the existence of the Great Sea Serpent wasn't definitely established until the last ten years. I'd settle for something smaller, though."

We had collecting plates out. They might well demonstrate the presence of the same sort of soupy life that was found on Uranus. Ben kept busy with his monitoring. I kept busy with my piloting.

I had helped on this venture because I was bored, thoroughly tired of doing nothing in particular. I had come to Neptune with only the mildest interest in proving Ben's case. Now, however, I began to feel pleased to be where I was. The view, as we drove ourselves through the currents of this gassy sea, was monotonous, monochromatic, but weirdly beautiful. This was another sort of world than any I had been used to. I liked it. It may sound funny, but I respected it for being itself in the same way that you respect a totally ugly girl who has come to terms with herself.

I was pleased that men should be here in this last dark corner of the Solar System, and glad that I was one of the men. There is a place in reference books for this, too, if only in a footnote with the hundreds of other people who have made first contacts.

It was a full five hours before we were back aboard our mother ship. Arlo Harlow helped us out of the bathyscaphe.

"How did it go?" he said.

"We won't know until we check through the data," Ben said. "We didn't see anything identifiable. Not where he drove."

I said, "You'll have to see it for yourself. I don't think I can describe it for you. You'll see. It's a real experience."

Arlo said, "Mike wants to talk to you. He's got news."

Ben and I went forward to talk to Mike back at Triton Base. The satellite was invisible ahead of us—with Neptune full, Triton was necessarily a new moon, and dark.

"Hello, Mike," I said. "Arlo says you have news. Did the starship check in?"

"No," he said. "The news is you. You two are a human interest story. The last planet landing in the Solar System. Hold on. The first fac sheet has already come through. The headline is 'NEPTUNE REACHED.' It begins, 'In these days of groups and organizations and institutions, in these days when man's first ship to the stars casts off with a crew of ten thousand, stories of individual human courage seem a thing of the distant past.' And it ends, 'If men like these bear our colors forward, the race of man shall yet prevail.'"

"I like that," Ben said. "That's very good."

Mike said, "There's also a story that wants to know why money was ever spent on such pointless flamboyance as this landing."

"Tell them in the first place that there wasn't any landing," I said. "We were in Neptune, not on it. Then make the point that the bathyscaphe was left over from the Uranus probe and that we put it in shape ourselves."

"I did that," Mike said. "They got it in the story. The first

ne. The writer applauds your courage in chancing your life
such a primitive and antiquated exploratory vehicle."

"Oh, hell," I said.

"Listen. They have some questions they want answered.
hey want to know why you went. Why did you go, Bob?"

"Tell them that it seemed like a good idea at the time," I
aid.

"I can't give them that."

"We wanted to find out whether there was life on Nep-
ane," Ben said.

"Did you find any?"

"As far as we know, we didn't," I said.

"Then I can't give them that. Try again."

I thought. After a moment, I said, "Tell them that we
idn't think it was right for men to go to the stars without
aving touched all the bases here."

As "touch all the bases," that line has passed into the fa-
niliar quotation books.

Ben and I are in the history books, too—in the footnotes
long with the hundreds of other people who made first land-
ags. If you count the starships, that list would run into the
nousands.

Ben isn't happy buried in the footnotes, and he and I don't
peak anymore. He's mad at me. He never discovered life on
Neptune, and nobody, it is clear, is ever likely to. On the oth-
r hand, I'm the author of one of history's minor taglines. He
nds that galling.

It isn't a great distinction to bear, I'll admit, but there have
een dark nights in my life when I've lain awake and won-
ered whether or not I would leave any ripples behind me.
hat line is enough of a ripple to bring me through to morn-
ag.

PLUTO

Pluto, like Neptune, was predicted before it was found. The discrepancies in the orbit of Uranus were not entirely corrected by taking Neptune into consideration. Could there be still another planet beyond Uranus, one that was even farther from the Sun than Neptune is? Percival Lowell was particularly assiduous in his searchings but had found nothing by the time of his death in 1916.

Others at his observatory continued the search, off and on: and finally in 1930 Clyde William Tombaugh located the planet. It was considerably farther than Neptune and considerably smaller, and it could only be seen as a spot of light.

Still, its orbit could be calculated, and it was found to be a very odd one. Pluto's orbit is the most eccentric ellipse of any of the major planets.

When Pluto is at its farthest from the Sun, it is 1.6 times as far away as Neptune. It is as much farther beyond Neptune as Neptune is beyond Uranus. But when Pluto swoops in to the near end of its orbit, it is actually some 50 million kilometers (30 million miles) *closer* to the Sun than Neptune is.

Right now Pluto is approaching perihelion and is moving in closer to the Sun than Neptune is. For some twenty years (a period repeated every two and a half centuries) Neptune, not Pluto, will be the farthest planet, something that is mentioned in "Wait It Out."

There is no danger of Pluto colliding with Neptune as

passes within Neptune's orbit, however, for Pluto's orbit is in a plane that is considerably tilted compared to Neptune's. That means that Pluto passes far below Neptune as it crosses orbits.

Still, this crossing of orbits is so strange that some astronomers have speculated that Pluto was once a satellite of Neptune and had been kicked free in some catastrophe.

This notion was strengthened by the fact that Pluto was not a gas giant. In fact, it proved to be rather small. As the decades passed after its discovery, and as small bits of information were gathered, the estimates of its size shrank. At first it seemed pretty certain that it was at least as large as Earth, but eventually it was decided that it was only as large as Mars. A Mars-sized world might easily have once been a satellite of Neptune.

Then, too, Pluto's light grew dimmer and brighter regularly, and it was decided that this represented its period of rotation, with one hemisphere being icier and brighter than the other. If so, Pluto's period of rotation equaled 6.39 days.

If we disregard Mercury and Venus as having had their rotation periods interfered with by the Sun's tidal effect, it turns out that Earth, Mars, Uranus, and Neptune all have rotation periods in the region of 24 hours, while Jupiter and Saturn have rotation periods in the region of 10 hours. A rotation period of 6.39 days is very slow—but if Pluto had once been revolving about Neptune, it might have had a period of revolution of 6.39 days, and the tidal forces of Neptune might have slowed the rotation till it was equal to the period of revolution.

Astronomers continued to think for a while that Pluto had to have a mass large enough to affect the orbits of Neptune and Uranus; and as it shrank in size, estimates of its density came to be many times as great as that of platinum. This high density is referred to in "Wait It Out," which was first published in 1968.

However, such high densities were really unthinkable and quickly went by the board. It had to be decided that Pluto was not only no larger than Mars, but no more massive either.

Then, on June 22, 1978, James W. Christy, examining photographs of Pluto, noticed a distinct bump on one side. He examined other photographs and finally decided that Pluto had a satellite. The satellite was only 20,000 kilometers (12,500 miles) from Pluto. Considering how close together the two objects were and how far away from us, it isn't surprising we tended to see them as a single object.

The satellite, named "Charon," circles Pluto in 6.39 days, which is just the time it takes for Pluto to turn on its axis. The two bodies have apparently slowed each other by tidal action, until each faces the same side to the other. They revolve about a common center of gravity like the two halves of a dumbbell about an invisible shaft.

From the distance of separation and the time of revolution, it can be showed that both bodies together have only about one-eighth the mass of our Moon. Pluto is far smaller than anyone had thought. Pluto is now thought to be about 3000 kilometers (1850 miles) in diameter and Charon about 1200 kilometers (750 miles) in diameter.

From now on, no one can write a science fiction story about Pluto without taking its very small size into account and without mentioning its satellite, which, although small, is larger compared to the planet it circles than any other satellite in the Solar System. Pluto-Charon make up the closest approach to a double planet in the system.

One thing is now clear. Pluto cannot explain the discrepancies in the motions of Uranus and Neptune. If there is an explanation, it must involve another planet, a larger one, and one that is still undiscovered. Does it exist? Perhaps probes will eventually tell us.

Wait It Out

LARRY NIVEN

Night on Pluto. Sharp and distinct, the horizon line cuts across my field of vision. Below that broken line is the dim gray-white of snow seen by starlight. Above, space-blackness and space-bright stars. From behind a jagged row of frozen mountains the stars pour up in singletons and clusters and streamers of cold white dots. Slowly they move, but visibly, just fast enough for a steady eye to capture their motion.

Something wrong there. Pluto's rotation period is long: 6.39 days. Time must have slowed for me.

It should have stopped.

I wonder if I may have made a mistake.

The planet's small size brings the horizon close. It seems even closer without a haze of atmosphere to fog the distances. Two sharp peaks protrude into the star swarm like the filed front teeth of a cannibal warrior. In the cleft between those peaks shines a sudden bright point.

I recognize the Sun, though it shows no more disk than any other, dimmer star. The sun shines as a cold point between the frozen peaks; it pulls free of the rocks and shines in my eyes.

The Sun is gone, the starfield has shifted. I must have passed out.

It figures.

Have I made a mistake? It won't kill me if I have. It could drive me mad, though.

I don't feel mad. I don't feel anything, not pain, not loss, not regret, not fear. Not even pity. Just: *What a situation.*

Gray-white against gray-white: the landing craft, short and wide and conical, stands half-submerged in an icy plain below the level of my eyes. Here I stand, looking east, waiting.

Take a lesson: this is what comes of not wanting to die.

Pluto was not the most distant planet. It had stopped being that in 1979, ten years ago. Now Pluto was at perihelion, as close to the Sun—and to Earth—as it would ever get. To ignore such an opportunity would have been sheer waste.

And so we came, Jerome and Sammy and I, in an inflated plastic bubble poised on an ion jet. We'd spent a year and a half in that bubble. After so long together, with so little privacy, perhaps we should have hated each other. We didn't. The UN psycho team must have chosen well.

But—just to be out of sight of the others, even for a few minutes. Just to have something to *do,* something that was not predictable. A new world could hold infinite surprises. As a matter of fact, so could our laboratory-tested hardware. I don't think any of us really trusted the Nerva-K under our landing craft.

Think it through. For long trips in space, you use an ion jet giving low thrust over long periods of time. The ion motor on our own craft had been decades in use. Where gravity is materially lower than Earth's, you land on dependable chemical rockets. For landings on Earth and Venus, you use heat shields and the braking power of the atmosphere. For landing on the gas giants—but who would want to?

The Nerva-class fission rockets are used only for takeoff from Earth, where thrust and efficiency count. Responsiveness and maneuverability count for too much during a powered landing. And a heavy planet will always have an atmosphere for braking.

Pluto didn't.

For Pluto, the chemical jets to take us down and bring us back up were too heavy to carry all that way. We needed a highly maneuverable Nerva-type atomic rocket motor using hydrogen for reaction mass.

And we had it. But we didn't trust it.

Jerome Glass and I went down, leaving Sammy Cross in orbit. He griped about that, of course. He'd started that back at the Cape and kept it up for a year and a half. But someone had to stay. Someone had to be aboard the Earth-return vehicle, to fix anything that went wrong, to relay communications to Earth, and to fire the bombs that would solve Pluto's one genuine mystery.

We never did solve that one. Where *does* Pluto get all that mass? The planet's a dozen times as dense as it has any right to be. We could have solved that with the bombs, the same way they solved the mystery of the makeup of the Earth, sometime in the last century. They mapped the patterns of earthquake ripples moving through the Earth's bulk. But those ripples were from natural causes, like the Krakatoa eruption. On Pluto the bombs would have done it better.

A bright star-sun blazes suddenly between two fangs of mountain. I wonder if they'll know the answers, when my vigil ends.

The sky jumps and steadies, and—

I'm looking east, out over the plain where we landed the ship. The plain and the mountains behind seem to be sinking like Atlantis: an illusion created by the flowing stars. We slide endlessly down the black sky, Jerome and I and the mired ship.

The Nerva-K behaved perfectly. We hovered for several minutes to melt our way through various layers of frozen gases and get ourselves something solid to land on. Condensing volatiles steamed around us and boiled below, so that we settled in a soft white glow of fog lit by the hydrogen flame.

Black wet ground appeared below the curve of the landing skirt. I let the ship drop carefully, carefully... and we touched.

It took us an hour to check the ship and get ready to go

outside. But who would be first? This was no idle matter. Pluto would be the solar system's last outpost for most of future history, and the statue to the first man on Pluto would probably remain untarnished forever.

Jerome won the toss. All for the sake of a turning coin, Jerome's would be the first name in the history books. I remember the grin I forced! I wish I could force one now. He was laughing and talking of marble statues as he went through the lock.

There's irony in that, if you like that sort of thing.

I was screwing down my helmet when Jerome started shouting obscenities into the helmet mike. I cut the checklist short and followed him out.

One look told it all.

The black wet dirt beneath our landing skirt had been dirty ice, water ice mixed haphazardly with lighter gases and ordinary rock. The heat draining out of the Nerva jet had melted that ice. The rocks within the ice had sunk, and so had the landing vehicle, so that when the water froze again it was halfway up the hull. Our landing craft was sunk solid in the ice.

We could have done some exploring before we tried to move the ship. When we called Sammy he suggested doing just that. But Sammy was up there in the Earth-return vehicle, and we were down here with our landing vehicle mired in the ice of another world.

We were terrified. Until we got clear we would be good for nothing, and we both knew it.

I wonder why I can't remember the fear.

We did have one chance. The landing vehicle was designed to move about on Pluto's surface; and so she had a skirt instead of landing jacks. Half a gravity of thrust would have given us a ground effect, safer and cheaper than using the ship like a ballistic missile. The landing skirt must have trapped gas underneath when the ship sank, leaving the Nerva-K engine in a bubble cavity.

We could melt our way out.

I know we were as careful as two terrified men could be. The heat rose in the Nerva-K, agonizingly slow. In flight there would have been a coolant effect as cold hydrogen fuel ran through the pile. We couldn't use that. But the environment of the motor was terribly cold. The two factors might compensate, or—

Suddenly dials went wild. Something had cracked from the savage temperature differential. Jerome used the damper rods without effect. Maybe they'd melted. Maybe wiring had cracked, or resistors had become superconductors in the cold. Maybe the pile—but it doesn't matter now.

I wonder why I can't remember the fear.

Sunlight—

And a logy, dreamy feeling. I'm conscious again. The same stars rise in formation over the same dark mountains.

Something heavy is nosing up against me. I feel its weight against my back and the backs of my legs. What is it? Why am I not terrified?

It slides around in front of me, questing. It looks like a huge amoeba, shapeless and translucent, with darker bodies showing within it. I'd guess it's about my own weight.

Life on Pluto! But how? Superfluids? Helium II contaminated by complex molecules? In that case the beast had best get moving; it will need shade come sunrise. Sunside temperature on Pluto is all of 50° Absolute.

No, come back! It's leaving, flowing down toward the splash crater. Did my thoughts send it away? Nonsense. It probably didn't like the taste of me. It must be terribly slow, that I can watch it move. The beast is still visible, blurred because I can't look directly at it, moving downhill toward the landing vehicle and the tiny statue to the first man to die on Pluto.

After the fiasco with the Nerva-K, one of us had to go down and see how much damage had been done. That meant tunneling down with the flame of a jet backpack, then crawling under the landing skirt. We didn't talk about the implications. We were probably dead. The man who went down into the bubble cavity was even more probably dead; but what of it? Dead is dead.

I feel no guilt. I'd have gone myself if I'd lost the toss.

The Nerva-K had spewed fused bits of the fission pile all over the bubble cavity. We were trapped for good. Rather, I was trapped, and Jerome was dead. The bubble cavity was a hell of radiation.

Jerome had been swearing softly as he went in. He came out perfectly silent. He'd used up all the good words on lighter matters, I think.

I remember I was crying, partly from grief and partly from fear. I remember that I kept my voice steady in spite of it. Jerome never knew. What he guessed is his own affair. He told me the situation, he told me goodbye, and then he strode out onto the ice and took off his helmet. A fuzzy white ball engulfed his head, exploded outward, then settled to the ground in microscopic snowflakes.

But all that seems infinitely remote. Jerome stands out there with his helmet clutched in his hands: a statue to himself, the first man on Pluto. A frost of recondensed moisture conceals his expression.

Sunrise. I hope the amoeba—

That was wild. The sun stood poised for an instant, a white point-source between twin peaks. Then it streaked upward—and the spinning sky jolted to a stop. No wonder I didn't catch it before. It happened so fast.

A horrible thought. What has happened to me could have happened to Jerome! I wonder—

There was Sammy in the Earth-return vehicle, but he couldn't get down to me. I couldn't get up. The life system was in good order, but sooner or later I would freeze to death or run out of air.

I stayed with the landing vehicle about thirty hours, taking ice and soil samples, analyzing them, delivering the data to Sammy via laser beam; delivering also high-minded last messages, and feeling sorry for myself. On my trips outside I kept passing Jerome's statue. For a corpse, and one which has not been prettified by the post-surgical skills of an embalmer, he looks damn good. His frost-dusted skin is indistinguishable from marble, and his eyes are lifted toward the stars in poignant yearning. Each time I passed him I wondered how I would look when my turn came.

"You've got to find an oxygen layer," Sammy kept saying.

"Why?"

"To keep you alive! Sooner or later they'll send a rescue ship. You can't give up now!"

I'd already given up. There was oxygen, but there was no such layer as Sammy kept hoping for. There were veins of oxygen mixed with other things, like veins of gold ore in rock. Too little, too finely distributed.

"Then use the water ice! That's only poetic justice, isn't it? You can get the oxygen out by electrolysis!"

But a rescue ship would take years. They'd have to build it from scratch, and redesign the landing vehicle too. Electrolysis takes power, and heat takes power. I had only the batteries.

Sooner or later I'd run out of power. Sammy couldn't see this. He was more desperate than I was. I didn't run out of last messages; I stopped sending them because they were driving Sammy crazy.

I passed Jerome's statue one time too many, and an idea came.

This is what comes of not wanting to die.

In Nevada, three billion miles from here, half a million corpses lie frozen in vaults surrounded by liquid nitrogen. Half a million dead men wait for an earthly resurrection, on the day medical science discovers how to unfreeze them safely, how to cure what was killing each one of them, how to cure the additional damage done by ice crystals breaking cell walls all through their brains and bodies.

Half a million fools? But what choice did they have? They were dying.

I was dying.

A man can stay conscious for tens of seconds in vacuum. If I moved fast, I could get out of my suit in that time. Without that insulation to protect me, Pluto's black night would suck warmth from my body in seconds. At 50° Absolute, I'd stay in frozen storage until one version or another of the Day of Resurrection.

Sunlight—

—And stars. No sign of the big blob that found me so singularly tasteless yesterday. But I could be looking in the wrong direction.

I hope it got to cover.

I'm looking east, out over the splash plain. In my peripheral vision the ship looks unchanged and undamaged.

My suit lies beside me on the ice. I stand on a peak of black rock, poised in my silvered underwear, looking eternally out at the horizon. Before the cold touched my brain I found a last moment in which to assume a heroic stance. Go east, young man. Wouldn't you know I'd get my directions mixed? But the fog of my breathing-air hid everything, and I was moving in terrible haste.

Sammy Cross must be on his way home now. He'll tell them where I am.

Stars pour up from behind the mountains. The mountains and the splash plain and Jerome and I sink endlessly beneath the sky.

My corpse must be the coldest in history. Even the hopeful dead of Earth are only stored at liquid nitrogen temperatures. Pluto's night makes that look torrid, after the 50° Absolute heat of day seeps away into space.

A superconductor is what I am. Sunlight raises the temperature too high, switching me off like a damned machine at every dawn. But at night my nervous system becomes a superconductor. Currents flow; thoughts flow; sensations flow. Sluggishly. The one hundred and fifty-three hours of Pluto's rotation flash by in what feels like fifteen minutes. At that rate I can wait it out.

I stand as a statue and a viewpoint. No wonder I can't get emotional about anything. Water is a rock here, and my glands are contoured ice within me. But I feel sensations: the pull of gravity, the pain in my ears, the tug of vacuum over every square inch of my body. The vacuum will not boil my blood. But the tensions are frozen into the ice of me, and my nerves tell me so. I feel the wind whistling from my lips, like an exhalation of cigarette smoke.

This is what comes of not wanting to die. What a joke if I got my wish!

Do you suppose they'll find me? Pluto's small for a planet. For a place to get lost in, a small planet is all too large. But there's the ship.

Though it seems to be covered with frost. Vaporized gases recondensed on the hull. Gray-white on gray-white, a lump on a dish of refrozen ice. I could stand here forever waiting for them to pick my ship from its surroundings.

Stop that.

Sunlight—

Stars rolling up the sky. The same patterns, endlessly rolling up from the same points. Does Jerome's corpse live the same half-life I live now? He should have stripped, as I did. My God! I wish I'd thought to wipe the ice from his eyes!

I wish that superfluid blob would come back.

Damn. It's *cold*.

Nikita Eisenhower Jones

ROBERT F. YOUNG

Near the southern fringe of Pluto's Great Ice Plain there is a range of mountains which resembles a Brobdingnagian man lying upon his back, staring eternally up at the stars. It begins with a lofty mesa, the prominences of which, when seen against the brooding star-specked sky, suggest a silhouetted profile. A brief ridge, comparable to a massive neck, leads to the range proper, the first great swell of which is easily identifiable as the upper section of a vast chest; then the range proper levels off for a hundred miles, drops gradually into a stomachlike plateau, and bifurcates finally into two thigh-like ridges, both of which terminate, some two hundred miles farther on, into almost identical footlike tors.

When the range is viewed from above—say from a height of about three hundred miles—the illusion is even stronger. Looking down you see an anthropomorphic formation of peaks and crevices and chimneys, of rocks and snow and ice. Two relatively smaller ranges, stretching out at near right angles on either side of the mother range, bring to mind outflung arms, and at the extremity of each is a deposit of moraine startlingly suggestive of a human hand. The face is an elusive pattern of shadows that changes subtly with each fitful play of starlight.

Now Pluto, as every schoolboy knows, is not a mountainous planet. It has, to be sure, interminable stretches of ice-clad hills that conceivably could have been mountains—a

270

hundred thousand Plutonian years ago. There are even, in the polar regions, eminences high enough to pass for frustrated foothills. In the region of the Great Ice Plain, however—with the glaring exception of the mountains in question—there is nothing but an endless succession of eroded ice ridges, souvenirs, no doubt, of the long-ago age when the wind still blew and the snow still fell. So it is odd to a degree that makes even mentioning the fact redundant that on a planet where the geology was not generally conducive to mountains that mountains should exist in a region where it was not conducive to them at all.

What planetary stress created the Brobdingnagian Mountains, or whatever they really are (if they *are* anything besides a massive upheaval of rocks and ice) constitutes a mystery that will probably never be resolved. But any mystery that can foster stories—be they legends or fairy tales, or both—has not endured in vain. The Brobdingnagian Mountains have fostered at least a hundred such stories, and you have merely to choose the one you think throws the most light upon their true origin. I am a romantic myself, and I prefer the romantic version—the one retired spacemen tell over their drinks-too-many in every spaceport bar from Alpha Centauri 4 to Betelgeuse 29. It is a true story, up to a point; whether it is true or not beyond that point is a question I am not qualified to answer.

You can judge best for yourself.

He had corkscrew hair and he was as black as space and his smile was as wide as the world. At the age of twelve he was five feet one—and five feet one was all he was ever going to be. He had the broad nose and the sloping forehead usually associated with his race; but in the almost feminine line of his lips there was a hint of sensitivity, and deep in his dark-brown eyes the latent tinder of intelligence awaited the right combination of flint and steel to bring it to life. His name was Nikita Eisenhower Jones.

Malaita, the island of his birth, had been the last of the Solomons to accept the white man's civilization. Now his people raised cucumbers and beans as well as yams and *kumara*, and collected comic books instead of heads. They still lived in the bush, but they gave their children white men's names and sent them to the British mission schools along the coast and wore dresses and slacks instead of lava-lavas and spoke English instead of Bêche-de-Mer.

In the schools the children learned among other things that the world was round, that it was one of nine planets orbiting the sun, that the sun was a star and that there were a zillion others roughly similar to it in the cosmos; that God had created the whole works and that old Kuvi-Kavi, who lived back in the bush and preached a different version of Genesis, was a liar of the first magnitude. But the children went right on listening to old Kuvi-Kavi's version anyway. Not that they had anything against the white man's version: it was just that old Kuvi-Kavi's packed a harder punch.

It went something like this:

In the beginning the world was water and the sky was without light. There were two gods—Kamikau, the rain god, and Murabongu, the sea god—and they hated each other cordially. Finally Kamikau got sick of riding around in the dark sky on his lonely rain cloud and caused land to emerge from the sea and caused coconut trees and yams and sweet potatoes to grow upon the land. From an armful of darkness and two cat's-eye shells he created the First Mary and brought her to life by blowing his breath into her mouth. Then he built the First Fire, and there was light and warmth. Meanwhile, Murabongu, the sea god, had become angry over the invasion of his domain, and now he emerged from the deeps to do battle with Kamikau. For ages the two gods battled in the light of the First Fire, while the First Mary watched from the scrub. At last the sea god tired and Kamikau was able to subdue him. He cut off Murabongu's head and cooked the rest of him over the First Fire, and he and the First Mary sat down to the First Feast. When they finished eating, Kamikau picked up the head and flung it high into the sky where it became the moon. Next he picked up the heart of the First Fire and flung it even higher into the sky where it became the sun. Finally he scattered the embers throughout the heavens where they became the stars. Not long afterward the first man was born of god and woman, and nineteenth- and twentieth-century ambassadors of civilization were assured of a good crop of native laborers, and twenty-first-century exponents of Western culture were provided with an excellent market for used comic books.

Nikita Eisenhower Jones was thirteen years old when a space comic first swam into his ken. It was like Keats first looking into Chapman's Homer. The round gaily colored planets and the sleek ships plying the immensities between them did something to his Melanesian soul that had never been done to it before, and he knew that henceforth he would never be the same again. Marrying a Mary and settling down in a vine-covered grass hut in the bush and raising yams and sweet potatoes and pickaninnies and working forty hours a week in the copra factory might be enough for his fellows, but it was not enough for him. He wanted the stars.

The space comic was the first of many. Obtaining them was no problem—by this time there were more comic books on the island than there were coconuts—and as the mission schools had long since given up assigning homework to their lackadaisical pupils, he had plenty of time to read. Space comics, however, were far from being ideal nourishment for a burgeoning young mind such as Nick's, and the time came when they failed utterly either to satisfy his curiosity or to titillate his imagination, whereupon he began visiting the mission-school library and availing himself of its limited supply of space books. Most of them were outdated and did not go beyond the first satellite launchings, but one of them dealt with the first Russian expedition to the moon, and reading it, his ambition was kindled anew. Once upon a time, Malaita had represented the whole universe in his mind: now it shrank beneath his feet to a mere speck of land, and planets of every size and color whirled dizzily round his head.

The mission schools covered only the elementary grades, and most of the islanders dropped out before completing them. But not Nick. The books he had read had done more than ignite his imagination: they had ignited the latent intellectual tinder, too, and the blaze that ensued greedily consumed every branch of knowledge he could lay his hands on. He shone forth like a nova among his schoolmates in every endeavor save one: like them, he was utterly incapable of pronouncing the letter "x," and whenever he said words such as "six" and "fix," they came out "sikkis" and "fikkis."

Noting his enthusiasm, and his marks, the headmaster urged him to take advantage of the British Solomon Islands Protectorate's new educational program, under which any eligible Solomon Islander could pursue his studies, expenses paid, in either the United States or Great Britain. Nick did so, and passed the eligibility examination without trouble. He chose the United States because of its more active role in the space race, and a few months later found himself in the Big Rock Candy Country.

By the time he graduated from high school he had managed to become a citizen. This automatically disqualified him for any further aid from the BSIP, but he had decided that being a permanent resident of the United States would be to his advantage in carrying out his plans. His next step was to apply for admittance to the Von Braun Space Academy. His size had already caused him considerable discomfiture in high school—the average American male now stood six feet two in his stocking feet—but he had not dreamed it would be a detriment to his becoming a spaceman. On the contrary, he had thought it would stand him in good stead. Theoretically, he was right; practically, he was not. The public wanted heroes for its tax dollars, and the public's conception of a hero had not deviated one iota from the moment Matt Dillon had first stalked down the cathodic streets of Dodge and shot up the first of a long line of drunks, card sharps, gunmen, ne'er-do-wells and sadomasochists. To be a hero, you had to be tall. You had to be big. You had to be handsome. Above all, you had to be a father figure. Small wonder then that when Nikita Eisenhower Jones applied for admission to the Academy he was laughed out the door.

But there are more ways of getting into space than becoming a pilot or an astronaut. This was not true in the beginning, of course, but by this time there were U.S. bases on Ganymede, the third moon of Jupiter, and on Miranda, the fifth moon of Uranus, and bases require personnel. In his Melanesian heart Nick knew that next to a well-filled wallet, the one thing white men cherish most is a well-filled stomach. So he became a cook. Not a good cook. Not even an excellent cook. But a superb cook. When he put in his application at the Planet Exploratory Agency—the joint civilian-military project that had superseded the Civilian Space Agency—and gave a demonstration of his prowess, he was laughed at, but he wasn't laughed out the door, and some months later PEA assigned him to the Miranda base, where, it was rumored, the most significant leap of all was about to take place—i.e., the Pluto shot.

According to section 20 of the Interplanetary Code set up by the U.N. in the latter part of the twentieth century, the first nation to plant its flag on a planet (said operation to be performed by human, rather than robotic, hands) could automatically claim that planet and all its satellites. In the case of a satellite, the entire planetary system could be claimed—with the exception, of course, of the Earth-moon system. The Soviet Union had long since planted its flag on the moon, and had followed the planting with the establishment of a huge moon base. After the code was set up, the United States pulled a coup by bypassing the moon, Mars and the asteroid belt, and planting its flag and setting up a base on Ganymede, thereby gaining title to the Jovian system. A Russian planting and base on Enceladus, the second moon of Saturn, soon followed, and was followed in turn by a U.S. planting and base on Miranda. Strategically speaking, the Miranda base was the most valuable one of all, because the Uranian system, while it was the seventh from the sun, marked the approximate halfway point between Earth and Pluto—or would, when opposition took place—and while Pluto, owing to the plane of the ecliptic, did not bring the nearer stars appreciably closer, the nation that reached it first would be the psychological winner of the solar-system race.

The Miranda base, Nikita Eisenhower Jones decided, was not precisely what he had had in mind on that distant day when he had laid aside the space comic and gazed up through the foliage of a banyan tree at a suddenly expanded sky. It was enclosed by a huge transparent pressure dome, and consisted of the oxygen-producing plant, the machine shop, the living quarters, the kitchen-dining-room-bar and the supply building. At one point on the perimeter of the dome stood the airtight tower, and several hundred yards from the tower, the *Starhope* pointed its proud nose at the brooding star-specked sky.

But the base was only partially responsible for his lack of enthusiasm. Most of it accrued from the sense of frustration that overcame him whenever he gazed through the roof of the dome at the stars. He had experienced the sense first when he had seen the huge mass of Jupiter in the viewport of the shuttle ship, and he had experienced it again—more poignantly this time—when he had glimpsed beringed Saturn, silvery and magnificent, against the black backdrop of the immensities. And whenever Miranda's rotation brought awesome Uranus into view, the sense was so overwhelming that he had to turn his eyes away. He did not understand the reason for his frustration, but one thing he did understand: being a part of the conquest of space was not enough—

He had to be the conqueror.

His day began at 0300 hours when he rose to prepare the

morning meal. At 0600 hours, when his work in the kitchen was caught up, he joined the maintenance crew in the *Starhope* in the unofficial capacity of water boy, handing and fetching them tools and materials, good-naturedly smiling at their constant jokes about his height, and religiously watching every move they made. At 1100 hours he returned to the kitchen and prepared the noon meal, and at 1400 hours he rejoined the maintenance crew and handed, fetched, smiled and watched till 1700 hours. The evening meal was at 1830 hours. Generally it took him an hour to clean up afterwards, and you'd have thought by then that his day would be done. But it wasn't. There were still his duties as bartender to be fulfilled.

The bar was strictly a morale item. The base was supplied with enough whiskey to permit each member of the crew to have two shots per night; but even if there had been no liquor available, the bar would have been a popular gathering place in view of the fact that the next nearest one was over a billion and a half miles away. To bring it into being, Nick simply folded up the aluminum chairs and piled them in one corner of the dining room, then he elevated the eating table to a height of three feet and aligned it with the nearest wall, leaving enough space behind it for him to walk back and forth. Finally he went out to the kitchen, unlocked the liquor chest and brought in the evening's ration.

In addition to Nick, there were fourteen men stationed at the base: Colonel Dennison, the commanding officer; the eight-man base maintenance crew; the four-man ship's maintenance crew; and Captain Cohill, the pilot of the *Starhope*. Two of the men—Blake and Barnaby—were teetotalers, and enjoyed a phenomenal popularity with the others, especially Captain Cohill. The way everybody hung around them and did them favors, you'd have thought they were a pair of pretty girls instead of a pair of burly grease monkeys. It was obvious from the start, though, that Captain Cohill had the inside track so far as their affections were concerned, and when, not long before the Great Event was scheduled to take place, he promised them souvenirs from Pluto's landscape if and when he came back, the others didn't stand a chance, and dropped out one by one.

Colonel Dennison usually spent the evening standing at the end of the bar, and Captain Cohill had a system all worked out for his benefit. First he would hang around Blake, his back to the colonel, and Blake would order his two shots in a double-shot glass. Not long afterwards, the two of them would leave, and the double-shot glass would be sitting there on the bar, drained to the last drop. Half an hour or so later, Captain Cohill would come in with Barnaby, and the procedure would be repeated. Finally Cohill would come in just before closing time—usually after everyone else had left—and order his own ration. By the time he finished drinking it he was ready—if not willing—to go to bed.

He struck up a warm friendship with Nick right from the start, calling him Keeper of the Golden Keys, Noble Bushman with the Heart of Gold, and King Solomon of the Spaceways, as the mood suited him, cautioning Nick never to reveal his duplicity to Colonel Dennison. Nick had a warm smile reserved just for him, and the two of them had many a pleasant conversation on the Captain's third visitation each evening. They were never at a loss for something to talk about: Captain Cohill's reminiscences about his various girl friends would have sufficed in themselves to keep the barroom bright with conversational cheer, and in addition to his reminiscences there were Nikita's endless questions about the Starhope, the physique of which Captain Cohill knew almost as thoroughly as he did the physiques of his girl friends.

Nick's curiosity about the ship was insatiable. "Big fella ship belong you," he said one night (he invariably employed Bêche-de-Mer when conversing with the men because he knew instinctively that it would be nothing in his favor for them to know he could speak English—with the exception of pronouncing his "X's"—better than they could.) "Big fella ship," he said, "you push'm up how?"

Cohill swirled—or tried to swirl—the final dram of rye filming the bottom of his shot glass. "You don't push'm up no how," he said. "You just go along for the ride." When Nick looked at him uncomprehendingly, he went on; "All they need the pilot for is to plant the flag. The ship operates itself."

"You no push'm on?"

"Oh, sure, you have to start it. That is," he amended, "you have to tell it what you want it to do. There's a little perforated card you feed into its brain box before you blast off and another one that you feed into it when you're ready to come back. They're all ready—hanging on the Christmas tree, so to speak, just waiting for you to use them." He signed. "A kid could do it. Even you could do it."

Nick smiled. He went into the kitchen, returned several minutes later with a quart can of whiskey. He set it on the bar, opened it. Disbelievingly, Cohill watched while he filled his shot glass to the brim. "Drink'm up," Nick said.

Cohill's big fingers plucked the glass from the bar; he raised it to his lips. "Noble Keeper of the Golden Keys, I salute you," he said, and downed the shot.

Nick poured him another. "Head belong you he savvee little bit too much," he said. "Head belong you he savvee ration belong Blake and he savvee ration belong Barnaby. He no savvee ration belong Nikita."

Cohill smote the center of his forehead with the palm of his hand. "Well I'll be damned!" he said. "You would rate a ration at that, seeing as how you're a member of the crew. And you've been saving it all this time. Saving it—for me!" His face grew radiant, especially his nose. "King Solomon of the Spaceways, I salute you!" he said, and downed the second.

Nick poured him one more and took the can back to the kitchen and locked it in the chest. "Sun he come up many times," he said, returning.

Cohill shook his head ruefully. "Not so many times," he

said. "Not for me, anyway." When Nick looked at him questioningly, he let the cat out of the bag, hoping it would obtain him another drink: "I'm blasting off day after tomorrow," he said. "At 0430, to be exact." In view of the fact that Colonel Dennison was going to release the information the next day and in view of the fact that it would come as no surprise to most of the men, the breach of security was but a minor one.

It came as no surprise to Nick either, but he didn't let on. He didn't go back to the kitchen and get the can of whiskey either. Cohill sighed. "And I thought you were my friend," he said.

"Nikita good fella friend belong you," Nick said. "Come along bar sun he go down long time little bit, you see."

Cohill beamed. "King Sholomon, I shalute you," he said, and staggered out into the night.

Nick's smile did not diminish. If anything, it grew wider. Before he turned in that night (he slept in a small room off the kitchen), he stepped outside and looked at the stars. Pluto was a smidgin of light no larger than a flyspeck, hanging low on the horizon; but to him it was diamond-bright and beautiful—the cynosure of the heavens. After a while he went back inside and lay down on his bunk and closed his eyes and tried to sleep.

Next night the bar was full all evening. Everyone wanted to toast Captain Cohill and wish him Godspeed, and during the course of the evening, everyone, including Colonel Dennison, did. Unfortunately for Cohill, however, the colonel never once left his side, and he was limited to his own ration, the two shots of which he dispatched in the first five seconds. Throughout the remainder of the proceedings he kept glancing at the clock and licking his lips.

Colonel Dennison lingered till after everyone else had gone. Just before he left he came over and shook Cohill's hand, placing his other hand on Cohill's shoulder. "Yours is a mission fraught with peril," he said sententiously. "But know that we here at the base who only stand and wait are with you in the spirit if not the flesh, and that when you plant the flag, our hands as well as yours will be upon the staff. Farewell, Captain. Godspeed!"

After he had gone, Nick dimmed the lights. Cohill was standing at the end of the bar, staring into a glass that had been empty hours ago. When he raised his eyes, Nick saw the naked fear in them, and his smile grew even wider than the world. He hurried into the kitchen, and this time when he returned, he bore two quart cans of whiskey.

Cohill's hand trembled as he tossed off the first three shots; after that, though, it steadied, and some of the fear faded from his eyes. He seemed inordinately eager to talk about his girl friends, and Nick, far from objecting, encouraged him. He dwelt longest on the red-headed nurse he had met on his last furlough. "Stacked, by God!" he said. "Stacked like a starship! And beautiful as space. Hair the color of Mars-light; eyes as blue as the belt of Orion; skin as golden as the sun ... Afterward, though, she was the same as all the others." He stared at his empty glass. Nick filled it again. "'s funny," Cohill went on. "The minute that happens, they change. They're not any good any more." He downed the shot. "It was the same way with Iphigenia."

Nick made no comment, but puzzlement must have shown in his brown eyes; either that, or Cohill wanted to talk about Iphigenia. "She was the starship I made my first solo in," he explained. "Tall, graceful, delicate—far lovelier than a real woman. A thousand times nobler. And yet when she gave me what I wanted I found out I didn't really want it after all. I wanted something else, I don't know what, and I hated her for not giving it to me. 's funny," he repeated.

Nick looked at him keenly, filled his glass again. Still he said nothing. "I hate 'em all," Cohill said, tossing off the shot. "They're all alike, every one of them!" He raised his eyes to the thick-paned window behind the bar and gazed at the distant silhouette of the *Starhope*. "I hate you too!" he shouted suddenly, and flung his glass at the panes.

The glass shattered, fell to the floor. Imperturbably, Nick

produced another, set it on the bar and filled it. Cohill's action had been more revelatory than a thousand words. He did not drink because he feared death—he drank because he wanted it and couldn't get it. He had become a pilot because he wanted it, and had pretended to himself that what he really wanted was the stars—

Abruptly Nick wondered why *he* really wanted the stars.

Cohill's outburst seemed to have calmed him. He raised the new glass to his lips, "Keeper of the Golden Keesh, I shalute you," he said, and downed the whiskey.

Nick smiled and filled the glass again. "Big fella marster colonel," he said. "He say'm good-by sun he come up?"

Cohill shook his head. "No more good-bys. Tomorrow morning I go straight to the ship when the CQ wakes me. The colonel and all the off-duty pershonnel will be in the tower for the countdown."

"Big fella marster colonel, he say'm good-by over talk-talk?"

Cohill looked at him blankly for a moment. Then: "Oh, you mean the radio." He shook his head again. "No. I repeat the last ten seconds of the countdown so they'll know I'm all right. Thash all."

Nick relaxed, not visibly, but inside him where the tight knot of worry was. It was a point that had bothered him: a spacesuit concealed your physical characteristics, but a radio did not do the same for your voice. Carrying on even a brief conversation might have betrayed him, but counting from ten to zero on the heels of someone else's words should give him no trouble.

He poured Cohill another shot. "Good old King Sholomon," Cohill said, downing it.

Nick continued to pour, Cohill to drink. The man had an alcoholic threshold as high as the moon. "Did I tell you about Iphigenia?" he asked presently. When Nick continued to smile warmly at him without answering, he went on: "Stacked, by God! Beautiful's space. Hair the color Marshlight; eyes blue's Orion's belt; skin's golden as the shun." He stared into the glass which Nick had just filled. "I tell you, Nick, she wash a woman!—but she washn't any good." He drank the whiskey. When he lowered his arm, his elbow missed the bar and he nearly went down. He righted himself with difficulty. "We went on a trip together, you know."

Half a can later, it was all over, and the captain was slumbering peacefully on the floor. Nick trussed him expertly, stuffed a bar rag in his mouth, secured it and dragged him into the kitchen. Doubled up, he fitted nicely into the flour bin. Avoiding the sentry, Nick made his way across the grounds to Cohill's private quarters and let himself inside. Cohill's spacesuit was hanging on the wall. He checked its gauges and connections, then tried it on for size. He found that by stuffing the feet with several odds and ends of Cohill's clothing he could manage it quite nicely. Finally he took off the suit, laid it on the bed, and armed with a length of rope, squatted down by the door to await the coming of the CQ.

"There he is now," Colonel Dennison said. "Right on time."

The other men in the tower room followed his eyes. 0430 represented dawn Earth time, but dawn was an unknown quality on Miranda, and the spacesuited figure walking slowly toward the locks was hardly more than a ghostly blur. "Looks kind of insignificant, doesn't he, sir," Barnaby said.

"Man is an insignificant creature when you use only his stature for a criterion," said the colonel. "But when you use his imagination as well, he is bigger than the cosmos." The colonel still believed that civilization was on the level.

"Yes sir, that's true," Barnaby said.

The spacesuited figure was obscured by the locks now. When it emerged a moment later at the tower's base, it waved one arm in an awkward farewell to the men gazing down from above. Then it started walking slowly across the ice-clad plain toward the *Starhope*.

Colonel Dennison began to fidget. He knew of course that

you had to walk slowly with only Miranda's tenuous gravity to hold you down, but it seemed to him that Cohill was overdoing it. It began to look as though the spacesuited figure would never reach the ship, but finally it did. Slowly, it started up the metal Jacob's ladder—

The officer in charge of countdown raised the mike to his lips. "Zero plus ten minutes."

Cohill should have been in the ship by now, strapping himself into the pilot's seat, but the spacesuited figure was only halfway up the ladder. The colonel resisted an impulse to grab the mike out of the countdown officer's hand and shout, "Hurry up, for God's sake hurry up!" There was plenty of time, he reassured himself: countdown schedules always allowed for unanticipated delays. Still and all, though—

He was relieved when the figure finally disappeared through the *Starhope*'s locks. "Zero plus five minutes," the countdown officer said.

Plenty of time, the colonel reassured himself again. After all, Cohill was a seasoned pilot and ought to know what he was doing if anybody did. A good dependable man, if ever there was one. He drank, sure, but lots of pilots drank. Cohill kind of overdid it sometimes, though—

"Zero plus four minutes—"

—Take that business of his drinking Barnaby's and Blake's rations. The colonel had been hep to what was going on, but he had overlooked it because he figured that a man with Cohill's responsibilities needed an extra drop or two—

"Zero plus three minutes—"

—to relax. The colonel had been careful not to let on he knew. That was the kind of commanding officer he was. Understanding. Kind. Mag—

"Zero plus two minutes—"

—Magnanimous. Most commanding officers would have lowered the boom. But not him. He, Colonel Dennison, understood men. He knew when to look the other way and when not to. He knew—

"Zero plus one minute . . . fifty-nine seconds—"

—He knew that the two main pursuits of off-duty spacemen were women and whiskey, and that when you deprived them of both you were asking for trouble. The colonel stood up a little straighter—

"Zero plus ten seconds—"

He listened eagerly for the next voice. It followed promptly on the heels of the countdown officer's: "Ten seconds." For some reason it sounded strained and unnatural.

"Nine."

"Nine."

(Slightly guttural, too.)

"Eight."

"Eight."

(Had Cohill been drinking?)

"Seven."

"Seven."

(Impossible!)

"Six."

"Sikkis."

(*Sikkis?*)

"Five."

"Five."

(Where had he heard that atrocious mispronunciation before?)

"Four."

"Four."

(Wildly, the colonel searched his mind.)

"Three."

"Three."

(Suddenly he remembered: the other night he had asked the messboy how much coffee there was left—)

"Two."

"Two."

(—and the messboy had replied, "Sikkis bokkises,"—)

"One."

"One."

(Good Lord!)

"Zero."

"Zero."

"Wait!" the colonel shouted, but he was too late. The *Starhope* had already become a star.

In trajectory, a spaceship is like a painted ship upon a painted ocean. There is no perceptible movement anywhere. The stars and the immensities between them compose the inner surface of a gigantic sphere, and in the precise center of the sphere the ship hangs poised like a shining needle, its wake a bright thin thread trailing behind it.

In the heart of the ship, if it is a manned one, sits the pilot. Day after day he sits there. Week after week. He has no function. He is a passenger, really. A flag man. The inverted bowl of the viewscope rims his head at eye level, and on its transparent inner surface he can see infinity, but he can do nothing about it, save look at it. The viewscope is a dunce cap, really, a dunce cap several sizes too big for his head which has slipped down over his eyes and which he lacks the inclination to raise. And the pilot's seat is the dunce stool on which he sits while the mechancial pupils carry out their tasks under the guidance of the mechanical teacher.

The man in this case was a small black one who had read a comic book underneath a banyan tree one day and had never been the same since. His name was Nikita Eisenhower Jones . . .

After leaving Miranda, Nick activated the radio long enough to inform the base that they would find Captain Cohill in the flour bin and the CQ in the closet of Cohill's room, then he turned it off in the middle of a furious outburst by Colonel Dennison and sat back to enjoy the ride.

Pluto was a pale yellow at first, but as the weeks passed, it transmuted gradually to a glinting blue. Neptune, far away on its orbit, did not enter into the picture at all, and Nick would have had no eyes for it if it had. Pluto, and Pluto alone, had reality.

Eagerly he watched it grow on the inner surface of the dunce cap. It was not a large planet—indeed, it was only a refugee moon—but with nothing save the distant stars to compare it to, it seemed larger than Saturn, larger even than Jupiter. True, it had no shining rings, no glowing red streak; but it was beautiful in its own right, and as he watched, its beauty grew and grew, and the sense of frustration he had known for so long gave way before a sense of pride.

Why pride? he wondered—and again he wondered why he really wanted the stars. To Cohill, they spelled death. What did they spell to *him*, deep in his unconscious where his true self lurked?

He shook his head. He did not know.

Turnover took him completely by surprise when it finally came. He had been expecting it momentarily in one part of his mind, but the rest of his mind had been so absorbed with the blue-glinting sphere snowballing toward him that his awareness was blunted. For a moment he could not understand where the planet had disappeared to, and panic touched him; then, remembering, he pulled down the viewscope mirror and looked through it at the opposite hemisphere of the scope. He saw the incandescent rapiers of the braking rockets lancing down, and the gouts of half-melted ice exploding from the surface. Again, absorption with his destination usurped him, and he did not notice the red flashes of the alarm signal, nor become aware of the insistent ringing of the bell, till it was too late. Possibly he wouldn't have had time to lower the third foot, which had failed to obey the impulse of the *Starhope*'s brain, in any case.

As crashes go, it was not a spectacular one. But it was an effective one insofar as his hopes of ever returning to Miranda were concerned. The *Starhope* fell on its side, the impact springing both the inner and the outer locks. Hearing the crescendoing hiss of escaping air, he wriggled quickly into

Cohill's spacesuit. He barely had time to seal the helmet before the interior of the ship became a vacuum with a mean temperature of −350 degrees Fahrenheit.

He tried the radio first, found it dead. Then for a long while he could not think. Finally he got the flag and managed to squeeze through the locks with it. Some distance from the ship he held the base of its staff to the ice and turned on the tiny motor that activated the roots. The steel roots penetrated deeply into the ice and spread out, and the steel staff and its flexible-foil flag became a new feature of the Plutonian landscape.

Nick raised his eyes then—and saw the plain. He turned—and saw the plain. He turned again, and again, and every time he turned he saw the vast glinting emptiness rolling away in wave after frozen wave to the dark star-flecked edge of space.

He dropped his eyes and went back to the ship, intending to re-enter it. But during his absence, it had settled still further, and the sprung locks had closed. He tried to open them, but the re-entry switch was dead—as dead as he was shortly going to be.

He turned away and started walking out over the plain. He did not intend to go far, but he was not thinking clearly, and he must have covered a quarter of a mile before he stopped and turned around. His shocked eyes took in nothingness. Blue-glinting nothingness. Both the ship and the flag had blended into the ice-bejeweled landscape.

He started back in the direction from which he thought he had come. A half hour passed, and the blue-glinting plain remained unchanged. He reversed his direction. To no avail. The ship and the flag were lost. Or perhaps it was he who was lost. He shrugged his shoulders. It did not matter. He would never see Miranda again anyway. Miranda or Malaita.

He went on walking. His heating unit was not functioning properly, and he could feel the in-creeping cold in his hands and feet. That did not matter either: there was only about a two-hour supply of oxygen left in his tanks, and if the cold didn't get him, asphyxiation would. After a while he began thinking that perhaps Pluto was inhabited. There might even be cities. Perhaps if he looked long enough he might find one. He looked and he looked. He was surprised when he came to the jungle. It was a Malaitan jungle—no question about that—though what it was doing on Pluto he could not fathom. He plunged into it eagerly, and the familiar trees rose reassuringly around him. He was overjoyed when he came to the yam patch, and he dropped down on his hands and knees and began digging in the rich dark soil with his hands.

After a while his fingers began to hurt, and raising them before his eyes he saw to his surprise that they were encased in thick unwieldy gloves. The yam patch faded away then, and the trees; and the plain came back, blue-glinting and malevolent, with the cold stars glittering above it.

He lay down upon his back and looked up at the stars. He was very tired. One of the stars was the sun, perhaps, but he had no idea which one it was. The heart of the First Fire that Kamikau, millennia before, had thrown into the sky. He smiled wanly. Old Kuvi-Kavi's cosmogony was badly in need of revision. It accounted for the moon and the sun and the stars, but how about the planets? Whose heads were they?

And suddenly Nikita Eisenhower Jones understood—in the last lucid moment ever to be granted to him—why *he* had wanted the stars.

He could have laughed if he had had the strength. It was ironic really. And it proved once and forever that the essential nature of man—regardless of his creed or color—had not changed since the first primate had climbed down from the trees and taken up residence in a cave; that, while man's goals might seem noble on the surface, they were basically no different from the selfish goals of his ancestors.

But perhaps the time might come when he would rise above himself and act out of nobler motives. And against that time, his primitive yearning for the stars would stand him in good stead. The conquest of the solar system was a part of a bridge that would eventually connect it with other systems; perhaps when the bridge was a finished product, man would be a finished product too.

He felt quite comfortable now—and warm, too, if you could call numbness warmth. But the lucid moment had passed. *What name you gammon along me, big fella marster God?* he said. *What name you gammon along me? Big fella sun he long way too much.* Kaikai, *he stop no more . . .* Around him, the plain stretched away to the dark and soundless sea of space, and above him the stars shone coldly down. He raised his arms with the last residue of his strength and tried to touch them . . . and as he did so he felt the ground stir beneath his back. Slowly, the plain, the ice, the very bedrock, became a cold integral part of him. He saw the blueglinting mountains of his shoulders spreading massively away into the pale distances and he became aware of the cold, crushing weight of his vast blue-glinting body. He felt the awesome breath of absolute zero reach out and touch his Brobdingnagian face. Lying there, he became mankind—mankind straining agonizingly outward, his attenuated body light-years long, reaching hungrily for the stars, and brushing their cold cruel light with his tense yearning fingertips.

COMETS

Except for the Sun and Moon and the five bright planets (Mercury, Venus, Mars, Jupiter, and Saturn) the only members of the solar system ever noted by human beings in pretelescopic days were occasional comets.

Because the comets came and went irregularly, because they had irregular shapes that could be imagined to resemble swords, or wailing women with loose streaming hair, they were thought to be omens of disaster, and their presence in the sky panicked populations.

One early scientific look at comets was by Aristotle in the fourth century B.C. Since he believed that the heavenly bodies all moved in absolutely regular motions and were otherwise changeless, he could not believe that the comets were heavenly bodies. He felt they were flaming gases that were part of the atmosphere. Of course, he felt the atmosphere extended to the Moon's orbit, so that comets could be atmospheric and yet still not be very close to Earth's surface.

It was not till 1577 that Tycho Brahe, by failing to measure the parallax of a bright comet, demonstrated them to exist beyond the orbit of the Moon, perhaps far beyond.

Then the telescope was invented and made possible closer and more accurate observations of positions and movements. Isaac Newton worked out his law of gravitation, which made it possible to determine what the movements *must* be. Finally, in 1705, Newton's friend Edmund Halley calculated the orbit of a

comet for the first time—and it has been known as Halley':
comet ever since.

It turned out that Halley's comet moved in a very elongate
cigar-shaped orbit that brought it quite near the Sun at one end
but took it far beyond the orbit of Saturn, then the farthest
known planet, at the other.

By 1930, when Pluto was discovered, a planet was finall
found whose orbit carried it beyond the extreme recession o
Halley's comet, but by then it was well known that other comet
looped around the Sun in such a way as to recede to distance
many times that of even Pluto. It is for this reason that ''The
Comet, the Cairn and the Capsule'' is placed last in the book.

The first hint as to the chemical structure of comets came i
the 1860s, when William Huggins analyzed the spectrum of one
and found that it contained carbon compounds. As the decade
passed, it seemed to make sense that the comets consist o
the lighter elements, as the outer planets did. After all, the com
ets are creatures of the outer regions of the Solar system
where the light elements and their compounds are not boiled of
by the heat of the Sun.

In 1949, Fred Lawrence Whipple suggested that the comet
were made up for the most part of icy materials in which rock
or metallic particles might be embedded as dust grains or sma
pebbles. That might be the structure all the way through, or i
some cases there might be a rocky core.

As comets move around the Sun, the ices vaporize when th
comets pass near the Sun. The dust particles are freed, sur
round the comet with a haze, and are swept back by the Sola
wind into a long tail facing away from the Sun. With each pas
sage around the Sun, cometary mass is lost until, after a perio
short in comparison with the duration of the Solar system, th
comet wastes away altogether. It may become nothing but dus
that spreads throughout the cometary orbit; or a rocky cor
may be left that will continue to circle the Sun without forming
tail and with only the merest haze to distinguish it from an aster
oid.

Whipple's theory has looked increasingly good with the years, and "The Comet, the Cairn and the Capsule" pictures a Whipple-like comet with considerable accurate detail.

But if comets are so short-lived, why do so many still circle the Sun? In 1950, Jan Hendrik Oort suggested that there is a kind of "cometoid belt" about the Sun, at a distance of one or two light-years. This contains as many as 100 billion tiny bodies made of hard-frozen icy materials.

Every once in a while, one of them, influenced by the gravitational pull of the nearer stars, will move away from the Solar system altogether, or will drop in toward the Sun. Those that enter the planetary regions will return periodically, and may be influenced by planetary attractions to remain there permanently. Once within the planetary system, a comet's lifetime is short—but new ones are always coming in.

"The Comet, the Cairn and the Capsule" was first published in mid-1972 and must therefore have been written in late 1971. Between the writing and publication Pioneer 10 was sent probing in March 1972, toward Jupiter. Pioneer 10 carried a message to the stars very much like the one described in the story, which is thus a startling and reasonably accurate prediction of something that was actually to happen.

To be sure, no comet ever observed has been found to have a distinctly hyperbolic orbit (one that would indicate it had come from another stellar system, would move around the Sun *once*, and would then leave forever). Still—you can never tell. The next large comet to appear may be such an object.

The Comet,
the Cairn and the Capsule

DUNCAN LUNAN

Three was the magic number in the design of the spaceship
Newtonian. At launch, there had been three reaction mass
tanks side by side in what older designers still called "Titan
III configuration." A and B tanks had given their all to re
dezvous orbit insertion and been jettisoned, taking with them
the auxiliary thrust chambers and large segments of radiation
shielding. (The turbines and as much as possible of the pump
system were on *this* side of the shielding, and of course the
helium feed tanks were right up *this* end, so EVA repair was
at least possible, if needed.) There remained the sustainer
motor, pile, shielding, C tank, then the service module and
crew sphere, flanked by two modified lunar shuttles. One was
topped by a capsule (Penetration Module), the other by a
winged Earth Lander. When the Lander was sunward and its
shadow fell on the crew sphere, it made the ship look like a
ceremonial trident hanging in space.

Inside the ship, three was anything but a magic number.
Paxton and Scherner had taken to sleeping in the Lander and
Penetration Module, respectively, to get away from Sullivan
and each other. It might be because, for the first time ever,
they were traveling at a velocity which would take them out
of the Solar System unless diminished; the psychologists at
Mission Control had no other explanation for the unforeseen
development; but the clash of personalities had arisen three

weeks out from Earth, and escalated over the weeks following. In the last few days they had been meeting only to collect their rations at feeding time, and had spoken only during
routine checks.

It might, Scherner thought, have something to do with the
visual aspect of what lay ahead. The comet was now putting
on its full display, less than a week from perihelion, and the
Newtonian was now very close indeed. The awesome spectacle of the tail, millions of miles long and beginning to curve
as the nucleus gained speed, was foreshortened out of existence; they saw only the shock wave of the coma, spraying
out from the bright spot of the nucleus, then pushed back by
solar wind into a great plume against the stars. The ship's
slow rotation wound the head around the forward window
like the sweep of a celestial radar, but from the side windows
only a faint mist could be seen, fading off into invisibility.
Something so big but only seen from a distance was disturbing, as if the head too might vanish as they approached it.

By now, however, more detail was showing. They could see
shells and smoky patterns in the gas coming off the nucleus,
and the bright star of the nucleus itself had become a sunlike
disk with spikes projecting from it. Behind the nucleus lay a
tunnel of shadow, blurring away at its edges till it vanished
into the glowing haze of the tail. Now the coma filled all the
sky ahead, and was beginning to move across the field of
view; it was time for the *Newtonian* to match orbit. Hyperbolic orbit, rare indeed, this comet was a stranger to the Solar System, and would never return.

The three astronauts strapped into their couches and got
down to work, with a minimum of conversation. Mission
Control, far enough away in any case to have little effect on
the quarrels, was taking a business attitude—the mission had
to go on, whatever the clash of personalities. The ship's rotation was halted, last refinements were applied to the burn
computations, and the *Newtonian* turned away from the comet. The burn was a relatively short one at max chamber tem-

perature, to boost the hydrogen jet past the comet altogether. If those superheated ions impinged on the coma, burning into those fragile shells, all the scientific objectives could be frustrated. There was no chance the crew would let that happen, taking out their resentments on the celestial body: each man's specialty was now taking absolute priority, as far as he was concerned.

They were much nearer the comet when Scherner saw it next, from the observation turret on the crew sphere, when the ship turned back to face it. The fuming gases around it seemed motionless, but after some minutes changes could be detected. The dazzling spikes around the nucleus were no longer sharp, but still too blurred overall by intervening gas and ice crystals for the telescope to resolve them. Probing with radar and laser beams, Paxton could tell even less about them; he was getting a general reflection from a layer about double the size of the nucleus, which by visual estimate was six hundred miles across. Scherner suspected that the spikes were internal reflections in a cloud of ice fragments orbiting the nucleus, but the changing light patterns he detected might just be due to the movement of gases out and back.

"At any rate," he reported, "I can't see any obvious hazards to Penetration."

"Radar seems to confirm that," Paxton broadcast. "The boundary layer I'm getting seems to be quite clearly defined. If we're following the programmed approach, we won't run suddenly into any problems."

They waited, still moving slowly toward the comet, for the signal to journey to Earth and the reply to amble back. A great deal of power was going into the *Newtonian* signal, to overcome their narrow separation from the sun. Interference had proved unexpectedly serious, and Sullivan's clamp-down on personal messages had been the first source of friction aboard. It wasn't as if they were overworking fuel cells, with power coming direct from the pile, and Scherner suspected that Sullivan, himself unmarried, was actively jealous of their daily hook-ups to their homes. Mission Control should have realized that a man without a wife and children could be most homesick of all and arranged someone to talk personally to the mission commander, but Scherner could hardly suggest that on open circuit with Sullivan right beside him. So Sullivan kept all radio time for business, and Scherner and Paxton lost a valued link with home.

The Mission Control bleep sounded. "Roger, no visible hazards. We agree that you should prepare for Penetration. Confirm launch readiness for final go/no-go decision. Over." *Bleep.*

"Okay, Dave," said Scherner, speaking directly to Paxton for the first time today. He didn't have much against Paxton, really, but he always felt he was talking across Sullivan when he addressed him. Perhaps the same feeling accounted for Paxton's incivility to *him.* "Why don't you move across into the PM, and I'll follow you through." He put the lens caps back on the turret instruments and stowed them for the next deceleration, then pulled himself feet-first back into the center section of the sphere. Sullivan didn't speak as he worked his way across, so neither did he.

Personnel selection had been almost wholly successful, he conceded as they checked out the Penetration Module. In space fiction (he'd never had time to read any, but he knew just what it was like) at least one member of the crew had to be a maniac, an agoraphobe, or something equally hard to detect, bent on aborting the mission five minutes after liftoff. But though the longest space flight yet had fallen down on compatibility, the conflict didn't even touch the mission program. After his unreasonable ruling on the signals, Sullivan had found it necessary to impose his authority in a string of minor matters, probably because he knew he had been unreasonable. He, Paxton and Scherner had worked up a real dislike of one another, but they weren't thinking of curtailing the flight.

There was a way to curtail the flight, but it was intended

for more serious difficulty than this. After perihelion they had an "abort window," a chance to fire the motor and drop right back, returning to Earth three months later. Otherwise riding outward with the comet as they studied it, they would make their separation burn not far from Earth's orbit and meet Earth itself nine months later. Fifteen months' voyage or six; and they were going for fifteen, without hesitation.

There could still be a scientific payoff if they had to abort. The Lander's cargo space contained a payload at present, a much less sophisticated payload than the PM's. If Penetration of the comet proved impossible, they could launch a nuclear device which, hopefully sinking to the nucleus before detonation, would supply some of the data they hoped to get less violently from Penetration, and the experimental package—in effect, a complete space probe—they would leave behind.

The checks went through without incident, and they received a go for launch. They counted down the separation and Paxton turned the craft for Sullivan's visual inspection. Then they moved out laterally, and Sullivan turned the Newtonian around once more. The final burn was gentle, the flaring gases missing the PM and the comet, bringing the spaceship to rest in the observation station it would hold for the next fourteen days. The PM traveled on with its original momentum, toward the hazed brilliance of the cometary nucleus.

There was no spectacle or sensation when they entered the coma. Like the end of the rainbow, the smoky plumes of gas receded and dissolved before them. But little by little the glow around the nucleus spread above them and below, waxing brighter and separating into bars and columns like auroras. Now the spikes were breaking up, visually, into discrete sources—tens, dozens, hundreds—each one brilliantly reflecting the sunlight along spikes to its own. By the time the streamers of haze completely surrounded the capsule, the nu

leus ahead was a lattice of light beams, with what seemed to
e a second sun at its heart.

"We're going to slow the ship," Paxton reported, activating
ly-by-wire. "Much of what looked solid from outside is sepa-
ating now. There's a huge shell of ice fragments, probably
rbiting in clusters, though gravity's so low you can't detect
t. If the nucleus itself was move massive, we'd probably get a
ing, like Saturn's. As it is, I don't see any problems in con-
inuing Penetration. We can treat this stuff as weightless and
tationary."

They burned their chemical motors to slow up; only briefly,
or gravitational acceleration was negligible. Making less
han five hundred miles an hour, the PM traveled into the
hree-dimensional ice field.

The "descent" was okay; they could see the solid surface
hey were making for, and bodies in their path separated vi-
ually and on radar in plenty of time to be avoided. Waves of
un-driven gases passed them from the huge bergs, too ten-
ous to affect visibility.

"By dead reckoning, we're two hundred miles inside," Pax-
on radioed. The PM's signals were being relayed through the
Newtonian to Earth (another reason for the ship's sunward
osition), and they'd had loss of signal several times as they
assed floating masses. "The concentration of material is in-
reasing, and we're cutting speed right now with another thir-
y-second burn. As well as ice masses, we're now seeing dark
rocky fragments, from which all the gases must have sub-
imed away. They're all of considerable size, up to hundreds
of feet across. Our micrometeor counters have not registered
any significant increases in impacts, and I'd deduce from that
that the smaller rock fragments are being carried out into the
tail by sunlight pressure and solar wind. This would seem to
confirm the origin of meteors along cometary orbits."

"Roger, Dave," Mission Control said eventually. "We're
happy with your fuel consumption, as indicated by Mike's

last set of figures, but there's some anxiety here about your frequent use of vernier and braking engines. Your last burn should reduce the need for frequent restarts. Of course, each engine should be able to take several hundred separate burns but we'd like you to keep to fewer, longer burns if possible."

This was a problem they had foreseen. In a stronger gravity field, descending, they could keep the motors burning steadily at low thrust; but for such an approach to the comet, with the drawn-out Penetration through the rock and ice field, they'd have to come in much too fast. Conversely, if they'd started slowly enough to make the Penetration on attitude control jets, it would have taken far too long. But by now the situation had changed.

"We're nearing shoals, that's the best way I can put it," said Paxton. "There's a lot of loose stuff ahead, forming an inclined plane across our line of Penetration. I'd say it's material which broke away from the nucleus in the first major solar heating, before the coma began to form and scatter the incident radiation. This ahead of us is the lighter stuff, beginning to drift backward as the cloud of new fragments takes up a conical shape. Its transverse velocity is pretty well negligible, and we should go through without trouble. We're going now to continuous vernier burn."

Tail-first, motors idling, they slid through the final barrier. Paxton held the ship confidently on fly-by-wire, turning the gimballed verniers for brief bursts to avoid denser clouds of fragments. Visibility was poorer now, with so many reflecting surfaces around that they were back to the lattice effect, softened now by the greater density of gases. Then suddenly the jeweled reefs were above them, and they began their final braking.

"We're now in the lee of the stone nucleus, starting our final approach. The body looks to be loosely compacted chunk of rock and ice, with gravity very low. The streams of gas and pieces breaking away are all coming from the area under direct sunlight, the surface appears stable along a broad strip toward the terminator."

"I'm getting a really bright radar echo from about two-thirds of the way up the terminator," Scherner added. "We have enough fuel to select that for our touchdown."

Paxton began the course change. "If it's an anomaly, we'll want a look at that."

The radar anomaly stayed conspicuous as the PM closed with it. "That's a bright echo," Scherner said. "It could almost be a metal outcrop."

"I'll land as close to it as I can. There's a promising site right next to the thing. I can see it now. It does look like metal. Put the radar into landing mode."

"Landing mode activated."

The icy horizon came up around them as Paxton throttled back. Ignoring the feeble attraction of the nucleus, he was flying the ship all the way to the surface. He shut off the braking engine and let the remnants of their approach velocity take them down. Scherner was calling off the approach figures, so he didn't see the anomaly come into view.

Paxton did, and he interrupted the commentary. "Control, the anomaly is artificial. I say again, the anomaly is an artificial object. We are go for touchdown, well within fuel reserves. . . . Contact light!"

"Contact light is on," Scherner confirmed. "The PM has landed. Our inclination is three degrees, repeat three degrees. Fuel and oxidizer residuals as follows . . ."

They were through the landing checks and had given themselves go for a three-minute stay when the Earth reaction came back. "We're getting pretty bad interference on your signal now, especially in the final stage of descent. Repeat description of the anomaly, repeat description of the anomaly." *Bleep.*

"I say again, the anomaly is an artificial object, repeat *artificial*. Now here we go for the details." Turning to the right, Paxton could just see the thing from his couch. "It looks like the bottom half of a totem pole. I'd say there are three distinct sections, one on top of the other. The bottom one is gold, or covered in gold foil, cylindrical, with heat radiator panels projecting. The one above that is roughly spherical, black and silver, with solar cell panels on the surface and projecting antennas. The top section is hexagonal for three-fourths of the way up, then it becomes a straight cylinder of lesser diameter. It too is gold, and some of the panels of the hexagon have solar cells. There are connecting rods from it on one side, anchoring it to the bottom section. I don't think they touch the sphere at all."

"We have your landing status report," said Mission Control. "On the basis of that, we'll give you go to stay for twelve hours. Let us have your computer readout, and we'll assess status for the full mission." *Bleep.*

"Roger," said Scherner. "Secondary antenna is now deployed and locked on *Newtonian* for telemetry. Computer readout begins in three seconds—two, one, mark!" He pressed the switch and the transmission light went on.

The reply to Paxton's description came back. "We copy the appearance of the object, Dave. Can you estimate the function or purpose of the device?" *Bleep.*

Paxton was still staring to the right. "The more I look at it, the more I think it's not one device but three. The three sections certainly don't add up to a unit like the three segments of the PM. Nor, I think, is any one of the sections a spacecraft in itself. I'd say each of them is a scientific package like the one in our cargo compartment. Over."

"We have your computer readout," said Mission Control. "You are go to stay for the full mission." *Bleep.*

"Great. Now let me see this thing." Scherner pushed off his straps and sat up on his couch, then rose and turned to see out of the port. Paxton sat up more slowly. They both looked out in silence until Control came back on.

"Dave, we could accept that some other national group

might have reached the comet some days ahead of us. But there hasn't been time for three complete scientific payloads to be landed even if three ships the size of *Newtonian* could be launched in secret." *Bleep.*

"Roger, Control, that confirms our assessment," said Paxton. Scherner glanced at him in surprise. "We're looking at objects from outside the Solar System altogether, like the comet itself. Sometime in the past, when this nucleus swung past another sun, there was another landing here—maybe more than one."

"If that's true, said Scherner, "then the object might be millions of years old. This is a fast comet, but over interstellar distances . . ."

"Not less than a million years," Paxton agreed. "Well, let's eat."

"Huh? Oh, yes." Their program called for a meal and then a sleep period. The discovery had knocked Scherner out of the routine, though he hadn't been thinking of going outside. The Penetration descent had left him fatigued, but he could have looked at the object a long time yet. "Okay, you break out the food packs and I'll get some pictures out of the window."

He even took some shots out of the other windows, of the comet's surface, and the bright columns of gas rising past the sun's disk from over the horizon. The sublimation mechanism was his speciality, was what he'd come here to study, but it was taking place in his thoughts.

Next "day" they depressurized the command module, and Paxton made his way carefully down the side of the ship. Gravity was so low that effectively they were still in free-fall, but the exhausts had softened the surface enough for the landing legs to grip. Scherner waited in the hatch while Paxton collected a contingency sample from the surface, sending it back up on his line; then he opened up the cargo section and began passing down the research tools. After he descended himself, they were to start taking cores and putting down probes into the comet, but obviously that had to wait. Taking the cameras, they maneuvered on their jet packs toward the object.

It was roughly the same height as the Penetration Module, but all three sections were greater than it in diameter. Scherner had thought, in the capsule, it was somewhat smaller; but sizes and distances were hard to judge. The irregular horizon was close everywhere, but there was a big outcrop of ice behind the object, and light reflected from the crag lit up the side away from the sun, giving the structure a luminous ethereality. Close up, they could see that the bottom section was clear of the surface. In the shadow beneath it their torches found a great golden spike, driven deep into the frozen gases of the comet.

"Whoever put down the first one, meant it to hold," said Paxton to Earth. "From the taper on the length we can see, which is about four feet, I would estimate that the spike would hold through at least one stellar passage even on the sunward side of the comet. Maybe the makers knew where the comet was going next, somewhere relatively close, and decided to use it as an interstellar probe. These radiator panels imply that there was a big power plant in here, enough to carry a signal over interstellar distances, maybe beaming its accumulated data once it got well out from the star again. It could be storing information to do that again right now, but the panels are at exactly the temperature of our surroundings, so I'd guess the pile's wholly inert. It's had millions of years to cool right down."

"Better say tens of millions, or even hundreds," Scherner corrected from above. "Once the probe was beyond use to its makers, it served as an anchorage for other people's. The spheroid was welded to its top, covering the antenna unit."

"And the top section added later still," said Paxton. "When I said the three didn't make anything in combination, I was wrong. What we have here is a cairn."

"Fantastic." Scherner was floating by the upper unit taking pictures. "These upper two could still be active, Dave, since they have solar cells. Maybe they're recording data on us right now."

"If the solar cells are still active after a million years in the interstellar dark, they're pretty good," said Paxton. "But if they have omnidirectional antennas, maybe we'll pick up something when we're tracking our own instrument package."

"That would be fantastic! If we could compare their transmissions with our probe's, we could maybe decode them. Then perhaps we could interrogate them about the planetary systems they originally passed through. It would be an interstellar probe for us—a time probe as well as a space one!"

"Great," said Paxton. "If we could get the second probe's recording of the *third* probe's system, we'd get some actual data about the people who put the third probe here."

But on closer examination, these were mere dreams. All three probes were inert, so thoroughly frozen that the ice crystals frosting them couldn't be brushed off. Scherner and Paxton didn't apply any force for fear that the whole structure would shatter; the metals must be nightmarishly brittle. There didn't seem to be any prospect of taking the probes apart, not even of removing data recorders that might be slowly warmed and interrogated. They couldn't find any access panels, not surprisingly; their own probe was a sealed unit, almost all solid-state, so its power would last as long as possible on the outward swing from the sun. They had no burning or cutting tools to force a way into the cairn; like their predecessors, they could only photograph the exterior and leave their own instruments in turn.

The work went on: studying the comet, as intended, as well as the unexpected marker it carried. Scherner ranged farther sunward day by day, taking rock and ice samples, studying the gas flow from the surface and the effects of the coma on sunlight and solar wind. Using a one-man jet platform, he penetrated the region where fragments were splitting off the comet, even landing there as the violence of the outbursts diminished. The comet was receding swiftly from the sun now, preceded by the vast length of the tail which would soon contract.

They were coming up to activation time for the automatic station they would leave behind. One question remained to be settled, however. It seemed fitting to add the package to the top of the cairn, but it had been planned to anchor it to the ice—like the lowest unit of the cairn, though to less depth. In that position it was to "listen" for tremors in the comet as the sunward face stabilized, and obviously these would be affected by transmission through the cairn. It would also measure the rate of ice fall as the coma gases froze and their crystals were drawn back to the nucleus. That was less of a problem because the precipitation on the upper face of the probe could be corrected for the height of the cairn, to give the values for the comet's surface. However, Mission Control had been holding up the decision.

When they did return to the subject, they had something very different in mind. "From the dimensions you've given us for the cylinder atop the cairn, it would be possible to grip it with the landing legs of the PM."

Scherner and Paxton looked at each other. Paxton raised his eyebrows. "That would be possible, Control," he replied. "We could lower the PM to the top of the cairn on the attitude control jets, and tighten up the jacks on the landing legs. We might even get a weld, with two metal surfaces pressed together in vacuum there; but I wouldn't expect the grip to hold if we tried to pull the cairn out of the ice."

"Surely that's not what they have in mind," said Scherner as they waited for the signals to course out and back.

"I can't think what else they want," said Paxton. "We couldn't use the central engine, but the four verniers could be angled sufficiently to keep the flames from impinging on the cairn. Maybe they want us to bring back the top section, but we haven't enough fuel even for that."

Scherner nodded. Neither of them put his own feelings into words; by now, they were of one mind concerning the cairn.

Mission Control replied. "As you may imagine, Dave, there's a big demand from scientists, and indeed from the public and their elected representatives, that the cairn be retrieved for study. The only way we can figure to do this involves sacrificing the backup capability of the PM and the Lander, so the final decision will rest with Bob Sullivan as mission commander. What we plan is for Bob to come down to you in the Lander and set the nuclear device in the ice at the edge of the current breakup zone. We calculate that an explosion at that point has the best chance of blasting the cairn out of the nucleus. Then we hope that you'd be able to get remote control of the PM and slow up the cairn with the vernier engines. With your present fuel reserves, it should return to the vicinity of the sun within a hundred years. We'd like to know whether you have any additional comments before we go to Bob for his decision." *Bleep.*

Paxton looked at Scherner. "You tell them," he said, looking sickened. "I can't."

Scherner swallowed hard. "Nothing to add, Control. Over."

After weighing up all the factors, Sullivan accepted the plan—surprising neither Paxton nor Scherner. His solo Penetration of the comet posed no real problems, because he knew what to expect. Only the landing might have been tricky, and for that he would have a talk-down. In due course they saw the bright flare of the Lander motors descending through the inclined belt of debris (bigger fragments now, more widely spaced), and with Scherner on the PM radar and Paxton outside, they talked him down without trouble.

Atop its booster, identical to the PM's, the winged Lander made an equilateral triangle with the PM and the cairn. Sullivan went through the routine checks, which took him quite a while on his own, then suited up immediately for EVA.

Paxton helped him out, and together they drifted across to the cairn. Scherner was already there waiting for them. They floated slowly up the structure, both scientists trying to read the mission commander's mind.

At the top of the cairn Sullivan cut his jets and hung there, sinking imperceptibly in the gravity of the nucleus. "I thought it might be an anticlimax," he said at last, "but that is absolutely beautiful. Not just in itself, though it has a strange unity of its own, but in all that it stands for."

"So it's got to you as well," Scherner said, inadequately.

"Yeah. Do you think it will survive disruption of the nucleus?"

"I doubt it." Paxton pointed to the ice bulk beyond. "That berg alone could crush it, just with the wallop it would pack tumbling over. That bomb is going to break loose everything on this side of the nucleus, maybe break the whole comet apart. I don't think we'll ever find the cairn again. There'll be nothing left of it to find."

"They only asked us whether it could be set up," Scherner said. "Not whether we thought it would work, or whether we should even *try* to retain the cairn. Earth wants, and Earth grabs. They'd sooner smash the cairn than let it go, if they can't have it."

Sullivan shook his head. Outside his helmet, the effect was just detectable. "Yeah. It's too bad."

"Come and see what Dave has been doing," said Scherner.

"What Dave has been doing?" Sullivan asked as they floated toward the PM. "Wait a minute. You fellows have been falling behind on the EVA program."

"I've been doing most of that lately," Scherner said wearily. "Sure it might have been a little risky, working so far from the ship on my own, but I stayed high enough with the platform to be in touch with Dave, except when I dropped to take samples. If I hadn't called again in thirty minutes, he'd have come for me."

The PM was before them, the four panels folded down

from the cargo hold like the armored ruff of some giant reptile. Paxton hung over the first of them, indicating his painstaking work on the interior of the panel.

"I brought down the rendezvous laser, unshipped from its housing, and refocused it," he said. "We can't use it to cut into the cairn, because we haven't a long enough power line; but it can engrave these panels, before we blow them clear. We were going to mount them around our probe, on top of the cairn. On this one I've put the sun, the Earth's orbit and the comet's, and the *Newtonian*'s path to the comet and back. I put the Moon beside the Earth so they could identify Earth in this second diagram at the side." He had shown the planets of the Solar System to scale, with their distances from the sun in astronomical units. "I've marked Earth E and the sun S, so ES is the astronomical unit, and I've put our numbers up to twenty-one along the bottom here so they can work them out. I couldn't figure any way to give them the actual distances, but as least they can chart the Solar System to scale.

"The next two"—he pointed across—"are star charts, north and south. I haven't put much stress on constellation figures because it'll be who knows how long before the comet goes through another inhabited system, but I've shown the relative positions of the Milky Way, the Galactic Poles, M-thirty-one, M-thirteen and other globulars, the Hyades, the Pleiades and the Magellanic Clouds. With those points of reference, people should be able to place where we are and when; even the open clusters should be good markers for a Galactic Year or so, provided they can be identified. That's for the scientists, the message is 'Here we are' and it doesn't matter that astronomical distances make it here we were."

Drifting around the hull, Sullivan met him again at the fourth panel. "This one should give them the identification. That's the Milky Way, with the cross in it showing our position now. There are the Magellanics, and there's Andromeda. I've started dotting in some globular clusters to show what they are, and then the Pleiades and the rest are obviously open clusters, by elimination. Then down here I'm going to put a stylized man, woman and child, to show what life is like on the Earth right now."

"Dave, those are incredible," said Sullivan at last.

"I've put a lot into them," said Paxton. "If you didn't feel as we do about the cairn, I might not have shown them to you. We could have blown them off and you'd never have known."

"Nobody will ever know if we blow up the comet," said Sullivan. "That's what you're trying to tell me. We have a chance here to add to what other intelligent races have begun, to make ourselves known to still others, perhaps, far from here in space and time. Or we can disrupt the comet and try to keep the cairn for ourselves." He fell silent for a moment, accepting that as mission commander the decision was his. "Well, I've always heard that it was bad luck to break the chain. But at this stage if we don't plant the bomb we'll obviously be disobeying Mission Control. Can we get around that?"

"We could mount the PM on the cairn, as ordered," said Scherner, "and take pictures to prove it. The ship will tell the next explorers of the comet still more about us. But before that, while Dave finishes the fourth panel, we tell Control that we're planting the bomb sunward, where they want it. But in fact we'll take it up with us for the first stage of the ascent, and cast it off when it has enough speed to leave the comet altogether. The excess fuel that we use for that first burn will cancel the excess we didn't use planting the charge."

"All right," said Sullivan. "You go back inside and tell Mission Control we're moving the Lander sunward. While Dave's finishing the panel, I'll take another look at that incredible thing over there."

They moved the PM, instrument package and all, to hover above the cairn, and this time Sullivan talked them down. With the legs pushed inward to grip the top cylinder, the PM looked entirely right sitting up there—shiny and new, still to

cquire the frost film of the lower components. They drew
ut the probe's antennas and instrument booms (the only
rost-deposit record they would get this way) and activated
he package. They were ready to tell Mission Control this
vas to get a clear location signal after the explosion, but they
ad lost touch with Earth. They could still hear the *Newtoni-*
n's automatic beacon, but the high-gain antennas out there
ad drifted off the planet, the nucleus or both. Probably the
ucleus sensors had wandered off along the illusory spikes.
The brilliant lattice overhead was opening now, beginning to
eparate into discrete objects reflecting the sunlight.

Paxton and Scherner backed out of the capsule, bringing
heir few belongings. It was strange to come out of the hatch
so high above the comet's surface; the original cairn was hidden by the bulk of the PM booster. "That's it, I guess," said
Paxton with a last glance at his artwork.

"I guess so." Sullivan had been talking pictures of the new
cairn, twice as high as before with the ship poised on top of
it. "I wish I'd had more time here."

They gathered at the Lander hatch, pulled themselves
through into the cabin. Sealing it up and pressurizing, they
left ice and vacuum behind for the last time. Down through
the prelaunch checks, without hitch to the moment of liftoff;
a pause at low thrust, as with the PM, to free the landing legs
from the ice, then up and away, through the roll maneuver
onto course for the *Newtonian*.

Central engine at low thrust, verniers flaring one way and
another, the Lander made its way up through the inclined
plane of fragments. Beyond it, coasting outward, they let the
bomb go. It drew ahead on its own solid charge, fast enough
to separate entirely from the comet. Sharing all its outward
velocity from the sun, by the time the comet next came to a
solar system the device would be too far away to be associated with it.

"I wonder if we'll ever tell what really happened?" mused
Scherner, watching it go.

"We might someday," said Sullivan. "Once people see the

pictures we're bringing back, they may turn against the Space Agency for having tried to kill the comet. The administration may be glad to hear then that we didn't plant the bomb."

A floating iceberg was growing in their path. They started their second burn, the verniers pushing the ship aside to miss the obstacle. Threading a path through the satellites of the nucleus, the motors fired again and again, until one of them cracked.

A cluster of red lights came on, the warning buzzer sounded and the ship was tumbled by the asymmetric thrust generated by the burn-out. Cutoff was automatic, and fly-by-wire brought the ship back into the burn attitude.

"Rate of approach to nearest hazard," Sullivan demanded.

"Distance one point four miles, three minutes to impact," Scherner replied smartly.

"Number three vernier has gone," said Sullivan. "We'll take a systems check on the others before we burn. Give me it from item thirty-one, Dave."

Out of touch with Mission Control, they had to get themselves through the emergency. They completed the check with a minute and a half to spare and made the next burn on the central engine alone. The approaching ice cliff, spread with gemlike points, slid past.

Sullivan studied the reefs ahead. "We'll have to take some way off this thing," he declared. "Set up a twenty-second burn for the central engine, Dave." He drew back the hand grip for a 180-degree rotation.

"We're going to be late back to the *Newtonian*," said Scherner as they decelerated.

"Mission Control will sweat," Sullivan agreed. "They think an atom bomb's going off down here. But they won't tell your families until they do hear from us, I expect."

De-Penetration was much harder now. With one vernier out of action, more work would fall on the central engine and the three verniers remaining; so there was a greater risk of another chamber failure. Either they could angle the ship for each burn, loading work onto the central engine, or roll to bring the other verniers to bear when the missing one was needed. To conserve fuel in the attitude-control thrusters, in fact, they would have to use the verniers as much as possible; but with all those roll maneuvers, they could get off the *Newtonian* beam; and if they emerged low on fuel there was no one over there to come and get them. Control was a three-man job, and the team clicked smoothly together.

Scherner, on radar and communications, kept them headed in the right direction. They emerged into the coma in approximately the right place, and not long afterward the *Newtonian*'s radio link locked onto them again. The Lander moved out toward clear space, the head behind them shrinking now as the new debris from the nucleus drifted into stronger sunlight and began adding its gases to the swelling tail.

"We were getting worried about you fellows for a while there," said Control. "But you should get back to the *Newtonian* and move out some way before the explosion." *Bleep*.

"Roger, Control," said Sullivan. "What will we tell them when there's no detonation?" he asked the others.

"No detonation," said Paxton.

"Right," said Sullivan, and they all chuckled, relaxed after the strain of the ascent.

Their hostility to one another was gone, Scherner realized; hadn't reared its head even after the stress was removed. The discovery of the cairn had overshadowed it and dissolved it. That was the reason—though it hadn't reached Earth yet—why the cairn had to remain intact, singing or silent, on its way between the stars. They had fulfilled the original objectives of their mission; and though photographs alone might never reveal the secrets of the cairn, they were bringing back the big reassurance that man wasn't alone in the immensity of space and time—and that was payload enough.

NOTES ABOUT THE AUTHORS

POUL ANDERSON

Born in 1926, Poul Anderson is one of the most honored and multitalented science fiction writers in the world. His almost seventy sf and fantasy books include such notable works as *Brain Wave* (1954), *The High Crusade* (1960), and *Tau Zero* (1970). He has also produced several series of great appeal, most especially his Nicholas Van Rijn stories. In a writing career that now exceeds thirty years he has been a Guest of Honor at numerous sf conventions and has won five Hugo Awards for his short fiction: "The Longest Voyage" (1961), "No Truce with Kings" (1964), "The Sharing of Flesh" (1969), the beautiful "Queen of Air and Darkness" (1972, Nebula Award 1971), and the haunting "Goat Song" (1973, Nebula 1972). He lives and works in California.

ISAAC ASIMOV

Born in 1920 in Russia, Isaac Asimov has been one of the leading figures in science fiction since the early 1940s. He received both the Hugo and Nebula awards for his novel *The Gods Themselves* (1973 and 1974), but is best known for the *Foundation* Trilogy and "I, Robot" and other stories on the future of artificial intelligence. He was the Guest of Honor at the 1955 World Science Convention. The author of more than 200 books and a leading science writer, his most recent efforts include *In Memory Yet Green* and *Opus 200*.

JAMES BLISH

The late (1921–1975) James Blish was a noted sf writer and critic who made a number of important contributions to the field. As an author, he has left us (from among more than twenty-five books) the notable macro-historical Cities in Flight series of novels (collected in one volume in 1969); the Hugo Award-winning *A Case of Conscience* (1958), one of the very best fusions of religious philosophy and science fiction; and the excellent

314

antropy series of stories collected as *The Seedling Stars* (1956). He was
also one of the pioneer literary critics within sf, and his best efforts (before
1970) can be found in *The Issue at Hand* (1964) and *More Issues at Hand*
(1970), both published under the pseudonym William Atheling, Jr.

TERRY CARR

Terry Carr's excellence as an editor and anthologist (the Ace Specials, one
of the leading Best of the Year series in both science fiction and fantasy,
and the Universe series, among many others) has tended to obscure his own
writing talent. In addition to the selection in this volume, his outstanding
short fiction includes "The Dance of the Changer and the Three" (1968),
"Ozymandias" (1972), and "Touchstone" (1964). *Circue* (1977) is an excellent and powerful novel.

ARTHUR C. CLARKE

Born in Somerset, England, in 1917, Arthur C. Clarke has been a major
figure in science fiction for more than twenty-five years. Best known for his
novel *Childhood's End* (1953) and for his co-authorship of the screenplay
of *2001: A Space Odyssey,* he has maintained a high level of excellence in
his more than twenty sf novels and collections. Among his many outstanding works are *Rendezvous with Rama,* which won the Nebula in 1973 and
the Hugo in 1974, *Sands of Mars* (1952), and *Against the Fall of Night*
(1953). He is also a talented short story writer, and his "Meeting with Me-
dusa" won the Nebula Award in 1972. An early champion of space travel,
he made major contributions to the propagation of the possibilities of space
flight in such nonfiction books as *The Exploration of Space* (1951). He is
a former chairman of the British Interplanetary Society.

FRITZ LEIBER

Born in Chicago in 1910, the son of the noted American actor of the same
name, Fritz Leiber is one of the very few writers who has achieved success
in both fantasy and science fiction. Among his almost thirty books and numerous stories, the following have won major sf awards: *The Big Time*
(Hugo 1958), *The Wanderer* (Hugo 1965), the story "Gonna Roll the
Bones" (Nebula 1967, Hugo 1968), the story "Ship of Shadows" (Hugo
1970), and the story "Ill Met in Lankhmar" (Nebula 1970, Hugo 1971).
Equally good are his novels *Conjure Wife* (1953) and *Gather, Darkness*
(1951). His best short fiction (including fantasy) can be found in *The Best
of Fritz Leiber* (1974).

DUNCAN LUNAN

The editors know very little about Mr. Lunan, except that he lives in Scot-
land and has written some very interesting science fiction, including stories

like "Here Comes the Sun" (1971), "How to Blow Up Asteroids" (1973 and "The Moon of Thin Reality" (1970). The great majority of his Amer can publications have been in *If* and *Galaxy*.

LARRY NIVEN

Born in Los Angeles in 1938, Larry Niven is widely considered one of th leading writers of "hard" science fiction. Since his first sf story in 1964, h has maintained a consistency of excellence difficult to equal. Among th honors he has won are the Hugo Award for the now classic *Neutron Sta* (1967); the Nebula Award (1970) and Hugo (1971) for *Ringworld;* an the Hugo for his story "Inconstant Moon" in 1972. His Known Space se ries, which includes such books and collections as *World of Ptavvs* (1966 *Protector* (1973), and *Tales of Known Space* (1975), is one of the bes constructed and carefully thought out of its type. He achieved considerabl commercial success with his collaborations with Jerry Pournelle, especiall the best-selling *Lucifer's Hammer* (1977).

ALAN E. NOURSE

Born in Des Moines, Iowa, in 1928, Alan E. Nourse is a practicing physs cian as well as an outstanding science fiction writer. His medical training i reflected in some of his sf, most notably in books like *The Blade Runne* (1974), *The Mercy Man* (1968), and *Rx for Tomorrow* (1971). Among h many excellent shorter works are the frequently reprinted "Nightmar Brother" (1953), "A Miracle Too Many" (1964), "The Coffin Cure (1957), and "Hard Bargain" (1958).

ALEXEI PANSHIN

Born in 1940, Alexei Panshin moved from the ranks of fandom (he won Hugo for fan writing in 1967) to the heights of professional success whe his novel *Rite of Passage* won the Nebula Award in 1968. His other book length work includes three novels in the Anthony Villiers series: *Starwe* *The Thurb Revolution* (both 1968), and *Masque World* (1969), his excel lent short story collection, *Farewell to Yesterday's Tomorrow* (1975) which contains his best short fiction, including "How Can We Sink Whe We Can Fly?" (1971), and "Sky Blue" (1972). He is also a noted critic producing one of the first book-length studies of a major sf writer, *Heinle in Dimension* (1968), and most recently, *SF in Dimension* (1978), a collec tion of critical essays.

ROBERT SHECKLEY

Born in New York City in 1928, Robert Sheckley has been one of the pre mier short story writers in science fiction for nearly thirty years. Durin the 1950s his work was featured in *Galaxy Science Fiction,* and helped to make that magazine the leader in the field in that decade. His short fiction can be found in eight collections, but he richly deserves a "Best of..." book. His novels include *Dimension of Miracles* (1968), *The Status Civilization* (1960), and *Immortality, Inc.* (1959).

THEODORE L. THOMAS

Born in 1920, Ted Thomas is one of the most underrated of modern sf writers. As Leonard Lockhard, he has produced a series of excellent stories on legal themes, which is natural, since he is a practicing lawyer. Noteworthy stories include "Early Bird" (1973), "Satellite Passage" (1958), "The Doctor" (1967), "The Weather Man" (1962), "December 28th" (1959), and the excellent "The Far Look" (1956). His novels include two collaborations with Kate Wilhelm, *The Clone* (1965), and *The Year of the Cloud* (1970).

ROBERT F. YOUNG

Born in Silver Creek, New York, in 1915, Robert F. Young has been quietly producing an impressive body of science fiction short stories for more than twenty-five years, and his work has been acclaimed by such writers as Fritz Leiber and Avram Davidson. A master of the short story, his lack of novel-length work has held down his reputation. He has had a number of stories selected in Best of the Year collections, including "Clay Suburb" (1975), "Not to Be Opened—" (1951), "Jungle Doctor" (1955), "The Dandelion Girl" (1961), "Ghosts" (1973), and "The Years" (1972). Among his most interesting work are three related stories extrapolating the "car culture" of the United States: "Chrome Pastures" (1956), "Thirty Days Had September" (1957), and "Romance in a Twenty-First Century Used-Car Lot" (1960).

**ISAAC ASIMOV, GRAND MASTER OF SCIENCE FICTION
NOW AVAILABLE IN PANTHER SCIENCE FICTION**

The Foundation Trilogy

Foundation	£1.25	☐
Foundation and Empire	£1.25	☐
Second Foundation	£1.25	☐

Other Titles

The Left Hand of the Electron (non-fiction)	75p	☐
The Stars in their Courses (non-fiction)	95p	☐
The Bicentennial Man	£1.50	☐
Buy Jupiter!	£1.25	☐
The Gods Themselves	£1.50	☐
The Early Asimov *Volume 1*	£1.25	☐
The Early Asimov *Volume 2*	£1.50	☐
The Early Asimov *Volume 3*	£1.25	☐
Earth is Room Enough	£1.25	☐
The Stars Like Dust	£1.25	☐
The Martian Way	£1.25	☐
The Currents of Space	£1.25	☐
Nightfall One	£1.25	☐
Nightfall Two	£1.25	☐
The End of Eternity	95p	☐
I, Robot	£1.25	☐
The Caves of Steel	£1.25	☐
The Rest of the Robots	£1.25	☐
Asimov's Mysteries	£1.25	☐
The Naked Sun	£1.25	☐

**THE WORLD'S GREATEST SCIENCE FICTION AUTHORS
NOW AVAILABLE IN PANTHER SCIENCE FICTION**

SF481

THE WORLD'S GREATEST SCIENCE FICTION AUTHORS NOW AVAILABLE IN PANTHER SCIENCE FICTION

Ray Bradbury

Fahrenheit 451	95p
The Small Assassin	£1.50
The October Country	£1.25
The Illustrated Man	£1.25
The Martian Chronicles	£1.25
Dandelion Wine	£1.50
The Golden Apples of the Sun	£1.25
Something Wicked This Way Comes	75p
The Machineries of Joy	95p
Long After Midnight	95p

Philip K Dick

Flow my Tears, The Policeman Said	80p
Do Androids Dream of Electric Sheep?	75p
Now Wait for Last Year	85p
Zap Gun	75p
The Three Stigmata of Palmer Eldritch	85p
The Penultimate Truth	95p
A Scanner Darkly	95p
Ubik	75p
A Handful of Darkness	95p
Our Friends from Frolix 8	60p
Clans of the Alphane Moon	50p

THE WORLD'S GREATEST SCIENCE FICTION AUTHORS
NOW AVAILABLE IN PANTHER SCIENCE FICTION

Frederick Pohl

The Man Who Ate the World	£1.25	☐
Survival Kit	£1.25	☐
Drunkard's Walk	£1.25	☐
Man Plus	£1.25	☐
The Age of the Pussyfoot	£1.25	☐
Jem	£1.50	☐
The Gold at the Starbow's End	40p	☐

Harlan Ellison

The Time of the Eye	£1.25	☐
All the Sounds of Fear	£1.25	☐

Jack Vance

Trullion: Alastor 2262	85p	☐
Fantasms and Magics	75p	☐
Servants of the Wankh	40p	☐
The Houses of Iszm	65p	☐
The Languages of Pao	65p	☐
Son of the Tree	65p	☐
The Five Gold Bands	95p	☐
The Blue World	60p	☐
The Pnume	50p	☐

Chelsea Quinn Yarbro

False Dawn	£1.50	☐

SF881

THE WORLD'S GREATEST SCIENCE FICTION AUTHORS
NOW AVAILABLE IN PANTHER SCIENCE FICTION

Piers Anthony
Cluster series

Vicinity Cluster	£1.25	☐
Chaining the Lady	£1.25	☐
Kirlian Quest	£1.25	☐

Other Titles

Phthor	85p	☐
Steppe	£1.25	☐

Fritz Leiber
Swords series

Swords in the Mist	85p	☐
Swords Against Wizardry	85p	☐
The Swords of Lankhmar	85p	☐
Swords and Ice Magic	85p	☐

Other Titles

A Spectre is Haunting Texas	£1.25	☐

All these books are available at your local bookshop or newsagent, or can be ordered direct from the publisher. Just tick the titles you want and fill in the form below.

Name _____

Address _____

_____

Write to Granada Cash Sales
PO Box 11, Falmouth, Cornwall TR10 9EN.

Please enclose remittance to the value of the cover price plus:

UK 40p for the first book, 18p for the second book plus 13p per copy for each additional book ordered to a maximum charge of £1.49.

BFPO and Eire 40p for the first book, 18p for the second book plus 13p per copy for the next 7 books, thereafter 7p per book.

Overseas 60p for the first book and 18p for each additional book.

Granada Publishing reserve the right to show new retail prices on covers, which may differ from those previously advertised in the text or elsewhere.

SF681